D1612965

Influenza virus

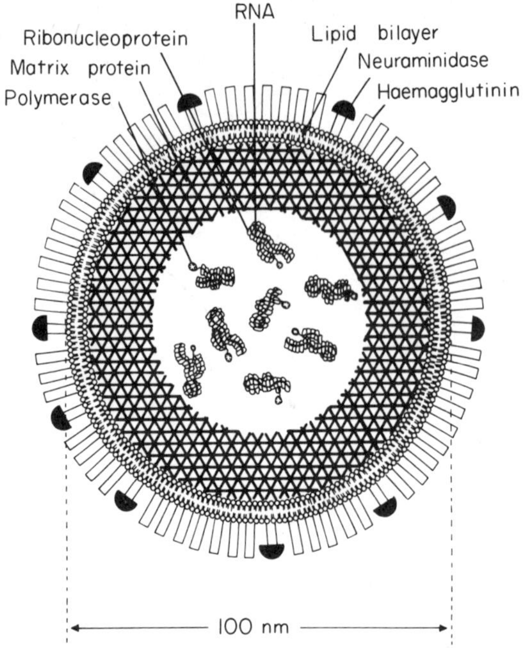

RNA
Ribonucleoprotein
Lipid bilayer
Neuraminidase
Matrix protein
Polymerase
Haemagglutinin
100 nm

Adenovirus

Hexon
Penton
Fibre
80 nm

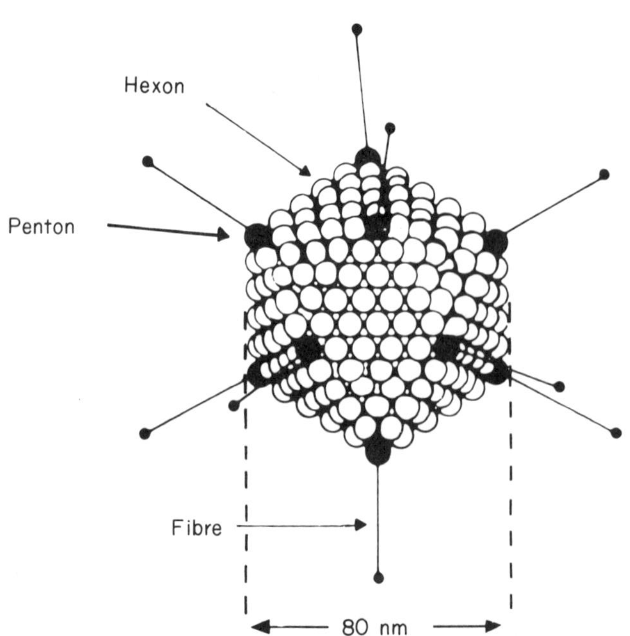

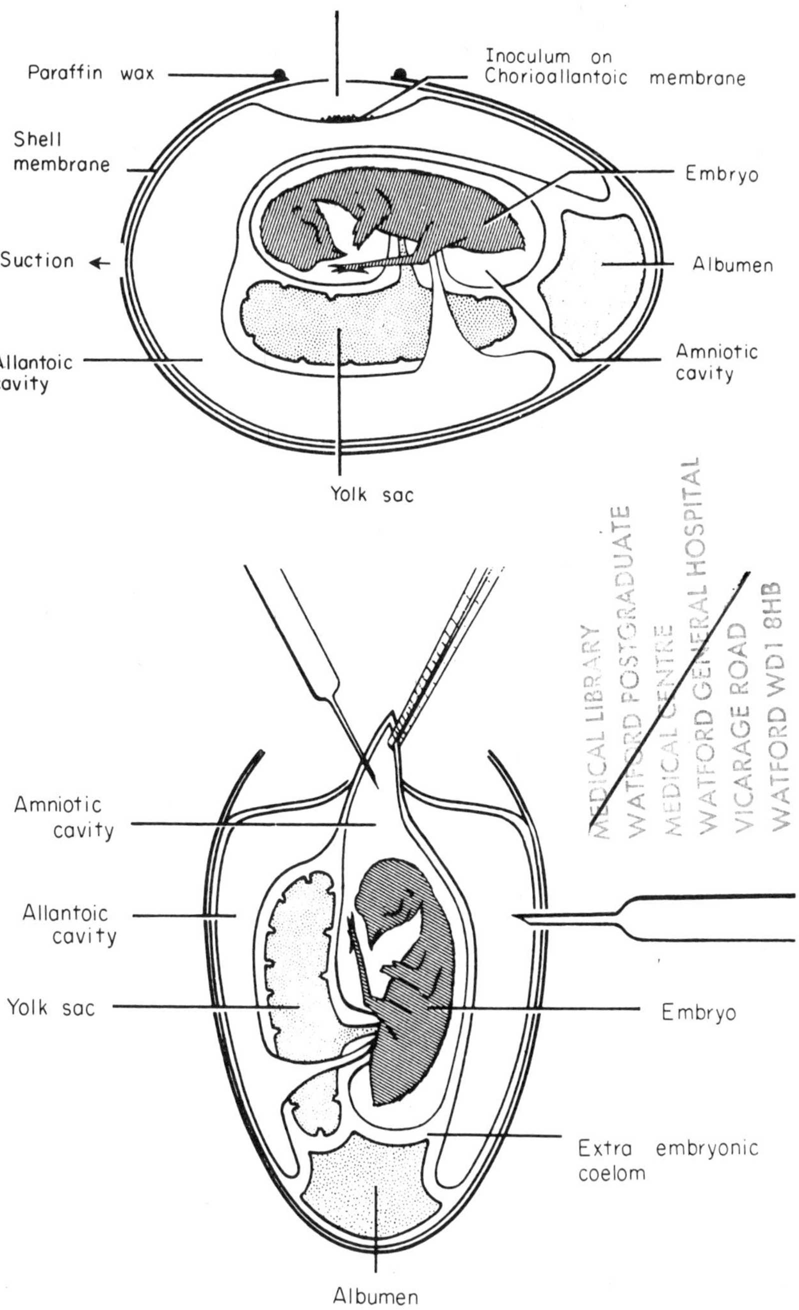
Artificial air sac
Paraffin wax
Inoculum on
Chorioallantoic membrane
Shell
membrane
Embryo
Suction ←
Albumen
Allantoic
cavity
Amniotic
cavity
Yolk sac
Amniotic
cavity
Allantoic
cavity
Yolk sac
Embryo
Extra embryonic
coelom
Albumen

A Dictionary of Virology

K. E. K. ROWSON
Reader in Virology
Institute of Laryngology and Otology
University of London

T. A. L. REES
Senior Lecturer in Bacteriology
Institute of Laryngology and Otology
University of London

B. W. J. MAHY
Huddersfield Lecturer in Special Pathology
University of Cambridge
Fellow of Wolfson College, Cambridge

BLACKWELL
SCIENTIFIC PUBLICATIONS
OXFORD LONDON
EDINBURGH BOSTON MELBOURNE

Editorial offices:
Osney Mead, Oxford, OX2 0EL
8 John Street, London, WC1N 2ES
9 Forrest Road, Edinburgh, EH1 2QH
52 Beacon Street, Boston
Massachusetts 02108, USA
214 Berkeley Street, Carlton
Victoria 3053, Australia

First published 1981

Printed in Great Britain
at the University Press, Cambridge

DISTRIBUTORS

USA
Blackwell Mosby Book Distributors
11830 Westline Industrial Drive
St Louis, Missouri 63141

Canada
Blackwell Mosby Book Distributors
120 Melford Drive, Scarborough
Ontario, M1B 2X4

Australia
Blackwell Scientific Book Distributors
214 Berkeley Street, Carlton
Victoria 3053

British Library
Cataloguing in Publication Data

Rowson, K E K
Dictionary of virology.
1. Virology – Dictionaries
I. Title II. Rees, T A L III. Mahy, Brian Wilfred John
576.64′03 QR358

ISBN 0-632-00697-8
ISBN 0-632-00784-2 Pbk

Introduction

Virologists are drawn from different branches of science – human and veterinary clinical practice, nucleic acid chemistry, genetics, electron microscopy and so on – and this dictionary is designed to aid them as well as others from outside virology to understand the specialist terminology which has developed as the subject has progressed and become diversified. It contains brief definitions of terms unique to virology or which have a particular usage in the subject. Terms common to other branches of science and which have no special virological connotation have been excluded. An attempt has also been made to include all those names which have been used in English language papers to identify specific viruses.

Virus nomenclature has been the active concern of the International Committee on Nomenclature of Viruses and its successor, the International Committee for the Taxonomy of Viruses (I.C.T.V.) since 1966, though it is still very much in its infancy. With regard to the viruses listed in this dictionary, we have proceeded as follows:

1 The *main entry* for each virus is made under the name approved by the I.C.T.V. and includes a list of synonyms, where these exist.

2 Where there is no approved name, the entry is made under a name which accords with I.C.T.V. rules. For example, the Herpesvirus Study Group has recommended that herpesviruses should be provisionally named after the taxonomic unit (family or subfamily) to which the primary natural host belongs. Thus the virus variously known as 'duck enteritis virus', 'duck-plague virus' and 'anatid herpesvirus' takes the name 'anserid herpesvirus' after the *Anseridae*, the family to which the duck belongs. Where more than one herpesvirus has been isolated from the same host family, a numbered series is created, e.g. cercopithecid herpesvirus 1, 2, 3, 4, 5 and 6.

3 Herpesviruses which have not yet been named officially have been given names by us, according to these rules.

4 Where no rules have been laid down for the naming of any particular virus, we have entered it under what seems to us to be the most suitable name, though in some cases this is not the one in common use.

5 With certain exceptions synonyms have also been entered separately, and each refers the reader to the appropriate main entry. Since many permutations can and have been made of names such as 'acute infectious gastro-enteritis virus of foals' we have not included all possible variations. In this example the entry is made under 'gastro-enteritis of foals virus'.

6 Words such as 'mouse' and 'murine', 'cat' and 'feline' are often used interchangeably in virus names without regard to their strict meaning. In this instance we have followed common usage, and if a particular virus cannot be found under one name the other should be tried.

7 Virus entries begin with the taxonomic status (family, genus or species) if this has been determined, and it is thus possible to trace a species back to its genus and family. Family characteristics are not repeated in the entry for the genus, and generic characteristics are not given for the species. To determine the properties of a species, both genus and family entries should be consulted where they exist.

8 Entries whose titles consist entirely of figures, e.g. 127 virus, are placed at the front of the dictionary, otherwise the order is strictly alphabetical. For this purpose, numbers forming only part of a title are disregarded except where they differentiate between otherwise identical names.

9 Chemicals are entered according to the initial letter of the first full syllable of the name, and prefixes such as Greek letters and numbers are ignored.

10 Prefix letters in the names of cell lines are always taken into account.

This dictionary is not in any way intended to serve the function of a virus textbook but rather as a data source, and many entries commence with references (not more than three) which are intended as a starting point for further reading. Where possible these are review articles or papers containing a good discussion of the subject. Preference has been given to recent publications rather than original descriptions, and to papers with a useful list of references.

We are indebted to the following for advice and assistance:
G. K. Darby, University of Cambridge;
H. H. Malherbe, University of Texas;
R. E. F. Matthews, University of Auckland;
J. B. Moe, U.S. Army Medical Research Institute of Infectious Diseases;
J. S. Porterfield, Oxford University;
B. Roizman, University of Chicago;
G. C. Schild, National Institute for Biological Standards and Control, London;
S. Siddell, University of Würzburg.

Abbreviations

APD	Average pore diameter
CAM	Chorioallantoic membrane
CFT	Complement fixation test
CNS	Central nervous system
CPE	Cytopathic effect
CSF	Cerebrospinal fluid
EM	Electron microscopy
HA	Haemagglutination
HAI	Haemagglutination inhibition
i/c	Intracerebral
i/d	Intradermal
i/m	Intramuscular
i/p	Intraperitoneal
i/v	Intravenous
mRNA	Messenger RNA
rRNA	Ribosomal RNA
s/c	Subcutaneous
tRNA	Transfer RNA

All other abbreviations are in accordance with the rules of *The Biochemical Journal*.

Cross references

Words printed in SMALL CAPITALS within any entry appear elsewhere in the dictionary as entries in their own right.

127 virus *See* egg drop syndrome 1976-associated virus.
2060 virus Classified originally as Echovirus 28. Now designated HUMAN RHINOVIRUS 1A.

AAV Abbreviation for ADENO-ASSOCIATED VIRUS.
Abelson leukaemia virus
Risser R. *et al.* (1978) *J. exp. Med.* **148**, 714
A strain of MOUSE TYPE C ONCOVIRUS isolated from prednisolone-treated BALB/c mice inoculated with MOLONEY LEUKAEMIA VIRUS. It has a short latent period and produces lymphoid leukaemia of B-cell type. It can transform 3T3 mouse cells *in vitro*. Requires a HELPER VIRUS for complete virus replication.
ABOB
Melander B. (1960) *Antibiotics Chemother.* **10**, 35
N1, N1-anhydrobis-(β-hydroxyethyl) biguanide-HCl. An antiviral drug claimed to be effective in the treatment of influenza infection in man.
abortive infection Infection in which some or all virus components are synthezised but no infective virus is produced. Also termed non-productive infection. Usually occurs because the host cell is NON-PERMISSIVE. May also result from infection with DEFECTIVE VIRUSES; in these cases it may be possible to rescue the virus by co-infection with a HELPER VIRUS or by co-cultivation.
abortive transformation TRANSFORMATION which is unstable. A few generations after transformation the cells revert to normal.
Absettarov virus A strain of TICK-BORNE ENCEPHALITIS VIRUS (CENTRAL EUROPEAN SUBTYPE). Isolated from a 3-year-old boy with biphasic fever and signs of meningitis. Found in Sweden, Finland, Poland, Czechoslovakia, Hungary, Austria, Bulgaria and western parts of U.S.S.R. Cannot be distinguished antigenically from HANZALOVA VIRUS or HYPR VIRUS, but causes a milder disease in man and is pathogenic in rhesus monkeys.
Abu Hammad virus An unclassified ARBOVIRUS serologically related to DERA GHAZI KHAN VIRUS. Isolated from a tick *Argas hermanni* in Egypt. Not reported to cause disease in humans.
Acado virus A species in the genus ORBIVIRUS. With CORRIPARTA VIRUS it forms the Corriparta antigenic group. Isolated from *Culex antennatus* and *C. univittatus neavi* in Ethiopia. Not reported to cause human disease.
Acara virus A species in the genus BUNYAVIRUS, serologically belonging to the CAPIM ANTIGENIC GROUP. Isolated from SENTINEL MICE, *Culex* sp. and the rodent *Nectomys squamipes* in Para, Brazil and in Panama. Not reported to cause human disease.
acetoxycycloheximide A glutarimide antibiotic. A potent reversible inhibitor of protein synthesis in animal cells.
2,3-bis-(acetylmercaptomethyl)quinoxalin
Bucchini D, and Girard M. (1975/76) *Intervirology* **6**, 285
An antiviral agent. Inhibits poliovirus RNA synthesis *in vitro* and *in vivo*. Inhibits HUMAN (ALPHA) HERPESVIRUS 1 multiplication *in vitro*. Does not interfere with ATTACHMENT, PENETRATION or DNA synthesis, but interrupts a late stage in virus assembly and/or maturation.
aciclovir W.H.O.-approved name for ACYCLOGUANOSINE.
acridine orange A fluorescent derivative of acridine which will bind to NUCLEIC ACIDS in cells or within the VIRION. When exposed to ultra-violet light, the dye fluoresces orange

if the nucleic acid is single-stranded; green if it is double-stranded. *See also* photodynamic inactivation.

acriflavine A photoreactive dye. *See* photodynamic inactivation.

acronym (Greek: *acro* = extreme + *onoma* = name) A special case of SIGLA. A word created from the initial letters of the principal words in a compound term. *See* CELO virus *and* ELIZA as examples.

actidione Synonym for cycloheximide.

actinomycin D A polypeptide antibiotic produced by the fungi *Streptomyces chrysomallus* and *S. antibioticus*. Inhibits TRANSCRIPTION. Interacts only with helical deoxypolynucleotides containing guanine. Not readily reversible by removal of drug from the culture medium. Blocks INTERFERON production by inhibiting mRNA synthesis. 1–5 μg/ml blocks DNA-dependent RNA synthesis, but apart from RETROVIRIDAE and INFLUENZAVIRUS, single-stranded RNA viruses are not affected.
SYN: dactinomycin; meractinomycin.

Acute anterior poliomyelitis virus Synonym for human poliovirus

Acute epidemic gastroenteritis virus of humans

Flewitt T.H. (1977) *Recent Adv. clin. Virol.* **1**, 151

An unclassified FAECAL VIRUS of type 1. Causes diarrhoea and vomiting in children and adults. There are at least 3 serological types: NORWALK, HAWAII, and WOLLAN. Virus particles are 27 nm in diameter, and are ether- and acid-stable. Found in the faeces by EM. Antibodies can be demonstrated in patients. The virus is very difficult to propagate *in vitro*. *See also* gastro-enteritis viruses of humans.

Acute haemorrhagic conjunctivitis virus

Yoshii T. *et al.* (1977) *J. gen. Virol.* **36**, 377

A species in the genus ENTEROVIRUS, designated ENTEROVIRUS 70. Causes acute haemorrhagic conjunctivitis in humans in all parts of the world except the Americas and Australia. The prototype strain J670/71 isolated in Japan multiplies optimally at 32–34° in monkey kidney cell cultures, but failed to replicate at 39°. A low temperature should be used for isolation, though the virus can be adapted to higher temperatures.

Acute laryngo-tracheo-bronchitis virus Synonym for parainfluenza virus type 2.

acycloguanosine

Jones B.R. *et al.* (1979) *Lancet* **i**, 243

Schaeffer H.J. *et al.* (1978) *Nature, Lond.* **272**, 583

9-(2-hydroxyethoxymethyl)guanine. A NUCLEOSIDE analogue. An antiviral agent with a potent and highly specific action against HUMAN HERPESVIRUS 1 and 2 both *in vitro* and in animal models of skin, eye and brain infections. The drug is selectively phosphorylated by herpesvirus-induced thymidine kinase, and once phosphorylated is a potent inhibitor of herpesvirus-induced DNA polymerase. In a clinical study, 24 patients with dendritic corneal epithelial ulcers were treated by minimal wiping debridement, 12 then receiving the drug topically as eye ointment, the others being given a placebo. Seven of the placebo group showed recurrence of herpetic corneal lesions within a week. There was no recurrence in the patients receiving acycloguanosine. Acute toxicity studies have shown that the drug has a very low toxicity.
SYN: Wellcome 248U; aciclovir; acyclovir; Zovirax.

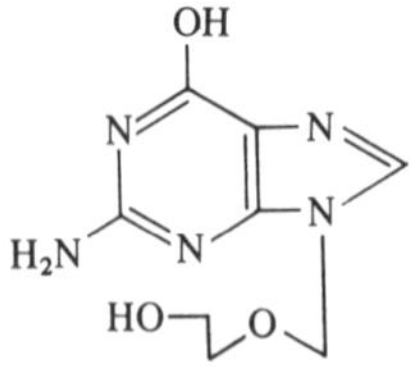

acyclovir U.S.A.N.-approved name for ACYCLOGUANOSINE.

1-adamantanamine hydrochloride *See* amantadine hydrochloride.

adenine arabinoside 9-β-D-arabinofuranosyladenine. An anti-viral agent. Synthesized in 1960, it was subsequently found as a naturally occurring NUCLEOSIDE in culture filtrates of *Streptomyces antibioticus*. Mode of action unclear but it probably inhibits viral DNA POLYMERASE. It neither directly inactivates virus nor prevents ATTACHMENT. In the body it is speedily converted to the hypoxanthine, with a decline to less than 50% of the original anti-viral activity. It is active against HERPESVIRUS and poxvirus; less so against adenovirus and PAPOVAVIRUS. With the exception of oncovirus the drug has no action against RNA viruses. Studies of its effect in viral encephalitis suggest that useful blood levels can be obtained with doses small enough to avoid toxicity. In some patients tremors, nausea, vomiting and toxic encephalopathy have been reported, particularly at high doses. It may be given i/v but is irritating on injection i/m. Also used as a 3% ophthalmic ointment. It is teratogenic in rats and rabbits.

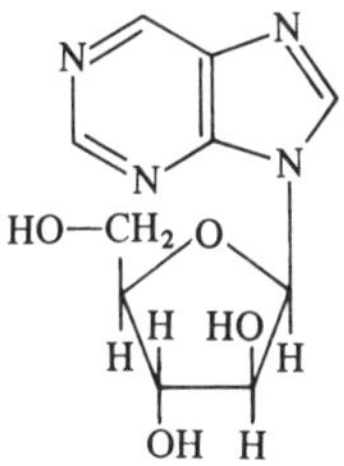

SYN: vidarabine

adenine arabinoside monophosphate

Spruance S. L. *et al.* (1979) *N. Eng. J. Med.* **300**, 1180.

A phosphorylated derivative of ADENINE ARABINOSIDE with greater solubility than the parent compound. Not yet evaluated.

Adeno-associated virus

Young J.F. & Mayor H.D. (1979) *Prog. med. Virol.* **25**, 113

Hoggan M.D. (1970) *Prog. med. Virol.* **12**, 211

Henry C.J. (1973) *Prog. exp. Tumor Res.* **18**, 273

A genus of the family PARVOVIRIDAE. Replication is dependent upon the presence of a HELPER adenovirus for complete virus production, but infectious DNA and antigens demonstrable by immunofluorescence are made in the presence of a helper herpes-type virus. Replicates in cells which support adenovirus replication and reaches a higher titre than the adenovirus whose replication may be depressed. Not genetically related to adenovirus. Mature virus particles contain either POSITIVE or NEGATIVE STRANDS of DNA which are COMPLEMENTARY, and after extraction anneal to form double-stranded DNA. There are a number of sero-types. The type species is type 1. Types 1, 2, 3, and 4 are primate ADENO-ASSOCIATED VIRUSES. There are also bovine, avian, ovine, equine and canine types. Antibodies can be found in human sera, but none of these viruses is known to be pathogenic.

SYN: adeno-satellite virus.

Adenoidal-pharyngeal-conjunctival agent Synonym for human adenovirus.

Adenoid degeneration agent Synonym for human adenovirus, for which it was the original name. Causes degeneration of human tonsillar tissue grown in culture.

Adeno-satellite virus Synonym for adeno-associated virus.

s-adenosyl-L-methionine *See* SAM.

Adenoviridae

Philipson L. *et al.* (1975) *Virology Monographs* **14**. Springer Verlag, Vienna

A family of double-stranded DNA viruses with icosahedral symmetry. The VIRION is 70–90 nm in diameter, formed of 252 CAPSOMERES 7–9 nm in diameter. The 12 vertex capsomeres consist of a base and an outward projection of fibre with a knob at its end. Each of these 12 is called a PENTON and has 5 neighbours. The virion is non-enveloped, resistant to lipid solvents and trypsin. BUOYANT DENSITY (CsCl) 1·33–1·35 g/ml, 795S. Inside the CAPSID is the CORE, consisting of protein and a linear molecule of double-stranded DNA mol. wt. 20–30 × 10^6 with no single-stranded breaks or TERMINAL REDUNDANCIES, though there are probably inverted TERMINAL REDUPLICATIONS because single-stranded DNA, formed by DENATURATION, forms rings on annealing. Viral maturation takes place in the nucleus. Virus is liberated by cell disruption. They may be divided on the basis of their host species and further on the basis of haemagglutination, antigenic structure and oncogenicity. Usually found in the respiratory tract where they are often associated with disease. There are two genera: MASTADENOVIRUS and AVIADENOVIRUS.

Adenovirus *See* Adenoviridae.

Adenovirus-SV$_{40}$ hybrids The first reported was between human adenovirus 7 and SV$_{40}$. An adenovirus 7 isolate was found to be contaminated with SV$_{40}$ after isolation and passage in primary rhesus monkey kidney cells. Infectious SV$_{40}$ virus was eliminated by passage in the presence of SV$_{40}$ antiserum but on injection into newborn hamsters the tumour cells produced contained adenovirus 7 and SV$_{40}$ T ANTIGENS. The virus could be neutralized by adenovirus antiserum and SV$_{40}$ GENOME sequences appeared to be in an adenovirus particle. The adenovirus SV$_{40}$ hybrid stock virus was named E46$^+$. It consisted of a mixture of complete adenovirus 7 particles and hybrid particles which contained incomplete genomes of both adenovirus 7 and SV$_{40}$. Adenovirus particles replicated in human embryo kidney cells but hybrid particles did not. In African green monkey kidney cells plaque formation followed two-hit kinetics. Adenovirus 7 and hybrid particles were produced. As adenovirus 7 will not replicate in monkey cells the hybrid must act as a HELPER. It has been called PARA or Particle Aiding Replication of Adenovirus. As the hybrid does not replicate in human cells it must have a DEFECTIVE adenovirus genome. As no plaques containing only hybrid virus were produced in monkey cells the hybrid must require the adenovirus as a helper. The viral DNAs in the hybrid virus are covalently linked. A number of hybrids between SV$_{40}$ and other adenoviruses have been described. They may be divided into those that produce free infective SV$_{40}$ virus and thus contain the complete SV$_{40}$ genome, and those that do not. Adenovirus SV$_{40}$ hybrid virus stocks are designated AD$_x^+$ and AD$_x^{++}$ (x is the adenovirus type number). The ADx refers to the adenovirus phenotype (CAPSID). (+) indicates the presence of SV$_{40}$ sequences in the hybrid genome and (+ +) indicates the hybrid contains the complete SV$_{40}$ genome. Thus E46$^+$ is AD$_7^+$. AD$_2^{++}$ is the best studied of the hybrid viruses producing SV$_{40}$ virus particles and there are strains containing different amounts of the adenoviral genome. AD$_2^{++}$ HEY (high-efficiency yielders) contains only a fragment of adenoviral genome and produces SV$_{40}$ virus particles with great efficiency. AD$_2^{++}$ LEY (low efficiency yielders) contains almost a complete adenovirus genome and produces SV$_{40}$ particles with low efficiency. Some AD$_2^+$ hybrids contain the complete adenoviral genome and a fragment of SV$_{40}$ genome. They cannot yield SV$_{40}$ but can replicate on their own in both human and monkey cells. Thus genetically pure stocks of these hybrids can be obtained and are designated AD$_2^+$ND, AD$_2^+$ND$_2$, AD$_2^+$ND$_3$ etc. (ND indicates that the particles are non-defective.)

adsorption *See* attachment.

adventitious viruses Contaminant viruses present by chance in a virus preparation or vaccine. Animals and cell cultures are often infected with adventitious viruses, whose presence may go unrecognized for a period.

African horse sickness virus

Davies F.G. & Otieno S. (1977) *Vet. Rec.* **100**, 291

A species in the genus ORBIVIRUS. There are 9 serotypes identified by NEUTRALIZATION tests. There is group-specific CF antigen. Causes disease in horses, mules and donkeys. In severe cases death occurs from pulmonary oedema. In chronic cases there is cardiac involvement with oedema of the head and neck. Some infections are mild. VIRAEMIA often occurs. Transmitted by nocturnal biting flies of the genus *Culicoides*. Goats are slightly susceptible but ferrets and dogs are infected more readily. Mice, rats and guinea pigs can be infected i/c. A mouse brain passage virus vaccine is effective. VIRION 55–80 nm in diameter, icosahedral and similar to BLUE TONGUE VIRUS. Infectivity is ether-resistant but acid-sensitive, being inactivated below pH 6. Horse erythrocytes are agglutinated. Virus contains double-stranded RNA in 6 segments. Multiplies in eggs in yolk-sac, and in cell cultures of many species.

African monkey cytomegalovirus Synonym for cercopithecid herpesvirus 2.

African swine fever virus

Coggins L. (1974) *Prog. med. Virol.* **18**, 48

A species in the family IRIDOVIRIDAE. Causes a fatal disease resembling classical swine fever in domestic pigs. There is high fever, cough and diarrhoea. Incubation period 7–9 days. Virus replication begins in the tonsils but soon becomes generalised: especially involved are lymph nodes and spleen. Surviving pigs may have VIRAEMIA for months. Natural hosts are probably wart hogs and bush pigs. Infection is by contact and fomites. Premises may be infective for months. However, virus has been recovered from argasid ticks and replication in the ticks demonstrated. Virus diameter 200 nm. ENVELOPE is acquired as it buds through the plasma membrane. An infectious DNA has been obtained. Survives dry at room temperature for years. Resists inactivation by some disinfectants but inactivated by 1% formaldehyde in 6 days, 2% sodium hydroxide in 24 days. Chloroform- and ether-resistant. Replicates in the yolk sac killing the embryo, and in cell culture of pig bone marrow. HAEMADSORPTION of pig erythrocytes is seen after 24 hours and CPE later. After 100 passes the virus loses virulence for pigs but does not give protection from infection with virulent virus. Antibodies do not give immunity. Originally observed in E., S. and W. Africa, reached Portugal and Spain in 1957, France in 1964, Italy in 1967 and Cuba in 1971. Outbreaks in Malta, Sardinia and Brazil in 1978. In Brazil the disease is mild and may be difficult to eradicate. Probably spread by waste food from ships and aeroplanes. In Europe the disease has become less severe, and chronically infected pigs perpetuate the infection.

SYN: wart-hog disease virus.

Agouti endogenous type C retrovirus

Sherwin S.A. *et al.* (1979) *Virology* **94**, 409

A species in the subgenus MAMMALIAN TYPE C ONCOVIRUS GROUP. Detected by appearance of REVERSE TRANSCRIPTASE activity when kidney tissue from a New World rodent, the agouti *Dasyprocta punctata*, was co-cultivated with human lung tumour cell line A549. Has been transmitted to human and cat cells. Nucleic acid HYBRIDIZATION demonstrated the presence of multiple copies of the viral GENOME in normal agouti DNA, and that there are related sequences in both New and Old World rodent cellular DNA.

Aguacate virus An ARBOVIRUS morphologically like BUNYAVIRUS but not serologically related to members of that genus. Serologically a member of the PHLEBOTOMUS FEVER GROUP. Isolated from *Lutzomyia* sp. in central Panama and Canal Zone. Not reported to cause disease in humans.

Aino virus

Takahashi K. *et al.* (1968) *Jap. J. med. Sci. Biol.* **21**, 95

Miura Y. *et al.* (1968) *Microbiol. Immunol.* **22**, 651

A species in the genus BUNYAVIRUS, belonging to the SIMBU ANTIGENIC GROUP. Isolated from *Culex tritaeniorhynchus* in Nagasaki Prefecture, Kyushu, Japan. Not reported to cause disease in humans. Antigenically indistinguishable from SAMFORD VIRUS, and cross-reacts with AKABANE VIRUS in CFT but not in NEUTRALIZATION or haemagglutination inhibition tests.

Akabane virus

Kurogi H. *et al.* (1975) *Arch. Virol.* **47**, 71

Kurogi H. *et al.* (1977) *Natn. Inst. Anim. Hlth Q.* **17**, 1, 27, and 184

Goto Y. *et al.* (1978) *Vet. Microbiol.* **3**, 89

A species in the genus BUNYAVIRUS, belonging to the SIMBU ANTIGENIC GROUP. Isolated from mosquitoes but flies of *Culicoides* sp. are the most probable vectors. Found in Guma Prefecture, Honshu, Japan, and in Queensland, Australia. There is serological evidence to associate infection with EPIZOOTIC bovine congenital arthrogryposis and hydranencephaly in Japan and Australia. Experimental infection of pregnant sheep and goats causes disease in the foetus. Not reported to cause disease in humans.

AKR mink cell focus inducing virus

Hartley J.W. *et al.* (1977) *Proc. natn Acad. Sci. U.S.A.* **74**, 789

A species in the subgenus MAMMALIAN TYPE C ONCOVIRUS GROUP. A HELPER independent virus isolated from AKR thymoma cells. Probably a recombinant between ECOTROPIC AKR MOUSE LEUKAEMIA VIRUS and a XENOTROPIC virus.

Alagoas virus A strain of VESICULAR STOMATITIS VIRUS isolated in suckling mice from the tongue epithelium of a mule with vesicular lesions of the tongue and feet. Found in Alagoas state, Brazil. Serological surveys suggest infection in humans, horses, donkeys, monkeys and bats in various states in Brazil. A few cases of febrile disease with headache and malaise have been reported in man.

Alastrim virus Synonym for variola minor virus. *See* variola virus.

Aleutian disease of mink virus

Shahrabadi M.S. *et al.* (1977) *J. Virol.* **23**, 353

Porter D.D. *et al.* (1977) *Intervirology* **8**, 129

A species in the genus PARVOVIRUS. Causes an economically important, lethal disease in ranch-raised mink. All types of mink are susceptible, but the Aleutian genotype, so named because the blue-grey coat colour is similar to that of the Aleutian blue fox, develop more severe lesions and die sooner. The virus can cross the placenta to infect the foetus, but chronically infected females produce few live kits. Animals infected *in utero* have a less severe disease than those infected after birth. Virus is excreted in the urine, faeces and saliva, and infection is readily transmitted by contact and handling. After infection there is rapid replication and high virus titres are present in spleen, liver and lymph nodes in 10 days. A proportion of non-Aleutian mink clear the virus and develop no disease. A chronic infection occurs in the majority and high antibody levels develop. VIRAEMIA persists for months. Virus/antibody complexes are formed and deposited in the tissues, producing glomerulonephritis, the usual cause of death, as well as arteritis of the coronary, hepatic, gastrointestinal and cerebral vessels. There is a systematic plasmacytosis involving bone marrow, spleen, lymph nodes, liver and kidneys. Ferrets and skunks can be infected experimentally, but not rabbits, guinea pigs, hamsters, rats or mice. Human infection is doubtful, though it would be prudent to handle the virus with caution. Replication in tissue culture is doubtful. VIRION diameter 23 nm, density 1·29–1·41 in CsCl. It is more resistant to heat than most, 60° for 30 minutes causing only partial inactivation. Resistant to lipid solvents and desoxycholate. Passes through a filter of average pore diameter 50 nm. Control of the disease can be obtained by killing all hyperglobulinaemic animals.

Alfuy virus A species in the genus FLAVIVIRUS. Isolated from mosquitoes in Queensland, Australia. Not reported to cause disease, but antibodies to it or to closely related virus are common in humans in N. Queensland.

algophages Synonym for cyanophages.

Allerton virus Synonym for bovid (alpha) herpesvirus 2.

Almpiwar virus An unclassified ARBOVIRUS. Isolated from a skink *Ablepharus boutonii virgatus* in N. Queensland, Australia. Not reported to cause disease in humans.

Alphaherpesvirinae

Knipe D.M. *et al.* (1978) *Proc. natn. Acad. Sci. U.S.A.* **75**, 3896

A subfamily of the family HERPESVIRIDAE. Replicate rapidly, usually with CPE. Latent infection is often demonstrable in nerve ganglia. Host range is very variable. DNA mol. wt. $85–110 \times 10^6$. There are two unique sequences separated by other sequences which repeat in an inverted orientation. Thus:

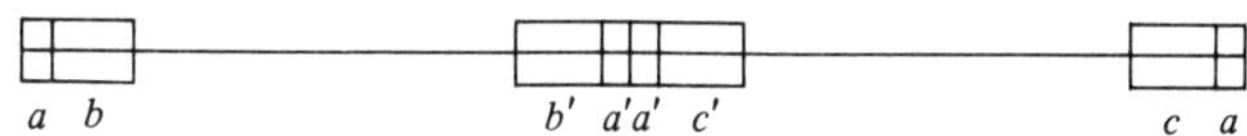

Prime sign indicates inverted sequence.

Two genera are identified so far but they have not been named. The type species of the first is HUMAN (ALPHA) HERPESVIRUS 1 and other species are HUMAN (ALPHA) HERPESVIRUS 2 and BOVID (ALPHA) HERPESVIRUS 2. The type species of the second genus is SUID (ALPHA) HERPESVIRUS 1 and another species is EQUID (ALPHA) HERPESVIRUS 1. Other probable species in the subfamily are EQUID HERPESVIRUS 2 and 3, FELID HERPESVIRUS 1, CERCOPITHECID HERPESVIRUS 1 and CANID HERPESVIRUS 1.

SYN: herpes simplex virus group.

Alphavirus

Chanas A.C. *et al.* (1976) *J. gen. Virol.* **32**, 295

A genus in the family of TOGAVIRIDAE. All species in this genus multiply in mosquitoes as well as in vertebrates. All are serologically related to each other but not to other members of the family. The HAI test is best for demonstrating an antigenic relationship between members of the genus and the CF test or NEUTRALIZATION test for differentiating between members. Cause encephalitis on i/c injection in suckling mice. The type species is SINDBIS VIRUS. There are 20 species.

Aura (C)
Bebaru (C)
Chikungunya* (C,H,B,Ba)
Eastern equine encephalomyelitis* (C,A,Cu,H,R,B,M)
Everglades* (C,A,R,M)
Getah (C,A)
Mayaro* (C,H)
Middleburg (C)
Mucambo* (C,H,R,B,M)
Ndumu (C)
O'Nyong-Nyong* (A,H)
Pixuna (C,A,R)
Ross river* (C,H,B,M)
Sagiyama (C)
Semliki Forest* (C,A,B)
Sindbis* (C,A,H,B)
Una (C,A)
Venezuelan equine encephalomyelitis* (C,A,H,R,Ba,M)
Western equine encephalomyelitis* (C,A,H,R,B)
Whataroa (C)

* *Can cause disease in man.*

Isolated from:

(*C*) *Culicine mosquitoes*
(*Cu*) *Culicoides*
(*R*) *Rodents*
(*M*) *Marsupials*
(*A*) *Anopheline mosquitoes*
(*H*) *Man*
(*B*) *Birds*
(*Ba*) *Bats*

Amaas virus Synonym for variola minor virus. *See* variola virus.

α-amanitin

Fiume L. & Wieland Th. (1970) *FEBS Letts* **8**, 1

Mahy B.W.J. *et al.* (1972) *Proc. natn. Acad. Sci. U.S.A.* **69**, 1421

A cyclic polypeptide. The principal toxin found in the poisonous mushroom *Amanita phalloides*. A potent and selective inhibitor of nucleoplasmic form II DNA-DEPENDENT RNA polymerase of eukaryotic cells. It binds to the RNA polymerase and blocks RNA synthesis after initiation, preventing chain elongation. Viruses which require cellular RNA POLYMERASE II for their replication e.g. ADENOVIRIDAE, INFLUENZAVIRUS and ONCOVIRINAE, are inhibited.

amantadine 1-adamantanamine hydrochloride. A pyrimidine NUCLEOSIDE with very limited prophylactic activity. Effective against INFLUENZA VIRUS A but not against INFLUENZA VIRUS B, nor MEASLES. Amantadine-resistant influenza virus mutants have been isolated.

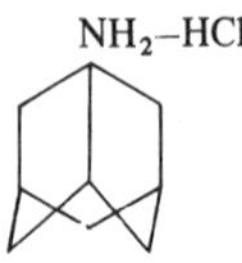

The drug does not inhibit viral ATTACHMENT but acts at an early stage by blocking either PENETRATION or UNCOATING. It may cause some mental disturbance in patients with a history of psychiatric disorder. Drowsiness, slurred speech, lethargy, dizziness and insomnia are side-effects. Available in 100 mg capsules.
SYN: Symmetrel

Amapari virus A species in the genus ARENAVIRUS, belonging to the TACARIBE ANTIGENIC GROUP. Isolated from forest rodents in the Amapari region of northern Brazil. Produces plaques in VERO CELL cultures. Not known to cause disease in humans.

amber Name given to a triplet codon (UAG) specifying chain termination. Other chain terminations are ochre (UAA) and opal (UGA). None of these three trinucleotides will bind aminoacyl tRNA. Some cells contain suppressor tRNA's which will cause the insertion of an amino acid instead of terminating the protein chain at the site of a chain termination codon. The name 'amber' was obtained by translation of the German name Bernstein, one of the contributors to the original work.

amber mutant Virus with mutation resulting in a chain termination codon UAG. *See* amber.

American haemorrhagic fever viruses
Johnson K.M. *et al.* (1967) *Prog. med. Virol.* **9**, 105
A group of species in the genus ARENAVIRUS. Sometimes used as a synonym for the TACARIBE ANTIGENIC GROUP VIRUSES, the New World arenaviruses. Two of them are associated with human haemorrhagic fever: JUNIN VIRUS in Argentina and MACHUPO VIRUS in Bolivia. PORTILLO VIRUS has been isolated from infants in Buenos Aires with a haemolytic-uraemic disease. Wild rodents are the natural hosts and transmission from man to man is rare. The viruses have also been isolated from mites and other ectoparasites, but it is doubtful if arthropods actually transmit them.

aminoacyl-tRNA An amino acid attached to its specific tRNA by covalent linkage between the carboxyl group on the amino acid and the 2′ or 3′ hydroxyl group on the ribose at the 3′ end of the tRNA. In this form the amino acid is said to be 'activated'.

aminoacyl-tRNA synthetases (amino acid-tRNA ligases) Enzymes which bring about the covalent bonding of amino acids to their specific tRNAs. Each enzyme is capable of selecting one of the 20 amino acids and uniting it with its specific tRNA. Once charged with their amino acids, the tRNA molecules are ready to provide them to the protein-synthesizing system.

7-amino-3-(β-D-ribofuranosyl)-pyrazolo[4,3-*d*]pyrimidine *See* formycin.

Amphotropic murine type C virus
Hartley J.W. & Rowe W.P. (1976) *J. Virol.* **19**, 19
A subspecies of the MOUSE TYPE C ONCOVIRUS which infects and replicates in murine and non-murine cells. It thus differs from the ECOTROPIC and XENOTROPIC sub-species. Further differentiation is possible on the basis of antigenicity and INTERFERENCE. Neither syncytia nor plaques are induced in XC cells. The virus is isolated from wild mice.

amphotropic virus A virus which will replicate in the cells of one or more species in addition to its natural host. Term usually applied to RETROVIRIDAE.

Anatid herpesvirus 1 Synonym for anserid herpesvirus.

Anhanga virus An ARBOVIRUS morphologically like BUNYAVIRUS but not serologically related to members of that genus. Belongs to the PHLEBOTOMUS FEVER ANTIGENIC GROUP. Isolated from the sloth *Choloepus brasiliensis* in Castanhal forest, Brazil. Not reported to cause disease in humans.

Anhembi virus A species in the genus BUNYAVIRUS, belonging serologically to the BUNYAMWERA ANTIGENIC GROUP. Isolated from the rodent *Proechimys iheringi* and an arthropod *Phoniomyia pilicauda* in São Paulo, Brazil. Not reported to cause disease in humans.

annealing Synonym for hybridization.

Anopheles A group viruses There are three mosquito-borne viruses in this serological group, morphologically like BUNYAVIRUS but unrelated antigenically to members of that genus. Isolated only from mosquitoes, and only in S. America.

Anopheles A
Lukuni
Tacaiuma

Anopheles A virus An ARBOVIRUS and a member of the ANOPHELES A GROUP. Isolated from *Anopheles* sp. in Colombia, S. America. Not reported to cause disease in humans.

Anopheles B virus An ARBOVIRUS, morphologically like BUNYAVIRUS, but unrelated antigenically to members of that genus. Isolated only from mosquitoes in S. America. Together with BORACEA VIRUS forms the Anopheles B antigenic group.

ansamycins Derivatives of RIFAMYCIN.

Anserid herpesvirus 1

Proctor S.J. (1976) *Arch. Virol.* **50**, 83

A species in the family HERPESVIRIDAE. A natural infection in domestic ducks, and possibly of mallard, in Britain. There is nasal and ocular discharge, and diarrhoea, with up to 97% mortality. Only ducks, geese, swans and day-old chicks can be infected experimentally. The virus can be cultivated on the CAM, killing the embryo in 4 days. Can be adapted to replicate in chick fibroblast cultures, but loses virulence. Attenuated virus vaccine is effective in control of the disease.

SYN: anatid herpesvirus; duck enteritis virus; duck-plague virus.

Ansteckende Schweinelahmung virus Synonym for porcine enterovirus.

Anterior poliomyelitis virus Synonym for human poliovirus.

anti-codon A group of three consecutive bases in a tRNA molecule which recognizes a CODON in an mRNA molecule. The bases pair in an antiparallel manner: A with U and G with C, at least as far as the first two bases in the codon are concerned. The pairing with the third base is more complicated as one tRNA can recognise several codons provided they differ only in the last place. This is the 'wobble' hypothesis which states that a certain amount of variation or 'wobble' is tolerated in the third nucleotide of the codon.

antigenaemia Presence of circulating viral antigen in the bloodstream. Occurs in viral hepatitis and possibly in smallpox, myxomatosis and yellow fever.

antigenic drift The appearance of a virus with slightly changed antigenicity after frequent passage in the natural host. This is presumably due to selection of mutants under pressure of the immune response. Commonly occurs in influenza infections, but also observed with other viruses e.g. APHTHO VIRUS.

antigenic shift A sudden and major change in the antigenicity of a virus. Presumably the result of RECOMBINATION (gene reassortment). Most likely to occur in viruses with fragmented GENOMES, but only reported in INFLUENZA VIRUS A to date.

antigenome The complementary positive RNA strand on which is made the negative-strand GENOME of viruses such as PARAINFLUENZA VIRUS TYPE 1 MURINE.

anti-H B_c Antibody to hepatitis B core antigen.

Anti-H B_e Antibody to hepatitis B e antigen.

anti-H B_s Antibody to hepatitis B surface antigen.

antimessage Viral RNA which is NEGATIVE-STRAND and cannot act as mRNA. It is transcribed by a viral transcriptase to a POSITIVE-STRAND which functions as mRNA.

Apeu virus A species in the genus BUNYAVIRUS, belonging serologically to the C GROUP VIRUSES. Isolated from the woolly opossum *Caluromys philander*, the murine opossum *Marmosa cinerea*, SENTINEL *Cebus* monkeys and mice. Also from mosquitoes in Para, Brazil. Has been associated with a few cases of febrile illness in humans.

Aphthous fever virus Synonym for aphtho virus.

Aphthovirus A genus of the family PICORNAVIRIDAE. Unstable below pH 5–6. BUOYANT DENSITY in CsCl 1·43–1·45. Type species APHTHO VIRUS.

Aphtho virus

Bachrach H.L. (1968) *Ann. Rev. Microbiol.* **22**, 201

Cooper P.D. *et al.* (1978) *Intervirology* **10**, 165

A species in the genus APHTHOVIRUS. Infection is endemic in continental Europe, Asia, Africa and S. America, but Australia, New Zealand, U.S.A. and Canada are free of it. Cattle are the most commonly infected species, but pigs, sheep, goats, deer, elephants and hedgehogs may also be infected. In cattle the disease is not usually fatal but causes loss of condition. There is fever and vesicular eruption in mouth, nose, hooves and udder. There may be myocardial damage. In pigs lameness is the most prominent sign; sheep and goats are less severely affected. The disease is extremely contagious. Guinea pigs and suckling mice can be infected experimentally. Virus multiplies in bovine, porcine, ovine and mouse embryo cell cultures. Calf thyroid cell cultures are also often used. There are 7 serological types: A, O, C, SAT1–3, and Asia 1. There are also subtypes, and 40 distinct antigenic strains are recognized. The virus is stable at pH 7·4–7·6 but is inactivated at pH 5. Control is by slaughter in non-endemic regions and by vaccination elsewhere. SYN: aphthous fever virus; foot and mouth disease virus.

Apoi virus A species in the genus FLAVIVIRUS. Isolated from healthy rodents *Apodemus speciosus ainu* and *A. argentus hokkaidi* on the foothills of Mount Apoi, Hokkaido, Japan. There is one report of infection in a laboratory worker who developed encephalitis.

Apollo virus Synonym for enterovirus 70. A name given to the virus isolated in central W. Africa from the first group of cases of acute haemorrhagic conjunctivitis. Named after the Apollo 11 mooncraft landing which took place about the same time.

ara A *See* adenine arabinoside.

9-β-D-arabinofuranosyladenine *See* adenine arabinoside.

1-β-D-arabinofuranosylcytosine hydrochloride *See* cytarabine hydrochloride.

1-β-D-arabinofuranosylthymidine *See* spongothymidine.

1-β-D-arabinofuranosyluracil *See* spongouridine.

arabinosyl adenine *See* adenine arabinoside.

arabinosyl cytosine *See* cytarabine hydrochloride.

ara C *See* cytarabine hydrochloride.

ara T *See* spongothymidine.

ara U *See* spongouridine.

arbovirus

Karabatsos N. (1978) *Am. J. trop. Med. Hyg.* **27**, suppl. 372

A term used to describe any virus of vertebrates which is transmitted by an arthropod. For inclusion in the catalogue of arboviruses they must be (1) isolated from a vertebrate and shown to be infectious to an arthropod, (2) isolated from an arthropod and shown to be pathogenic to a vertebrate, e.g. mice, or (3) be isolated from a vertebrate or an arthropod and shown to be antigenically related to an established arbovirus. A number of antigenic groups have been designated. An antigenic group is created when a newly-discovered virus can be shown to be serologically related to, but clearly distinguishable form, a previously isolated arbovirus. The original groups were A, B, and C but now new groups take the name of the first discovered member of the group. Groups A and B form the genera ALPHAVIRUS and FLAVIVIRUS respectively of the family TOGAVIRIDAE. Other arboviruses belong to the families ARENAVIRIDAE, BUNYAVIRIDAE, REOVIRIDAE (genus ORBIVIRUS) and RHABDOVIRIDAE. A few are unclassified and there is one virus in each of the taxa IRIDOVIRUS, PARAMYXOVIRUS, and POXVIRUS. The name 'arbovirus' is not accepted as a legitimate taxonomic term since it has no relevance to chemistry, morphology or mode of viral replication. There follows an alphabetical listing of presumed or provisional arthropod-borne viruses:

Name	Abbr.	Genus	Antigenic group
Absettarov	ABS	Flavivirus	B
Abu Hammad	AH		DGK
Acado	ACD	Orbivirus	COR
Acara	ACA	Bunyavirus	CAP
African horsesickness	AHS	Orbivirus	AHS
African swine fever	ASF	Iridovirus	
Aguacate	AGU		PHL
Aino	AINO	Bunyavirus	SIM
Akabane	AKA	Bunyavirus	SIM
Alfuy	ALF	Flavivirus	B
Almpiwar	ALM		
Amapari	AMA	Arenavirus	TCR
Anhanga	ANH		PHL
Anhembi	AMB	Bunyavirus	BUN
Anopheles A	ANA		ANA
Anopheles B	ANB		ANB
Apeu	APEU	Bunyavirus	C
Apoi	APOI	Flavivirus	B
Aride	ARI		
Arkonam	ARK		
Aruac	ARU		
Arumowot	AMT		PHL
Aura	AURA	Alphavirus	A
Avalon	AVA		SAK
Bagaza	BAG	Flavivirus	B
Bahig	BAH	Bunyavirus	TETE
Bakau	BAK		BAK
Baku	BAKU	Orbivirus	KEM
Bandia	BDA		QYB
Bangoran	BGN		
Bangui	BGI		
Banzi	BAN		B
Barur	BAR	Vesiculovirus	
Batai	BAT	Bunyavirus	BUN
Batken	BKN		
Batu Cave	BC		B
Bauline	BAU	Orbivirus	KEM
Bebaru	BEB		A

Name	Abbr.	Genus	Antigenic group
Belmont	BEL		
Bertioga	BER	Bunyavirus	GMA
Bhanja	BHA		
Bimbo	BBO		
Bimiti	BIM	Bunyavirus	GMA
Birao	BIR	Bunyavirus	BUN
Bluetongue	BLU	Orbivirus	BLU
Bobaya	BOB	Bunyavirus	OLI
Bocas	BOC	Bunyavirus	CAL
Boracea	BOR		ANB
Botambi	BOT	Bunyavirus	SBU
Boteke	BTK	Bunyavirus	BTK
bovine ephemeral fever	BEF		
Bouboui	BOU	Flavivirus	B
Bujaru	BUJ		PHL
Bunyamwera	BUN	Bunyavirus	BUN
Burg el Arab	BEA		MTY
Bushbush	BSB	Bunyavirus	CAP
Bussuquara	BSQ	Flavivirus	B
Buttonwillow	BUT	Bunyavirus	SIM
Bwamba	BWA	Bunyavirus	BWA
Cacao	CAC		PHL
Cache Valley	CV	Bunyavirus	BUN
Caimito	CAI		PHL
California enc.	CE	Bunyavirus	CAL
Calovo	CVO	Bunyavirus	BUN
Candiru	CDU		PHL
Cape Wrath	CW	Orbivirus	KEM
Capim	CAP	Bunyavirus	CAP
Caraparu	CAR	Bunyavirus	C
Carey Island	CI	Flavivirus	B
Catu	CATU	Bunyavirus	GMA
Chaco	CHO		TIM
Chagres	CHG		PHL
Chandipura	CHP	Vesiculovirus	VSV
Changuinola	CGL	Orbivirus	CGL
Charleville	CHV		
Chenuda	CNU	Orbivirus	KEM
Chikungunya	CHIK	Alphavirus	A
Chilibre	CHI		PHL
Chobar gorge	CG		
Clo Mor	CM		SAK
Cocal	COC	Vesiculovirus	VSV
Colorado tick fever	CTF	Orbivirus	CTF
Congo	CON		CON
Corriparta	COR	Orbivirus	COR
Cotia	COT		
Cowbone Ridge	CR	Flavivirus	B
D'Aguilar	DAG	Orbivirus	PAL

Name	Abbr.	Genus	Antigenic group
Dakar bat	DB	Flavivirus	B
dengue-1	DEN-1	Flavivirus	B
dengue-2	DEN-2	Flavivirus	B
dengue-3	DEN-3	Flavivirus	B
dengue-4	DEN-4	Flavivirus	B
Dera Ghazi Khan	DGK		DGK
Dhori	DHO		
Dugbe	DUG		NSD
east. equine enc.	EEE	Alphavirus	A
Ebola	EBO		MBG
Edge Hill	EH	Flavivirus	B
Entebbe bat	ENT	Flavivirus	B
epizootic haem. dis.	EHD		EHD
Eubenangee	EUB	Orbivirus	EUB
Everglades	EVE	Alphavirus	A
Eyach	EYA	Orbivirus	CTF
Flanders	FLA	Vesiculovirus	
Frijoles	FRI		PHL
Gamboa	GAM	Bunyavirus	
Ganjam	GAN		NSD
Garba	GAR		MTY
Germiston	GER	Bunyavirus	BUN
Getah	GET	Alphavirus	A
Gomoka	GOM		
Gordil	GOR		PHL
Gossas	GOS		
Grand Arbaud	GA		UUK
Great Island	GI	Orbivirus	KEM
Guajara	GJA	Bunyavirus	CAP
Guama	GMA	Bunyavirus	GMA
Guaratuba	GTB	Bunyavirus	
Guaroa	GRO	Bunyavirus	BUN
Gumbo limbo	GL	Bunyavirus	C
Hanzalova	HAN	Flavivirus	B
Hart Park	HP	Vesiculovirus	
Hazara	HAZ		CON
Huacho	HUA	Orbivirus	KEM
Hughes	HUG		HUG
hypr	HYPR	Flavivirus	B
Ibaraki	IBA	Orbivirus	
Icoaraci	ICO		PHL
Ieri	IERI		
Ilesha	ILE	Bunyavirus	BUN
Ilheus	ILH	Flavivirus	B
Ingwavuma	ING	Bunyavirus	SIM
Inkoo	INK	Bunyavirus	CAL
Ippy	IPPY		
Irituia	IRI	Orbivirus	CGL
Isfahan	ISF	Vesiculovirus	VSV

Name	Abbr.	Genus	Antigenic group
Israel Turkey men.	IT		B
Issyk-kul	IK		
Itaporanga	ITP		PHL
Itaqui	ITQ	Bunyavirus	C
Jamestown Canyon	JC	Bunyavirus	CAL
Japanaut	JAP	Orbivirus	
Japanese enc.	JE	Flavivirus	B
Jerry slough	JS	Bunyavirus	CAL
Johnston Atoll	JA		QRF
Joinjakaka	JOI	Vesiculovirus	
Juan Diaz	JD	Bunyavirus	CAP
Jugra	JUG	Flavivirus	B
Junin	JUN	Arenavirus	TCR
Jurona	JUR	Bunyavirus	
Jutiapa	JUT	Flavivirus	B
Kadam	KAD	Flavivirus	B
Kaeng Khoi	KK	Bunyavirus	
Kaikalur	KAI	Bunyavirus	SIM
Kairi	KRI	Bunyavirus	BUN
Kaisodi	KSO		KSO
Kamese	KAM		MOS
Kammavanpettai	KMP		
Kannamangalam	KAN		
Kao shuan	KS		DGK
Karimabad	KAR		PHL
Karshi	KSI	Flavivirus	B
Kasba	KAS	Orbivirus	PAL
Kemerovo	KEM	Orbivirus	KEM
Kern Canyon	KC	Vesiculovirus	
Ketapang	KET		BAK
Keterah	KTR		
Keuraliba	KEU		
Keystone	KEY	Bunyavirus	CAL
Khasan	KHA	Bunyavirus	
Klamath	KLA		
Kokobera	KOK	Flavivirus	B
Kolongo	KOL		
Koongol	KOO	Bunyavirus	KOO
Koutango	KOH	Flavivirus	B
Kowanyama	KOW		
Kumlinge	KUM	Flavivirus	B
Kunjin	KUN	Flavivirus	B
Kununurra	KNA		
Kwatta	KWA		KWA
Kyasanur for. dis.	KFD	Flavivirus	B
La Crosse	LAC	Bunyavirus	CAL
Lagos bat	LB	Lyssavirus	
La Joya	LJ		
Landjia	LJA		

Name	Abbr.	Genus	Antigenic group
Langat	LGT	Flavivirus	B
Lanjan	LJN		KSO
Lassa	LAS	Arenavirus	TCR
Latino	LAT	Arenavirus	TCR
Lebombo	LEB	Orbivirus	
Le Dantec	LD		
Lipovnik	LIP	Orbivirus	KEM
Lokern	LOK	Bunyavirus	BUN
Lone Star	LS		
Louping-ill	LI	Flavivirus	B
Lukuni	LUK		ANA
Machupo	MAC	Arenavirus	TCR
Madrid	MAD	Bunyavirus	C
Maguari	MAG	Bunyavirus	BUN
Mahogany hammock	MH	Bunyavirus	GMA
Main drain	MD	Bunyavirus	BUN
Malakal	MAL		MAL
Manawa	MWA		UUK
Manzanilla	MAN	Bunyavirus	SIM
Mapputta	MAP		MAP
Maprik	MPK		MAP
Marburg	MBG		
Marco	MCO		
Marituba	MTB	Bunyavirus	C
Matariya	MTY		MTY
Matruh	MTR	Bunyavirus	TETE
Matucare	MAT		
Mayaro	MAY	Alphavirus	A
Melao	MEL	Bunyavirus	CAL
Mermet	MER	Bunyavirus	SIM
Middleburg	MID	Alphavirus	A
Minatitlan	MNT	Bunyavirus	
Minnal	MIN		
Mirim	MIR	Bunyavirus	SBU
Mitchell River	MR	Orbivirus	WAR
Modoc	MOD	Flavivirus	B
Moju	MOJU	Bunyavirus	GMA
Mono Lake	ML	Orbivirus	KEM
Mont. Myotis leuk.	MML	Flavivirus	B
Moriche	MOR	Bunyavirus	CAP
Mossuril	MOS		MOS
Mount Elgon bat	MEB		
M'poko	MPO		TUR
Mucambo	MUC	Alphavirus	A
Murray Valley enc.	MVE	Flavivirus	B
Murutucu	MUR	Bunyavirus	C
Nairobi sheep dis.	NSD		NSD
Nariva	NAR		
Navarro	NAV		

Name	Abbr.	Genus	Antigenic group
Ndumu	NDU	Alphavirus	A
Negishi	NEG	Flavivirus	B
Nepuyo	NEP		C
Ngaingan	NGA		
Nique	NIQ		PHL
Nkolbisson	NKO		
Nodamura	NOD		
Nola	NOLA	Bunyavirus	SIM
Northway	NOR	Bunyavirus	BUN
Ntaya	NTA	Flavivirus	B
Nugget	NUG	Orbivirus	KEM
Nyamanini	NYM		
Nyando	NDO		NDO
Okhotskiy	OKH	Orbivirus	KEM
Okola	OKO		
Olifantsvlei	OLI	Bunyavirus	OLI
Omsk haem. fever	OMSK	Flavivirus	B
O'Nyong Nyong	ONN	Alphavirus	A
Oriboca	ORI	Bunyavirus	C
Oropouche	ORO	Bunyavirus	SIM
Orungo	ORU	Orbivirus	
Ossa	OSSA	Bunyavirus	C
Ouango	OUA		
Oubangui	OUB		
Pacora	PCA		
Pacui	PAC		PHL
Pahayokee	PAH	Bunyavirus	PAT
Palyam	PAL	Orbivirus	PAL
Paramushir	PMR		
Parana	PAR	Arenavirus	TCR
Pata	PATA	Orbivirus	EUB
Pathum Thani	PTH		DGK
Patois	PAT	Bunyavirus	PAT
Phnom-Penh bat	PPB	Flavivirus	B
Pichinde	PIC	Arenavirus	TCR
Piry	PIRY	Vesiculovirus	VSV
Pixuna	PIX	Alphavirus	A
Pongola	PGA	Bunyavirus	BWA
Ponteves	PTV		UUK
Powassan	POW	Flavivirus	B
Pretoria	PRE		DGK
Puchong	PUC		MAL
Punta Salinas	PS		HUG
Punta Toro	PT		PHL
Qalyub	QYB		QYB
Quaranfil	QRF		QRF
Razdan	RAZ		
Restan	RES	Bunyavirus	C
Rift Valley fever	RVF		

Name	Abbr.	Genus	Antigenic group
Rio Bravo	RB	Flavivirus	B
Rio Grande	RG		PHL
Rocio	ROC	Flavivirus	B
Ross River	RR	Alphavirus	A
Royal farm	RF	Flavivirus	B
Russ. spr. sum. enc.	RSSE	Flavivirus	B
Sabo	SABO	Bunyavirus	SIM
Saboya	SAB	Flavivirus	B
Safiyama	SAG	Alphavirus	A
Saint-Floris	SAF		
Saint Louis enc.	SLE	Flavivirus	B
Sakhalin	SAK		SAK
Salanga	SGA		
Salehabad	SAL		PHL
Samford	SAM	Bunyavirus	SIM
San Angelo	SA	Bunyavirus	CAL
Sandfly f. (Naples)	SFN		PHL
Sandfly f. (Sicilian)	SFS		PHL
Sandjimba	SJA		SIM
Sango	SAN	Bunyavirus	Sim
Sathuperi	SAT	Bunyavirus	SIM
Saumarez Reef	SRE	Flavivirus	B
Sawgrass	SAW		
Sebokele	SEB		
Seletar	SEL	Orbivirus	KEM
Sembalam	SEM		
Semliki Forest	SF	Alphavirus	A
Sepik	SEP	Flavivirus	B
Shamonda	SHA	Bunyavirus	SIM
Shark river	SR	Bunyavirus	PAT
Shuni	SHU	Bunyavirus	SIM
Silverwater	SIL		KSO
Simbu	SIM	Bunyavirus	SIM
Simian haem. fever	SHF		
Sindbis	SIN	Alphavirus	A
Sixgun City	SC	Orbivirus	KEM
Snowshoe hare	SSH	Bunyavirus	CAL
Sokoluk	SOK	Flavivirus	B
Soldado	SOL		HUG
Sororoca	SOR	Bunyavirus	BUN
Spondweni	SPO	Flavivirus	B
Stratford	STR	Flavivirus	B
Sunday Canyon	SCA		
Tacaiuma	TCM		ANA
Tacaribe	TCR	Arenavirus	TCR
Taggert	TAG		SAK
Tahyna	TAH	Bunyavirus	CAL
Tamdy	TDY		
Tamiami	TAM	Arenavirus	TCR

Name	Abbr.	Genus	Antigenic group
Tanga	TAN		
Tanjong Rabok	TR		
Tataguine	TAT		
Tembe	TME		
Tembusu	TMU	Flavivirus	B
Tensaw	TEN	Bunyavirus	BUN
Tete	TETE	Bunyavirus	TETE
Tettnang	TET		
Thimiri	THI	Bunyavirus	SIM
Thogoto	THO		THO
Thottapalayam	TPM		
Timbo	TIM		TIM
Tlacotalpan	TLA	Bunyavirus	BUN
Toure	TOU		
Tribec	TRB	Orbivirus	KEM
Triniti	TNT		
Trivittatus	TVT	Bunyavirus	CAL
Trubanaman	TRU		MAP
Tsuruse	TSU	Bunyavirus	
Turlock	TUR		TUR
Tyuleniy	TYU	Flavivirus	B
Uganda S	UGS	Flavivirus	B
Umatilla	UMA	Orbivirus	
Umbre	UMB		TUR
Una	UNA	Alphavirus	A
Upolu	UPO		
Urucuri	URU		PHL
Usutu	USU	Flavivirus	B
Uukeniemi	UUK		UUK
Vellore	VEL	Orbivirus	PAL
Ven. equine enc.	VEE	Alphavirus	A
Venkatapuram	VKT		
VSV-Alagoas	VSA	Vesiculovirus	VSV
VSV-Indiana	VSI	Vesiculovirus	VSV
VSV-New Jersey	VSNJ	Vesiculovirus	VSV
Wad Medani	WM	Orbivirus	
Wallal	WAL		
Wanowrie	WAN		
Warrego	WAR	Orbivirus	WAR
Wesselsbron	WSL	Flavivirus	B
West. equine enc.	WEE	Alphavirus	A
West Nile	WN	Flavivirus	B
Whataroa	WHA	Alphavirus	A
Witwatersrand	WIT		
Wongal	WON	Bunyavirus	KOO
Wongorr	WGR		
Wyeomyia	WHO	Bunyavirus	BUN
Yaquina Head	YH	Orbivirus	KEM
Yata	YATA		

Name	Abbr.	Genus	Antigenic group
Yellow fever	YF	Flavivirus	B
Yogue	YOG		
Zaliv Terpeniya	ZT		UUK
Zegla	ZEG	Bunyavirus	PAT
Zika	ZIKA	Flavivirus	B
Zinga	ZGA		
Zingilamo	ZGO	Bunyavirus	BTK
Zirqa	ZIR		HUG

Arenaviridae (Latin: *arenosus* = sandy)

Pfau C.J. (1974) *Prog. med. Virol.* **18**, 64

Pfau C.J. *et al.* (1974) *Intervirology* **4**, 207

Vezza A.C. *et al.* (1978) *J. Virol.* **26**, 485

A family of RNA viruses 50–300 nm in diameter, spherical or pleomorphic. They have a dense lipid bi-layer membrane covered with projections, surrounding a CORE which contains ribosome-like particles. VIRION proteins include two glycopeptides and two polypeptides. GENOME consists of two species of single-stranded RNA with mol. wt. of $3{\cdot}2 \times 10^6$ and $1{\cdot}6 \times 10^6$. Viral RNA is probably transcribed by virion polymerase into complementary RNA which acts as mRNA. Synthesized in the cytoplasm and matures by budding through the cell membrane. Infectivity sensitive to lipid solvents. There is one genus: ARENAVIRUS. The name was at first spelled aren*o*virus but this was altered to avoid confusion with the adenoviruses.

Arenavirus

Wulff H. *et al.* (1978) *Intervirology* **9**, 344

A genus in the family ARENAVIRIDAE. All species are antigenically related but can be divided into two serological groups: (1) the Old World Arenaviruses *viz.* LASSA VIRUS and LYMPHOCYTIC CHORIOMENINGITIS VIRUS; (2) New World Arenaviruses *viz.* the TACARIBE ANTIGENIC GROUP VIRUSES. Most species have a single rodent or bat host in which they cause a persistent infection with VIRAEMIA and/or VIRURIA. Type species: Lymphocytic choriomeningitis virus (LCM).

	Virus	Locality	Disease in humans
A	LCM	Widespread	Aseptic meningitis
B	Lassa	W. Africa	Pan-systemic
C	Junin	Argentina	Arg. haemorrhagic fever
	Machupo	Bolivia	Bol. haemorrhagic fever
D	Tacaribe	Trinidad	Not reported
	Tamiami	U.S.A.	
	Pichinde	Colombia	
	Parara	Paraguay	
	Latino	Bolivia	
	Amapara	Brazil	

Argentina virus Synonym for Indiana 2A strain of vesicular stomatitis virus.

Argentine haemorrhagic fever virus Synonym for junin virus.

Aride virus

Converse J.D. *et al.* (1976) *Arch. Virol.* **50**, 237

An unclassified ARBOVIRUS, isolated in suckling mice from a pool of *Amblyomma loculosum* ticks collected from dead Roseate Terns on Bird Island, Seychelles. Not known to infect man.

arildone

Diana G.D. *et al.* (1977) *J. med. Chem.* **20**, 750

McSharry J.J. *et al.* (1979) *Virology* **97**, 307

An aryl-alkyl-diketone (4-[6-(2-chloro-4-methoxyphenoxy)hexyl]-3,5-heptanedione) which inhibits replication of several viruses, including HUMAN POLIOVIRUS, at non-cytotoxic concentrations. Probably acts by inhibiting UNCOATING.

Arkonam virus An unclassified ARBOVIRUS. Isolated from the mosquitoes *Anopheles subpictus*, *A. hyrcanus* and *Culex tritaeniorhynchus* in Tamil Nadu, India. Not reported to cause disease in humans.

Aruac virus An unclassified ARBOVIRUS. Isolated from the mosquito *Trichoprosopon theobaldi* in Trinidad. Not reported to cause disease in humans.

Arumowot virus An ARBOVIRUS morphologically like BUNYAVIRUS but not serologically related to members of that genus. Serologically a member of the PHLEBOTOMUS FEVER ANTIGENIC GROUP. Isolated from the mosquito *Culex antennatus*, the mice *Thamnomys macmillani* and *Lemniscomys striatus*, a shrew of *Crocidura* sp., the Kusu Rat *Arvicanthis niloticus* and Kemp's Gerbil *Tatera kempi* in Sudan, Nigeria, Ethiopia and the Central African Republic.

aseptic meningitis Meningitis in which the raised cell count in the CSF is predominantly lymphocytic, and the protein level is only moderately raised (80–120 mg/ml). Most commonly caused by a viral infection, but the term is not synonymous with viral meningitis because the condition may be caused by leptospirosis, syphilis, tuberculosis, brucellosis, cryptococcosis, infiltration of the meninges with malignant or granulomatous tissue, cerebral abscess, and meningeal infiltration in collagen disease, or following the introduction of drugs or contrast media. The viral causes are MUMPS VIRUS, LYMPHOCYTIC CHORIOMENINGITIS VIRUS, ENTEROVIRUSES, and ARBOVIRUSES. Enteroviruses of most types have been isolated from cases of aseptic meningitis. Outbreaks have been associated with ECHOVIRUS 2, 3, 4, 7, 9, 11, 14, 15, 16, 17, 18, 19, 25, 27, 30, 33, COXSACKIEVIRUS A7, A9, B1, B2, B3, B4, B5, B6, and enterovirus 71.

Astra virus

Butenko A.M. & Chumakov M.P. (1971) *Akad. Med. Nauk. SSR*, part 2, 111

An isolate of DHORI VIRUS made from the tick *Hyalomma plumbeum* and the mosquito *Anopheles hyrcanus* in USSR.

Astrovirus

Woode G.N. & Bridger J.P. (1978) *J. med. Microbiol.* **11**, 441

Kurtz J.B. *et al.* (1979) *J. med. Virol.* **3**, 221

Virus particles found in the faeces of normal infants and patients with diarrhoea. Named because of their star-like appearance, which is accentuated because there is no space in the centre as with CALICIVIRUS. Diameter 27–29 nm. Has not been replicated in cell cultures. Relationship to gastro-enteritis under investigation. Infectivity ether-resistant. Similar virus particles have been seen in the faeces of calves.

Ataxia of cats virus Synonym for feline panleucopenia virus.

attachment

Lonberg-Holm K. & Philipson L. (1974) *Monogr. Virol.* vol. **9**. publ. S. Karger, Basel

The first stage of infection of a cell by a virus following chance collision of the virus with a suitable receptor area on the cell. It is dependent on electrostatic forces but independent of temperature except that collisions are more frequent at higher temperatures. Absence of suitable receptor areas can give a cell immunity from infection.

attachment interference *See* interference.

attenuated strains Mutant strains with low virulence or which are avirulent for their natural host species, and in which they can thus be used as a vaccine. Obtained by passage in cell culture or in a host different from the one in which they usually cause disease.

A-type virus particles

Bernard W. (1960) *Cancer Res.* **20**, 712

Dalton A.J. (1972) *J. natn. Cancer Inst.* **49**, 323

A term used originally by electron microscopists to designate a morphologically defined group of RNA virus particles, often found in tumour cells. They are double-shelled spherical particles, appearing in thin sections as two concentric rings, the outer with a diameter of 65–75 nm and the inner with a diameter of approximately 50 nm. The inner ring usually appears more dense. The centre is electron-lucent but contains some amorphous material. They are always intracellular and morphologically similar but there are at least two groups: (1) Intracytoplasmic particles within the ground substance of the cytoplasm where they may form large paranuclear masses within or close to the Golgi area. They are typically seen in mouse mammary tumour cells but are also present in cells of lymphomas in mice with the mammary tumour virus. Some observers believe that the intracytoplasmic A type particles can bud through the cell membrane to become enveloped A type particles which are also known as immature C TYPE PARTICLES. Others believe that immature C type particles arise by condensation under the cell membrane and bud through without any previous existance as A type particles. Budding B TYPE PARTICLES contain a structure morphologically indistinguishable from an A type particle. Whether or not A type particles become either B or C type particles or both is not certain. (2) Intracysternal particles which appear by budding from the inner surface of the cysternae of the endoplasmic reticulum. They are more variable in size than the first group of A type particles and are not considered to be related to other morphological types such as B and C type particles. Their biological role is unknown.

atypical pneumonia of rats *See* pneumonia of rats.

Atypischen Geflügelpest virus Synonym for Newcastle disease virus.

Aujesky's disease virus Synonym for suid (alpha) herpesvirus 1.

Aura virus

Causey O.R. *et al.* (1963) *Am. J. trop. Med. Hyg.* **12**, 777

A species in the genus ALPHAVIRUS. Isolated from mosquitoes in Brazil. No known association with disease. Antibodies found in low percentage of humans, rodents, marsupials and horses but not in monkeys, bats, lizards, cows and sheep.

Australia antigen An antigen first found in the blood of an Australian aboriginal and later identified as hepatitis B surface antigen.

SYN: H B_s Ag

Australian X-disease virus Synonym for Murray Valley encephalitis virus.

autointerference *See* interference.

Avalon virus An unclassified ARBOVIRUS of the SAKHALIN ANTIGENIC GROUP. Isolated from mosquitoes on Great Island, Witless Bay, Newfoundland, Canada. Not reported to cause disease in humans.

Av-3 cells (CCL 21) A line of normal human amnion cells.

Aviadenovirus

McFerran J.B. & Connor T.J. (1977) *Avian Dis.* **21**, 585

A genus in the family ADENOVIRIDAE comprised of the viruses isolated from birds of many different species in many countries. They share a common antigen which does not cross react with the MASTADENOVIRUS common antigen. The 12 vertex CAPSOMERES each have 2 filaments of different lengths. GENOME mol. wt. 30×10^6. G+C CONTENT 54–55%. GALLUS-ADENO-LIKE VIRUS agglutinates rat erythrocytes and is the only species to do so. Type species CHICKEN EMBRYO LETHAL ORPHAN VIRUS. There are at least 11 serologically distinct fowl adenoviruses but type strains have not yet been designated as there are a number of intermediate strains. Two serologically distinct types have been isolated from turkeys and two from geese. Other strains have been isolated from pheasants, guinea fowl and goshawks.

Avian adeno-associated virus

Yates V.J. *et al.* (1973) *Infect. Immun.* **7**, 973

Yates V.J. *et al.* (1976) *Avian Dis.* **20**, 146

A species in the genus ADENO-ASSOCIATED VIRUS. Antigenically distinct from primate adeno-associated viruses. May be a common virus. No evidence of pathogenicity.

SYN: quail parvovirus.

Avian adenovirus *See* aviadenovirus.

Avian arthritis virus

Taylor D.L. *et al.* (1966) *Avian Dis.* **10**, 462

A species in the family POXVIRIDAE. Unrelated to FOWL POX VIRUS. Ether- and chloroform-resistant. Replicates in yolk sac of embryonated eggs. Causes arthritis on injection into the footpads of chicks.

Avian diarrhoea virus Synonym for infectious enteritis virus. *See also* blue comb virus.

Avian encephalomyelitis virus

Calnek B.W. *et al.* (1961) *Avian Dis.* **5**, 456

A species in the genus ENTEROVIRUS. There are at least 15 serotypes. A widespread and silent infection of adult domestic fowls, but causes severe disease in 2- to 3-week-old chicks. There is ataxia followed by tremors of the head, somnolence and often death. Young ducks, turkeys and pigeons can be infected experimentally but not mammals. Virus is present in the excreta and in the eggs which may contain antibodies protective for the chick. Strains vary in virulence. Inoculation of eggs may kill the embryo. Replicates in chick embryo cell cultures.

Avian enteric cytopathogenic viruses An old term used for GALLUS-ADENO-LIKE VIRUS when it was thought to be a picornavirus.

Avian enteroviruses Include AVIAN ENCEPHALOMYELITIS VIRUS and DUCK HEPATITIS VIRUS as well as a number of strains isolated from normal birds.

Avian erythroblastosis virus

Ishizaki R. & Shimizu T. (1970) *Cancer Res.* **30**, 2827

Hayman M.J. *et al.* (1979) *Virology* **92**, 31

A mixture of viruses belonging to the subgenus AVIAN TYPE C ONCOVIRUS GROUP. Consists of a transforming virus and a leukaemia virus which acts as HELPER for the defective transforming virus. The helper belongs to subgroup B of the CHICKEN LEUKOSIS SARCOMA VIRUS. The transforming virus is very closely related to the transforming component in avian myeloblastosis. On i/v injection into chickens it causes rapid erythroblastosis and anaemia but on i/m injection sarcomas are produced. Transforms fibroblasts and bone marrow cells *in vitro*. Non-producer cells can be obtained and the defective GENOME rescued by superinfection with a chicken leukosis sarcoma virus. The anaemia and the occasional case of lymphatic leukaemia produced are probably due to the helper virus.

SYN: erythroblastosis virus.

Avian infectious bronchitis virus

Cunningham C.H. (1970) *Adv. vet. Sci. comp. Med.* **14**, 105

The type species of the genus CORONAVIRUS. The cause of a common, contagious, acute respiratory disease of chicks. NEUTRALIZATION TESTS using chick embryos indicate 2 antigenic types, Connecticut and Massachusetts. All strains show some antigenic relationships but are unrelated to other coronaviruses. Beaudette strain (IBV-42) is serologically similar to Massachusetts strain, though on egg passage has become lethal for chick embryos but lost infectivity for older birds. Chicks up to 4 weeks old are most susceptible. They show depression and gasping; rales are heard. The disease lasts 6–18 days and the mortality is up to 90%. In laying birds there is a drop in egg production and eggs are defective. Pheasants may be infected. Mild endemic infection may result in poor egg production and predispose to bacterial respiratory disease. Avian nephrosis and visceral gout may be caused by the virus, possibly by certain strains. The virus is very

infectious and spreads by respiratory route. Birds are infectious for up to 35 days after recovery but there is no evidence of a carrier state. Virus can be isolated from eggs and semen of experimentally infected birds. An attenuated vaccine has been used. Antibodies have been found in humans who handle poultry. Replicates on the CAM but produces no definite pocks. In chick embryo cell cultures there is replication with syncytium formation and cell necrosis. The viral RNA is a single piece of single-stranded RNA of mol. wt. $6{\cdot}9 \times 10^6$. There are 7 or less viral polypeptides of mol. wt. 14,000–180,000.
SYN: gasping disease virus.

Avian infectious laryngotracheitis virus Synonym for gallid herpesvirus 3.

avianized virus Virus adapted to birds.

Avian leukaemia virus *See* chicken leukosis sarcoma virus.

Avian leukosis virus *See* chicken leukosis sarcoma virus.

Avian lymphoid leukosis virus *See* chicken leukosis sarcoma virus.

Avian lymphomatosis virus *See* chicken leukosis sarcoma virus.

Avian monocytosis virus Synonym for infectious enteritis virus. *See also* blue comb virus.

Avian myeloblastosis virus (AMV)

Moscovici C. (1975) *Current Topics Microbiol. Immunol.* **71**, 79

A mixture of viruses belonging to the subgenus AVIAN TYPE C ONCOVIRUS. The strain, reported by Ellerman and Bang in 1908 has been lost. The most widely used strain is BAI strain A (BAI denotes Bureau of Animal Industry) which originated from a 1941 isolate from 2 birds with neurolymphomatosis. After several passages from nerve and bone marrow tissue a virus with leukaemogenic activity was obtained. BAI strain A is a complex of several viruses. Two viruses AMV-1 and AMV-2 have been isolated from it. They belong on ENVELOPE properties to CHICKEN LEUKOSIS SARCOMA VIRUS subgroups A & B respectively and on injection into day-old chicks cause osteopetrosis and kidney tumours, but not leukaemia. They have been renamed MYELOBLASTOSIS-ASSOCIATED VIRUS (MAV-1 and MAV-2). It is suggested that the original mixture of viruses be called 'standard' AMV, which contains cell-transforming and leukaemogenic viruses, as well as the non-transforming MAV-1 and 2. There are stocks of AMV free of subgroup A virus which are referred to as subgroup B AMV. No subgroup A AMV with leukaemogenic activity is reported. 'Standard' AMV causes myeloblastosis, osteopetrosis, lymphoid leukosis and nephroblastoma in chickens. It seems likely that the different conditions are caused by individual viruses or combinations of viruses in the 'standard' AMV. AMV can cause TRANSFORMATION of yolk-sac or bone-marrow cells *in vitro*. The transforming virus is probably DEFECTIVE. Non-producer transformed cells can be obtained and from these cells leukaemogenic virus can be rescued by superinfection with chicken leukosis sarcoma virus of subgroup B, C or D. MAV of subgroup A does not rescue transforming AMV.

Avian myelocytomatosis virus MC29

Bister K. *et al.* (1977) *Virology* **82**, 431

Hu S.S.F. *et al.* (1979) *Proc. natn. Acad. Sci. U.S.A.* **76**, 1265

A species in the subgenus AVIAN TYPE C ONCOVIRUS. It causes myelocytomatosis, renal and liver tumours and occasionally erythroblastosis in chickens. Causes cell TRANSFORMATION *in vitro* and can produce foci of such cells in chick embryo monolayers. The transforming virus is DEFECTIVE, and non-producer cells can be obtained from which infective virus is produced on superinfection with CHICKEN LEUKOSIS SARCOMA VIRUSES such as ROUS-ASSOCIATED VIRUS or RING-NECKED PHEASANT VIRUS.

Avian nephrosis virus Synonym for infectious bursal disease virus.

Avian papilloma virus Synonym for fringilla papilloma virus.

Avian paramyxoviruses Include NEWCASTLE DISEASE VIRUS and a number of viruses isolated from birds which are antigenically distinguishable from it and from each other. They include YUCAIPA VIRUS, BANGOR VIRUS, TURKEY PARAINFLUENZA VIRUS, BUDGERIGAR PARAINFLUENZA VIRUS and KUNITACHI VIRUS.

Avian pneumo-encephalitis virus Synonym for Newcastle disease virus.

Avian reticuloendotheliosis virus

Purchase H.G. & Witter R.L. (1975) *Current Topics Microbiol. Immunol.* **71**, 103

Hoelzer J.D. *et al.* (1979) *Virology* **93**, 20

A species in the subgenus AVIAN TYPE C ONCOVIRUS. There are four strains: chick syncytial virus (CS), duck infectious anaemia virus (DIA), duck spleen necrosis virus (SN) and turkey strain T reticuloendotheliosis virus (T). All strains are very closely related antigenically but cross-react very slightly with CHICKEN LEUKOSIS SARCOMA VIRUSES. They can be distinguished morphologically from these viruses and do not have their group specific antigen, or NUCLEOTIDE sequences in common with them. They are probably widely distributed among turkeys and wild water fowl especially ducks and geese. The only spontaneous disease produced appears to be turkey leukosis. Chickens, quail, ducklings, goslings, turkeys, pheasants and guinea keets are susceptible to virus injected by any route. A large dose causes death in 3 days. With smaller doses or in older animals death is not so rapid and some animals survive. Such birds are often thin, anaemic, retarded and have poor feather development. Histological changes produced by the virus are visceral or neural; proliferative lesions and necrotizing lesions. The proportion of each varies with the strain of virus. In the proliferative lesions the cells are histiocytoid and probably malignant. The virus replicates in chick embryo fibroblast cultures, producing a transitory CPE followed by TRANSFORMATION.

Avian retroviruses Synonym for avian type C oncovirus group.

Avian sarcoma virus *See* chicken leukosis sarcoma virus.

Avian type C oncovirus group

Vogt P.K. (1965) *Adv. Virus Res.* **11**, 293

Bishop J.M. (1979) *Ann. Rev. Biochem.* **35**, 1

Wang L.-H. (1978) *Ann. Rev. Microbiol.* **32**, 561

A subgenus of the genus TYPE C ONCOVIRUS GROUP. The natural host range is restricted to birds, though some will infect mammalian cells experimentally. There are two species or groups of subspecies: (1) the chicken leukosis and sarcoma viruses, and (2) the AVIAN RETICULOENDOTHELIOSIS VIRUSES. There are five internal structural proteins and two ENVELOPE glycoproteins. It has been suggested that CHICKEN LEUKOSIS SARCOMA VIRUSES can be divided into three groups: (1) sarcoma viruses, e.g. ROUS SARCOMA VIRUS and FUJINAMI VIRUS; (2) AVIAN LYMPHOID LEUKAEMIA VIRUSES, e.g. RESISTANCE-INDUCING FACTORS and ROUS-ASSOCIATED VIRUSES; (3) avian acute leukaemia viruses e.g. AVIAN MYELOBLASTOSIS VIRUS and AVIAN ERYTHROBLASTOSIS VIRUS.

Avipoxvirus

Holt G. & Krogsrud J. (1973) *Acta vet. Scand.* **14**, 201

A genus of the subfamily CHORDOPOXVIRINAE, consisting of viruses of birds. Ether-resistant. Species are antigenically related. Infected cells develop type A inclusion bodies which are rich in lipid. Haemagglutinin is not formed. Mechanical transmission by arthropods is common. Type species FOWL POX VIRUS. Other species are canary, junco, pigeon, quail, sparrow, starling and turkey pox viruses. All are closely related and can infect several species. The four species most worked on are fowl, pigeon, turkey and canary pox viruses. SYN: fowl pox subgroup viruses.

Baboon endogenous virus Synonym for baboon type C oncovirus.

Baboon lymphotropic herpesvirus Synonym for cercopithecid herpesvirus 4.

Baboon type C oncovirus

Hu S. *et al.* (1977) *J. Virol.* **23**, 345

Schnitzer T.J. (1979) *J. gen. Virol.* **42**, 199

A species in the sub-genus MAMMALIAN TYPE C ONCOVIRUS GROUP. A vertically transmitted

ENDOGENOUS virus. Isolated from a baboon *Papio cynocephalus* by CO-CULTIVATION of the cells with various mammalian cells. Replication was most efficient in foetal canine thymus cells. Virus can be isolated directly from placental extract. The virus designated M7 has REVERSE TRANSCRIPTASE and group-specific protein immunologically distinct from other C TYPE VIRUSES. However, there is some relationship to RD114 VIRUS. It is suggested that the CCC CAT ENDOGENOUS VIRUS may have evolved from this baboon endogenous virus. SYN: baboon endogenous virus.

bacteriocinogen

Hardy K.G. (1975) *Bact. Revs* **39**, 464

A plasmid DNA present in certain strains of bacteria, which specifies production of a bacteriocin. Normally the bacteriocinogen is repressed, and the cell carrying it does not produce bacteriocin. The circumstances under which derepression occurs are complex and not completely understood.

bacteriocins

Hardy, K.G. (1975) *Bact. Rev.* **39**, 464

Protein substances of varying complexity released by some types of bacteria which kill bacteria of certain strains within the same species. The producing strain is generally immune to the effects of its own bacteriocins. When purified, bacteriocins seem to fall into two classes. Some are simple proteins or proteins associated with cell wall components; others resemble BACTERIOPHAGES or fragments of them. Bacteriocin formation is due to a bacteriocinogen in the cell, which is normally repressed and behaves like a defective PROPHAGE. Bacteriocins adsorb to specific receptors on the cell wall, and bacterial mutants which lack these receptors may arise and will be resistant. The potency of bacteriocins is exceedingly high, and in several cases it has been shown that the lethal action is mediated without PENETRATION of the cell. Some bacteriocins appear to be enzymes which cause cell lysis.

bacteriophage A virus which replicates inside a bacterium.

Bagaza virus A species in the genus FLAVIVIRUS. Isolated in suckling mice from a pool of *Culex* mosquitoes collected from man at Bagaza, Central African Republic. Has also been found in Cameroon and Senegal. Not reported to cause disease in humans.

Bahig virus A species in the genus BUNYAVIRUS, belonging to the TETE ANTIGENIC GROUP. Isolated from birds in Egypt and Italy. Serological surveys suggest presence in Cyprus and Israel. Not reported to cause human disease.

Bakalasa virus A species in the genus FLAVIVIRUS with no known arthropod vector. Isolated from bats of *Tadarida* sp. in Uganda.

Bakau virus An ARBOVIRUS morphologically like BUNYAVIRUS but not serologically related to members of that genus. With KETAPANG VIRUS forms the Bakau antigenic group. Isolated from mosquitoes in Malaya and Pakistan. Not reported to cause disease in humans.

Baku virus A species in the genus ORBIVIRUS, belonging to the KEMEROVO ANTIGENIC GROUP. Isolated from a tick *Ornithodoros capensis*. Antibodies found in nestlings of a bird *Larus argentatus* on Glinyanyi Island in the Caspian Sea. Not reported to cause disease in humans.

Balano-posthitis virus of sheep

Tunnicliff, E.A. (1949) *Am. J. vet. Res.* **10**, 240

A species in the genus PARAPOXVIRUS causing venereal infection in sheep in America. It can cause ulcerative dermatitis as well as balanitis and ulcerative vulvitis. Similar disease pictures are reported from Australia, S. Africa and Britain. They may be caused by the same virus but the relationships of these viruses to other parapoxviruses require study.

BALB/c (Mo) mice

Jaenisch, R. (1976) *Proc. natn. Acad. Sci. U.S.A.* **73**, 1260

A strain of mice derived from a pre-implantation embryo infected with MOLONEY

LEUKAEMIA VIRUS. They have the viral DNA transmitted as a single Mendelian gene. Heterozygous animals have one copy of the viral DNA in each diploid cell, homozygous individuals have two. Infective virus is produced in their tissues and 90% of the mice develop thymus-derived lymphomas before they are 10 months old.

BALB/3T3 cells Heteroploid fibroblast cell line developed, as 3T3 cells, but from disaggregated 14–17 day old embryos of inbred Balb/c mice. Exhibits low saturation density, extremely sensitive to CONTACT INHIBITION, grow at high dilution, and highly susceptible to TRANSFORMATION by the oncogenic DNA virus SIMIAN VIRUS 40 and MOUSE SARCOMA VIRUS. Do not form tumours on injection into weanling irradiated Balb/c mice whereas 3T12-B cells do. Also known as 3T3-B cells.

Balkan nephropathy virus

Apostolov K. *et al.* (1975) *Lancet* **ii**, 1271

Virus particles morphologically resembling CORONAVIRUSES seen in sections of kidney tissue from human cases of a slowly progressive kidney disease. This disease occurs only in the Balkans, mainly Bulgaria, and is rare in muslims. Virus antigen in tissue sections reacts with patients' serum, but does not react with pig or bird coronavirus antiserum.

Baltimore virus

Light J.S. & Hodes H.L. (1949) *J. exp. Med.* **90**, 113

Hodes H.L. (1977) *Am. J. Dis. Child* **131**, 729

A virus isolated in 1942 from four nursery outbreaks of gastroenteritis. Caused severe diarrhoea in calves. Diameter 40–80 nm. Examination of faeces from these calves and infants 32 years later showed the presence of ROTAVIRUS-like particles.

Bamble disease

Miles J. (1971) *History of Medicine* **3**(4), 28

This disease was first described in 1872 in Norway, and takes its name from the village in which it was prevalent. There is an incubation period of 2–4 days followed by sudden onset, with 'stitch-like' pain in chest, epigastrium, abdomen, and more rarely, the limb muscles, and accompanied by fever, headache, coughing and hiccough. May be caused by COXSACKIE VIRUSES types B1–6, A4, 6, 9, and 10, or ECHOVIRUS types 4, 6, and 9. The first N. American outbreak was described in 1888 by Dabney, whose name was officially bestowed on the disease in U.S.A. in 1923. The Bornholm outbreak was not described until 1932.

SYN: Bornholm disease; Dabney's grippe or grip; devil's clutch; devil's grippe or grip; epidemic myalgia; pleurodynia; Taarbaek disease.

Bandia virus An unclassified ARBOVIRUS. With QALYUB VIRUS forms the Qalyub antigenic group. Isolated from mice and ticks of *Ornithodoros* sp. from the Bandia forest, Senegal. Not reported to cause disease in humans.

Bangoran virus An unclassified ARBOVIRUS. Isolated from the mosquito *Culex perfuscus* and the Kurrichane Thrush *Turdus liboyanus* in the Central African Republic. Not reported to cause human disease.

Bangor virus

McFerran J.B. *et al.* (1974) *Arch. ges. Virusforsch* **46**, 281

A species in the genus PARAMYXOVIRUS. Isolated from a finch in Northern Ireland. Antigenically related to, but distinct from YUCAIPA VIRUS. A similar virus has been isolated from a parrot (Collings D.F. *et al.* (1975) *Res. vet. Sci.* **19**, 219).

Bangui virus An unclassified ARBOVIRUS. Isolated from a man with fever, headache and rash in Bangui, Central African Republic.

Banzi virus A species in the genus FLAVIVIRUS. Isolated in S. Africa from a boy with a fever. Mosquito-borne. Natural hosts may be cattle and sheep. Found in S. Africa, Kenya, Tanzania, Zimbabwe and Mozambique. Does not appear to be a common cause of disease in humans.

Barur virus A species in the genus VESICULOVIRUS. Isolated from *Rattus rattus* and from the goat ticks *Haemaphysalis intermedia* in Karnatka, India. Also found in northern Canada. Not reported to cause disease in humans.

base analogue A substance with a structure resembling one of the purine or pyrimidine bases found in NUCLEIC ACID. It can be incorporated into a growing nucleic acid chain by substitution for the proper base, resulting in mutations or cessation of growth. It is thus an antimetabolite. Examples are 5-bromo-thymidine which substitutes for thymine in bacterial DNA, and 5-fluorouracil which substitutes for uracil in bacterial RNA.

Batai virus A species in the genus BUNYAVIRUS, belonging antigenically to the BUNYAMWERA ANTIGENIC GROUP. Isolated in India, Malaya, Thailand, Czechoslovakia and Ukrainian S.S.R. Mosquito-borne. Not reported to cause disease in humans.

Batken virus An unclassified ARBOVIRUS. Isolated from the sheep tick *Hyalomma p. plumbeum.* Found in Kirghiz S.S.R. Not reported to cause disease in humans.

Bat salivary virus Synonym for Rio Bravo virus.

Batu cave virus A species in the genus FLAVIVIRUS. Isolated from bats in Malaysia. Not reported to cause disease in humans.

Bauline virus A species in the genus ORBIVIRUS belonging to the KEMEROVO ANTIGENIC GROUP. Isolated from the tick *Ixodes uriae* on Great island, Newfoundland, Canada. Antibodies present in puffins and petrels. Not reported to cause disease in humans.

B14-150 cells (CCL 14·1) Heteroploid peritoneal cells from the Chinese hamster *Cricetulus griseus.* Initiated from the original B14 cell line by selection of cells resistant to BROMO-DEOXYURIDINE in the culture medium. This was later replaced by IDOXURIDINE to which the cells are now resistant.

Bebaru virus

Scherer W.F. *et al.* (1962) *Am. J. trop. Med. Hyg.* **11**, 269

A species in the genus ALPHAVIRUS. Isolated in Malaya from mosquitoes. No known association with disease in man.

Bedsonia Synonym for Chlamydia.

Belmont virus An unclassified ARBOVIRUS. Isolated from *Culex annulirostris* in eastern Queensland, Australia. Antibodies found in cattle, wallabies and kangaroos. Not known to cause disease in humans.

Benign epidermal monkey pox virus Synonym for tanapox virus.

Benign inoculation lymphoreticulosis virus Synonym for cat-scratch disease virus.

benzo[de]isoquinoline-1,3-diones

Garcia-Gancedo A. *et al.* (1979) *Chemother.* **25**, 83

5-nitro-2-(2-dimethylaminoethyl)- and 5-nitro-2-[2-(1-pyrrolidine)-ethyl]-benzo[de]isoquinoline-1,3-dione are both reported to inhibit replication of HUMAN (ALPHA) HERPESVIRUS 1 and VACCINIA VIRUS in chick embryo cultures. The inhibitory effect is time-related but not VIRUCIDAL. SINDBIS VIRUS and HUMAN INFLUENZA VIRUS are not affected. Infection of rabbit skin or eye with vaccinia virus could be prevented or reduced in severity by treatment with either drug.

Berry–Dedrick phenomenon

Berry G.P. & Dedrick H.M. (1936) *J. Bact.* **31**, 50

An example of nongenetic REACTIVATION. Rabbits infected with a mixture of heat-inactivated MYXOMA VIRUS and infectious RABBIT FIBROMA VIRUS die of myxomatosis. It was thought to be an example of genetic cross-reactivation, but appears to result from use by the inactivated virus of the DNA-DEPENDENT RNA POLYMERASE of the active virus to make its own mRNA.

Bertioga virus A species in the genus BUNYAVIRUS. With GAMBOA VIRUS forms the Gamboa Antigenic Group. Isolated from sentinel mice in Bertioga State of Sao Paulo, Brazil. Not reported to cause disease in humans.

Betaherpesvirinae A subfamily of the family HERPESVIRIDAE. Replicate relatively slowly with spreading CPE. Cause enlargement of infected cells, hence the common name

cytomegalovirus. Latent infection in the salivary glands and other tissues is frequent. INCLUSION BODIES containing DNA are often present in the nuclei and cytoplasm late in infection. The host range is usually narrow and they generally replicate best in fibroblasts. DNA mol. wt. 130–150 × 10^6. G+C CONTENT 56%. Sequences from either or both termini may be present in an inverted form internally. Two genera are identified but they have not been named. The type species of the first is HUMAN (BETA) HERPESVIRUS 5 and of the second MURID (BETA) HERPESVIRUS 1. Other possible species in the subfamily are SUID HERPESVIRUS 2, MURID HERPESVIRUS 2 and CAVIID HERPESVIRUS 1.
SYN: cytomegalovirus group.

Bhanja virus
Gaidamovich S.Ya. *et al.* (1979) *Intervirology* **11**, 288
An unclassified ARBOVIRUS, morphologically like BUNYAVIRUS but not serologically related to members of that genus. Isolated from ticks in India, Nigeria, Cameroon, Senegal, Yugoslavia and Italy. Also from cattle, sheep, hedgehog and squirrel. Has been described in association with a febrile disease in man.

BHK-21 cells (CCL 10)
Stoker M. & Macpherson I. (1964) *Nature, Lond.* **203**, 1355
Heteroploid cells derived from kidneys of 5 unsexed day-old Syrian or Golden hamsters *Mesocricetus auratus*. Has been used for POLYOMA VIRUS TRANSFORMATION, APHTHO VIRUS, RABIES and many ARBOVIRUS replication studies.

Big bone disease virus Synonym for osteopetrosis virus.

Bimbo virus An unclassified ARBOVIRUS. Isolated from a healthy specimen of the Golden Bishop Bird *Buplectes afer* in Central African Republic. Not reported to cause disease in humans.

Bimiti virus A species in the genus BUNYAVIRUS, belonging to the GUAMA ANTIGENIC GROUP. Isolated from *Culex spissipes* in Trinidad. Also found in Brazil, French Guiana and Surinam. Not reported to cause disease in humans.

Biphasic milk fever virus Synonym for tick-borne encephalitis virus (Central European subtype).

Birao virus A species in the genus BUNYAVIRUS, belonging to the BUNYAMWERA ANTIGENIC GROUP. Isolated from *Anopheles pharoensis* and *A. squamosus* in Central African Republic. Not reported to cause disease in humans.

Bird papilloma virus Synonym for fringilla papilloma virus.

Bird pox virus Synonym for fowl pox virus.

Bittner virus The first of the MOUSE MAMMARY TUMOUR VIRUSES isolated from C_3H mice. It is a highly oncogenic virus transmitted in the milk. Foster-nursed mice are free of the virus but may continue to carry a mammary tumour virus of low oncogenicity. The virus is also known as C_3H mammary tumour virus and as MTV-S.
SYN: milk factor.

Biundulant meningo-encephalitis virus Synonym for tick-borne encephalitis virus (Central European subtype).

BK virus
Yang, R.C.A. & Wu R. (1979) *Science* **206**, 456
Gardner S.D. (1977) *Recent Adv. in Clin. Virol.* **1**, 93. Ed. A.P. Waterson, Publ. Churchill Livingstone
A species in the genus POLYOMAVIRUS. Distinct from JC VIRUS and other members of the genus. Agglutinates human group O erythrocytes. Originally isolated from the urine of a patient on immunosuppressive therapy after renal transplantation. Presence of antibodies in humans suggests it is a common infection of man, probably of the kidneys, usually silent but activated by immunosuppressive therapy. Can be propagated in VERO CELLS or primary human foetal kidney cells. Has not been associated with progressive multifocal leukoencephalopathy. Transforms rat and hamster cells in culture and is oncogenic on injection into new-born hamsters.

blind passage Transmission of material from an inoculated animal or cell culture which shows no evidence of infection, to a fresh animal or cell culture.

Blue comb virus This term has been used for two viruses causing similar diseases, *viz.* TURKEY BLUECOMB DISEASE VIRUS and INFECTIOUS ENTERITIS VIRUS. In some early papers it is difficult to decide which virus is being discussed.

blue-green algal viruses. Synonym for cyanophages.

Blue tongue antigenic group

Gorman B.M. (1979) *J. gen. Virol.* **44**, 1

Three groups of viruses sharing a common CF antigen, but distinguishable by NEUTRALIZATION TESTS. Since they have segmented GENOMES, genetic reassortment can occur in mixed infection with the generation of multiple antigenic types. They are:

(1) BLUE TONGUE VIRUS: 20 serotypes.

(2) EPIZOOTIC HAEMORRHAGIC DISEASE OF DEER VIRUS: 8 serotypes.

(3) the former Eubenangee antigenic group consisting of EUBENANGEE VIRUS, PATA VIRUS, TILLIGERRY VIRUS and IBARAKI VIRUS.

Blue tongue virus

Bowne J.G. (1971) *Adv. vet. Sci. comp. Med.* **15**, 1

Howell P.G. & Verwoerd D.W. (1971) *Virol. Monographs.* **9**, 35

Hoff G. & Trainer D.O. (1978) *Adv. Vet. Sci. comp. Med.* **22**, 111

A species in the genus ORBIVIRUS. 20 serotypes can be identified by NEUTRALIZATION TESTS. There is a group specific CF antigen. Causes a serious disease of sheep with a mortality of 5–30%. There is fever, oedema of the head and neck, cyanosis, erosions around the mouth, sometimes pulmonary oedema and lameness due to involvement of the hooves and muscle damage. Cattle and goats develop a much milder disease. Foot-lesions occur in pigs. Wild ruminants are often infected. The infection is prevalent mainly in Africa, especially in the east and south, but has occurred recently in Cyprus, Palestine, Turkey, Spain, Portugal, Pakistan, India, Japan and southern and western U.S.A. The virus is transmitted by nocturnal biting flies of the genus *Culicoides*. Virus replication occurs in the insects but there is no evidence of transovarial transmission. Infectivity is ether-resistant. VIRIONS have a BUOYANT DENSITY of 1·38–1·36 g/cm³, SEDIMENTATION COEFFICIENT of 600 S and contain 20% double-stranded RNA which is in 10 segments. There is also some single-stranded RNA of unknown function. Virions are icosahedral, 53–68 nm in diameter. Unlike REOVIRIDAE there is a diffuse outer case removed by exposure to CsCl. The outer COAT may contain 92 CAPSOMERES. The inner shell has a diameter of 54–64 nm and contains 32 capsomeres. Replication occurs on yolk sac inoculation of 6 day old eggs at 33·5 °C. Replication with CPE occurs in cell cultures of lamb kidney, hamster and chick embryo tissue and in BHK-21 CELLS. An egg-attenuated vaccine is effective if polyvalent.

SYN: ovine catarrhal fever virus; sore mouth virus.

Bobaya virus A species in the genus BUNYAVIRUS. With OLIFANTSVLEI VIRUS forms the Olifantsvlei antigenic group. Isolated in suckling mice from the pooled brain, liver and heart of an adult African thrush *Turdus libonyanus* netted at M'Boko, Central African Republic. Not known to infect humans.

Bocas virus

Bardos V. *et al.* (1980) *Intervirology* **13**, 275

Closely related to or identical with MOUSE HEPATITIS VIRUS. On first isolation thought to be an ARBOVIRUS of the CALIFORNIA ANTIGENIC GROUP.

Bolivian haemorrhagic fever virus Synonym for Machupo virus.

Bollinger bodies Intracytoplasmic acidophilic INCLUSION BODIES found in cells infected with FOWL POX VIRUS.

Boracea virus An unclassified ARBOVIRUS, morphologically like BUNYAVIRUS but not serologically related to members of that genus. Isolated from *Anopheles cruzii* and *Phoniomyia pilicauda* in Casa Grande, State of Sao Paulo, Brazil. Not reported to cause disease in humans. Together with ANOPHELES B VIRUS forms the Anopheles B antigenic group.

Border disease virus

Barlow R.M. *et al.* (1979) *Vet. Rec.* **104**, 334

Vautsis J.T. *et al.* (1976) *J. comp. Path.* **86**, 111

A species in the genus PESTIVIRUS. Causes a disease first described from the borders of Wales. A congenital condition of new-born lambs characterised by an abnormally hairy birthcoat and a tremor. There is defective myelination of the CNS caused by the virus crossing the placenta to infect the foetus. Virus can be isolated from the CNS of affected lambs. A similar disease has been described in Germany, Australia and New Zealand. The virus replicates in cultures of primary calf and foetal lamb kidney cells. Cell depletion is seen and infected cells can be stained with fluorescent-labelled antiserum. Infected lambs develop antibodies to HOG CHOLERA VIRUS and to MUCOSAL DISEASE VIRUS to which border disease virus is antigenically related. Injection of non-pregnant ewes causes no obvious disease, but in pregnant animals there is necrotizing carunculitis, abortion, and border disease in those young which are not aborted.

SYN: pestivirus ovis.

Borna disease virus

Mayr A. & Danner K. (1974) *Infektion* **2**, 64

An unclassified ARBOVIRUS. Causes lassitude, followed by excitation with tonic spasms and later paralysis in horses. A similar disease is produced in sheep, cattle and probably deer. Experimental infection of rabbits produces a similar disease. Guinea pigs, rats and mice are less susceptible. Human infection is not reported. Occurs mainly in Saxony but also in other parts of Germany, Poland, Rumania, Russia, Syria and Egypt. A virus causing staggers in horses in Nigeria may be the same. The virus has been isolated from ticks of several genera and from the brains of herons and other wild birds. Transmission by oral and nasal secretions is possible. A virus vaccine has been used with success. Virus passes through a 20 nm APD membrane. Replicates on the CAM and in cultures of lamb testis and monkey kidney cells with CPE.

Bornholm disease A name assigned in Denmark in 1932 to a local outbreak of a disease more accurately referred to as BAMBLE DISEASE.

Borrel bodies Minute granules composing the BOLLINGER BODIES found in FOWL POX VIRUS infected cells.

Borrielota variolae bovis

Goodpasture E.W. (1933) *Science* **77**, 119

ELEMENTARY BODIES associated with cells infected with VACCINIA VIRUS.

Borrielota variolae hominis

Goodpasture E.W. (1933) *Science* **77**, 119

ELEMENTARY BODIES associated with cells infected with SMALLPOX VIRUS.

Botambi virus A species in the genus BUNYAVIRUS. Not assigned to an antigenic group. Isolated from *Culex guiarti* in Central African Republic. Not reported to cause disease in humans.

Boteke virus An unclassified ARBOVIRUS. Together with ZINGILAMO VIRUS forms the Boteke antigenic group. Isolated from the mosquito *Mansonia maculipennis* in Central African Republic. Not reported to cause disease in humans.

Bothid herpesvirus 1

Buchanan J.S. *et al.* (1978) *Vet. Rec.* **102**, 527

A species in the family HERPESVIRIDAE. Isolated from turbot *Scophthalmus maximus* in a fish farm where many fish were dying. Probably endemic in wild fish.

SYN: turbot herpesvirus.

Bouboui virus A species in the genus FLAVIVIRUS. Isolated from mosquitoes, and a baboon

Papio papio, in the Central African Republic, Senegal and Cameroon. Probably present in Zaire. Not reported to cause disease in humans.

Bovid (alpha) herpesvirus 2 A species in the family HERPESVIRIDAE. Not distinguishable from Allerton virus isolated in S. Africa from lumpy skin disease and thought to be the cause of this condition. Causes deep, slowly healing ulcers on the teats and udders of milking cows, and lesions are produced on the lips of calves which suckle them. In S. Africa the virus may be transmitted by insects. Infection of day-old rats, mice and hamsters may lead to stunted growth, rashes and death. There is replication in calf kidney cell cultures with formation of large syncytia. A viable unattenuated virus given i/m gives some protection. Shares 14% of DNA sequences with HUMAN HERPESVIRUS 1.

SYN: Allerton virus; bovine mammillitis virus; bovine ulcerative mammillitis virus.

Bovid herpesvirus 1

Gibbs E.P.J. & Rweyemamu M.M. (1977) *Vet. Bull.* **47**, 317

Narita M. *et al.* (1979) *Brit. J. exp. Path.* **60**, 11

A species in the family HERPESVIRIDAE. A natural world wide infection in cattle, but antibodies can be found in mule deer *Odontocoileus* sp. May cause a silent, mild infection, or acute disease of the whole respiratory tract. Mortality can be as high as 75%. In Europe it has been known to cause conjunctivitis, and, notably, disease of the genital tract, when lesions appear on the external genitalia. There is no evidence of antigenic difference between the respiratory and genital strains. Young goats infected experimentally develop fever; in rabbits there is meningo-encephalitis with paralysis of the hind legs. Transmission of the virus is by contact, expecially under crowded conditions. Has been cultivated in bovine embryo cell cultures, with CPE in 1–2 days, but there is loss of virulence. Replication also occurs in pig, sheep, goat and horse kidney cell cultures and in human amnion cultures. There is TRANSFORMATION of hamster cells *in vitro*. No growth in eggs. All strains are antigenically very similar and an attenuated virus can be used as a vaccine.

SYN: infectious bovine rhinotracheitis virus; infectious pustular vulvo-vaginitis virus; necrotic rhinitis virus; red nose virus.

Bovid herpesvirus 2 Synonym for bovid (alpha) herpesvirus 2.

Bovid herpesvirus 3

Straver P.J. & Bekkum J.G. van (1979) *Res. vet. Sci.* **26**, 165

A species in the family HERPESVIRIDAE. Causes a widespread, sporadic, very fatal disease of cattle, with fever, acute inflammation of nasal and oral membranes, and involvement of pharynx and lungs. There is often keratitis and nervous symptoms. Epidemiological evidence suggests that infection can be transmitted to cattle from wildebeest and sheep which may have a SILENT INFECTION. The virus can be transmitted experimentally to cattle and rabbits. There is replication in bovine thyroid and adrenal cell culture; doubtful in eggs.

SYN: bovine epitheliosis virus; malignant catarrhal fever virus; Snotsiekte virus; wildebeest herpesvirus.

Bovid herpesvirus 4

Martin W.B. *et al.* (1976) *Nature, Lond.* **264**, 183

A species in the family HERPESVIRIDAE. Isolated in Britain and Africa from pulmonary adenomatosis of sheep, but is probably not the cause. Cell-free transmission to cultures is possible, but animals are not infected by cultivated virus. Infection is probably by the respiratory route, but most contact experiments failed. May be a cause of respiratory disease in calves which predisposes them to bacterial disease of the respiratory tract.

Bovid herpesvirus 5 (Number assigned by us)

Berrios P.E. *et al.* (1975) *Am. J. vet. Res.* **36**, 1755, 1763

A species in the family HERPESVIRIDAE. Isolated from kids *Capra hircus* with a severe generalised infection. Experimental infection of these animals produces a severe febrile

disease, and in adult pregnant goats there is fever and abortion. Not pathogenic for lambs and calves. The virus replicates in bovine, rabbit and lamb cell cultures with CPE, but not in HELA, VERO, or chick embryo cells. It is antigenically distinct from BOVID HERPESVIRUS 1.
SYN: caprine herpesvirus 1; goat herpesvirus; herpesvirus caprae.

Bovine adeno-associated virus
Luchsinger E. & Wellemans G. (1971) *Arch. ges. Virusforsch.* **35**, 203
A species in the genus ADENO-ASSOCIATED VIRUS. Found in association with BOVINE ADENOVIRUS. Not known to be pathogenic.

Bovine adenovirus
Darbyshire J.H. (1973) *Prog. exp. tumor res.* **18**, 56
Mohanty S.B. (1978). *Adv. vet. Sci. comp. Med.* **22**, 83
A species in the genus MASTADENOVIRUS. Ten serotypes are described. Associated with respiratory infection and conjunctivitis in cattle. Serological evidence suggests a high incidence of infection. Replication with CPE in bovine kidney cell cultures. Agglutination of erythrocytes of several species: mouse, monkey, cattle, horse, goats, guinea pig, and hamster. Types 3 and 8 are oncogenic in new-born hamsters.

Bovine coronavirus Synonym for neonatal calf diarrhoea coronavirus.

Bovine diarrhoea virus Synonym for pestivirus diarrhoea virus.

Bovine enteroviruses
Kalter S.S. (1960) *Bull. W.H.O.* **22**, 319
Picornaviruses isolated in cell cultures from bovine tissues or excreta. There are many serotypes and some agglutinate bovine erythrocytes at 5°–8°. One strain is reported to produce diarrhoea in colostrum-deprived calves. They may be a cause of infertility in bulls.
SYN: ecboviruses

Bovine ephemeral fever virus Synonym for ephemeral fever virus.

Bovine epitheliosis virus Synonym for bovid herpesvirus 3.

Bovine epizootic fever virus Synonym for ephemeral fever virus.

Bovine haemadsorbing enteric virus Synonym for bovine parvovirus.

Bovine influenza virus Synonym for ephemeral fever virus.

Bovine leukaemia virus Synonym for bovine type C oncovirus.

Bovine mammillitis virus Synonym for bovid (alpha) herpesvirus 2.

Bovine papilloma virus
Lancaster W.D. *et al.* (1979) *Intervirology* **11**, 227
Meischke H.R.C. (1979) *J. gen. Virol.* **43**, 473
Pfister H. *et al.* (1979) *Virology* **96**, 1
A species in the genus PAPILLOMAVIRUS. A natural infection of cattle causing papillomas with underlying fibroma mainly on the head and neck but also in mouth and oesophagus. The same or similar virus may be involved in the aetiology of bladder tumours and carcinomas of the upper alimentary tract. Produces slowly growing fibrosarcomas on injection into hamsters and C_3H/EB mice, and connective tissue tumours in horses. Causes TRANSFORMATION of embryo cultures of mouse, hamster and bovine tissues. Virus particles (full or empty) agglutinate mouse erythrocytes at 4° between pH 6·8 and 8·4. Elutes readily at 37°. Receptors not destroyed by INFLUENZA VIRUS NEURAMINIDASE.

Bovine papular stomatitis virus
Menna, A. *et al.* (1979) *Arch. Virol.* **59**, 145
A species in the genus PARAPOXVIRUS. Causes a usually benign, non-febrile disease, most often in young cattle. There are crateriform ulcers up to 1 cm in diameter in the mouth. Some strains may infect sheep and goats. Transmission to man is reported.
SYN: erosive stomatitis virus of cattle; papular stomatitis of cattle virus; pseudo-aphthous stomatitis of cattle virus; stomatitis papulosa of cattle virus; ulcerative stomatitis of cattle virus.

Bovine parvovirus A species in the genus PARVOVIRUS. A common infection of cattle. Isolated from the genito-urinary tract. Role as a pathogen is doubtful but probably can cause diarrhoea in calves. Has usually been isolated from faecal specimens from calves with enteric disease, but can be isolated from many tissues after injection into colostrum-deprived calves. The only strains antigenically different from the original haden strain of bovine parvovirus 1 have been isolated in Japan. Unrelated antigenically to other parvoviruses. Agglutinates erythrocytes of several species including guinea pig and man. Replicates in bovine embryo kidney cell cultures with CPE.
SYN: bovine haemadsorbing enteric virus; HADEN virus; haemadsorbing enteric virus of calves.

Bovine respiratory syncytial virus

Lehmkuhl H.D. *et al.* (1979) *Am. J. vet. Res.* **40**, 124

A species in the genus PNEUMOVIRUS. Causes a mild respiratory disease in cattle. Replicates in bovine kidney and lung cell cultures causing syncytia. Inactivated by lipid solvents. Reciprocal antigenic cross-reaction with human respiratory syncytial virus. Does not replicate in human, monkey, hamster or sheep cells.
SYN: respiratory syncytial virus of bovines.

Bovine respiratory viruses

Mohanty S.B. (1978) *Adv. Vet. Sci. comp. Med.* **22**, 83.

Respiratory disease is an important problem in the cattle industry. Viruses appear to be the primary cause but stress plays an important role and viral infection predisposes to bacterial invasion. The viruses are:

bovid herpesvirus 1, 3 and 4
bovine adenovirus
parainfluenza type 3
bovine respiratory syncytial
bovine diarrhoea
reovirus
bovine rhinovirus
ephemeral fever

Bovine rhinovirus

Bögel K. (1968) *J. Am. vet. med. Ass.* **152**, 780

Hussain A. & Mohanty S.B. (1979) *Arch. Virol.* **59**, 17.

A species in the genus RHINOVIRUS. Two serotypes have been described. Replicates best in calf kidney cells at 33 ° and low bicarbonate. A widespread infection with low pathogenicity for calves, causing nasal discharge. Does not infect other animals.

Bovine syncytial virus

Dermott E. *et al.* (1971) *J. gen. Virol.* **12**, 105

Woode G.N. & Smith K. (1973) *J. gen. Virol.* **21**, 425

Greig A.S. (1978) *Canad. J. comp. Med.* **43**, 112

A species in the subfamily SPUMAVIRINAE. Isolated from buffy coat, spleen, lymph nodes and milk of lymphosarcomatous and normal cattle. Can be propagated in BHK 21 CELLS producing syncytia. Little free virus is produced. Infection appears to be common in cattle in U.S.A. and Europe. Produces a persistent infection. Different from BOVINE RESPIRATORY SYNCYTIAL VIRUS.

Bovine type C oncovirus

Piper C.E. *et al.* (1979) *J. nat. Cancer Inst.* **62**, 165

Mussgay M. & Kaaden, O.R. (1978) *Current Topics Microbiol. Immunol.* **79**, 43

A species of the subgenus MAMMALIAN TYPE C ONCOVIRUS. Mitogen-stimulated cultures of lymphocytes from infected cattle produce virus, but in bovine cells only a little virus is produced. However, in bat lung cells, foetal lamb kidney and several other cell lines, virus is continuously released in abundant quantity. Cattle, sheep and goats injected with the virus become infected, produce antibodies to the viral internal antigen, and some sheep and cattle later develop lymphosarcoma. Human, simian, bovine, ovine, bat and caprine cells exposed to the virus or bovine leukaemic cells form syncytia, probably by cell fusion. Antiserum prevents syncytia formation. This can be used to assay both virus and

antiserum. Antibody-positive animals are common in herds with high incidence of leukaemia and colostrum provides protection against infection in the first 5–6 months of life. Infection is acquired by contact with infected animals after the maternal antibody has disappeared. The virus differs from other mammalian type C oncoviruses in producing syncytia, in not having the interspecies mammalian antigen, and in having a DNA polymerase with preferential activity for Mg^{2+}.
SYN: bovine leukaemia virus; enzootic bovine leukosis virus.

Bovine ulcerative mammillitis virus Synonym for bovid (alpha) herpesvirus 2.

Bovine visna-like virus

Van der Maaten M.J. *et al.* (1972) *J. natn. Cancer Inst.* **49**, 1649
Georgiades J.A. *et al.* (1978) *J. gen. Virol.* **38**, 375

Probably a species of the subfamily LENTIVIRINAE. Isolated from a cow with persistent lymphocytosis. Replicates in cultures of bovine embryonic spleen cells, with the slow formation of multinuclear giant cells similar to those produced by BOVINE SYNCYTIAL VIRUS. However, the two viruses differ morphologically and antigenically. Experimental infection of cows results in enlarged peripheral lymph nodes and hyperlymphocytosis. The disease may last over a year, during which time the virus can be re-isolated.

Brazil virus Synonym for Indiana 3 strain of vesicular stomatitis virus. Probably the same as ALAGOAS VIRUS.

Breakbone fever virus Synonym for dengue virus.

brilliant cresyl blue A photoreactive dye. *See* photodynamic inactivation.

bromelain

Compans R.W. *et al.* (1970) *Virology* **42**, 880

A proteolytic enzyme isolated from pineapple stem which can be used to remove the PEPLOMERS from the surface of enveloped viruses such as influenza.

5-bromo-2-deoxyuridine A halogenated pyrimidine which can become incorporated into cellular DNA in place of thymidine. Incorporation may activate the transcription of viral RNA from genes integrated into the cellular DNA, such as those of RETROVIRIDAE.

Bryan strain of Rous sarcoma virus A high titre strain, highly oncogenic and much used in experimental work.

BS-C-1 (CCL 26) A continuous cell line from kidneys of the African green monkey *Cercopithecus aethiops*. Develops characteristic CPE when infected with SIMIAN VIRUS 40. A valuable tool for viral diagnostic studies.

B type particles

Bernard W. (1960) *Cancer Res.* **20**, 712
Dalton A.J. (1972) *J. natn. Cancer Inst.* **49**, 323

A term used originally by electron microscopists to describe a morphologically defined group of enveloped RNA virus particles seen typically outside the cells in mouse mammary carcinoma. They are always extracellular. They have a dense body or CORE (nucleoid) 40 to 60 nm in diameter contained within a membranous sac or ENVELOPE 90 to 120 nm in diameter. The membrane is covered with protrusions. The nucleoid is usually eccentrically located within the envelope. Occasionally one envelope may contain more than one nucleoid. B TYPE PARTICLES bud through the cell membrane and contain an internal constituent morphologically indistinguishable from an A TYPE PARTICLE which becomes the core.

budding A method of virus release from the cell in which replication has taken place. Occurs with all enveloped animal viruses. The viral ribonucleoprotein, with or without a surrounding membrane protein, associates with an area of the cell membrane which starts to form a COAT around the virus protein. In electron micrographs it appears as a crescentic structure. The cell membrane closes around the virus and the particle leaves the cell. During the budding process, all cellular proteins in the area of membrane destined to become the virus coat are replaced by virus-coded proteins. Thus, in the mature virus particle, the ENVELOPE lipid is host-cell derived, but all proteins are virus-coded. The exact mechanism of this process is unknown.

Budgerigar parainfluenza virus

Mustaffa-Babjee A. *et al.* (1974) *Avian Dis.* **18**, 226

A species in the genus PARAMYXOVIRUS. Isolated from caged budgerigars during an outbreak of severe enteritis. Similar to NEWCASTLE DISEASE VIRUS but distinct from it and from YUCAIPA VIRUS.

Buffalo pox virus

Baxby D. & Hill B.J. (1969) *Vet. Rec.* **85**, 315

A species in the genus ORTHOPOXVIRUS. Causes outbreaks of severe disease in India. The pocks produced on the CAM are similar to those produced by VACCINIA VIRUS, but they do not appear at temperatures above 38 °. Though some strains are obviously different from vaccinia virus, many cases of clinical disease in buffaloes are caused by viruses which appear to be identical to it. Very similar to LENNY VIRUS.

Bu(IMR-31) cells (CCL 40) A line of near diploid fibroblasts from male yearling buffalo *Bison bison*. Finite life-expectancy of at least 30 passages. Supports replication of a large number of viruses.

Buist bodies

Buist, J.B. (1886) *Proc. R. Soc. Edin.* **13**, 603

A synonym and probably the proper name for the elementary particles known as PASCHEN BODIES. The credit for their discovery is usually given to Paschen (1906), but Buist's account anticipates this by many years.

Buistia pascheni

Mackie T.J. & van Rooyen C.E. (1937) *Edin. med. J.* **44**, 72

A synonym proposed for PASCHEN BODIES in order to commemorate the work of both Paschen and Buist. *See* Buist bodies.

Bujaru virus An unclassified ARBOVIRUS, morphologically like BUNYAVIRUS but unrelated serologically to members of that genus. Isolated from the rodent *Proechimys guyannensis oris* in Para, Brazil. Not known to cause disease in humans.

Bukalasa bat virus A species in the genus FLAVIVIRUS. Isolated from bats in West Africa. No known arthropod vector.

Bunyamwera antigenic group viruses Eighteen serologically related viruses in the genus BUNYAVIRUS.

Anhembi (C,R)
Batai (C,A)
Birao (A)
Bunyamwera* (C,H)
Cache Valley (C,A)
Calovo*† (A)
Germiston* (C,H,R)
Guaroa* (A,H)
Ilesha* (A,H)
Kairi (C,R)
Lokern (C,Cu)
Maguari‡ (C,A)
Main Drain (Cu)
Northway (C)
Sororoca (C)
Tensaw*‡ (C,A)
Tlacotalpan‡ (C,A)
Wyeomyia* (C,A,H)

Isolated from:
(C) *Culicine mosquitoes*
(A) *Anopheline mosquitoes*
(Cu) *Culicoides flies*
(H) *Humans*
(R) *Rodents*
* *Can cause disease in man.*
† *Strain of Batai virus.*
‡ *Strains of Cache Valley virus.*

Bunyamwera supergroup of arboviruses Old name for the genus BUNYAVIRUS.

Bunyamwera virus A species in the genus BUNYAVIRUS. A member of the BUNYAMWERA ANTIGENIC GROUP. Isolated in Uganda, Nigeria, Cameroon, Kenya and Central African Republic where it has caused a few cases of fever with a rash in humans. Mosquito-borne.

Bunyaviridae

Bishop D.H.L. & Shope R.E. (1979) in *Comprehensive Virology*, **14**, 1
Porterfield J.S. (1976) *Intervirology* **6**, 13
Obijeski J.F. & Murphy F.A. (1977) *J. gen. Virol.* **37**, 1

A family of enveloped spherical viruses 90–100 nm in diameter. The lipid ENVELOPE contains at least one virus-specific glycopeptide. The internal ribonucleoprotein consists of long strands 2–2·5 nm wide. The GENOME is single-stranded RNA of mol. wt. $6–7 \times 10^6$ in 3 pieces with mol. wt. of 4, 2 and $0{\cdot}8 \times 10^6$. Develop in the cytoplasm and mature by budding into smooth-surfaced vesicles in the Golgi region or nearby. Contains 1 genus at present, BUNYAVIRUS. There are in addition 10 serological groups and 7 ungrouped viruses which will probably be placed in 2 or more genera to be created within the family. The 10 serological groups are:

Uukuniemi
Anopheles A
Anopheles B
Bakau
Congo
Kaisodi
Mapputta
Nairobi Sheep Disease
Phlebotomus fever
Turlock

The ungrouped viruses are:

Bhanja
Kowanyama
Lone Star
Rift Valley fever
Tataguine
Thogoto
Witwatersrand

Bunyavirus A genus of the family BUNYAVIRIDAE consisting of at least 87 species of virus which show some degree of antigenic relationship, though not so close as exists between species of the genus ALPHAVIRUS or FLAVIVIRUS. They can be divided into 10 antigenic groups and a number of as yet ungrouped viruses. The antigenic groups are:

Bunyamwera
C.
Capim
Koongol
Simbu
Bwamba
California
Guama
Patois
Tete

The ungrouped species are:

Botambi
Guaratuba
Kaeng Khoi
Mirim
Gamboa
Jurona
Minatitlan

Most are mosquito-borne but some (Tete group) are tick-borne. Some show transovarial transmission.

buoyant density The density of a particle expressed in terms of the density of a fluid in which it neither sinks nor floats. *See* isopycnic gradient centrifugation.

Burg el Arab virus An unclassified ARBOVIRUS belonging to the MATARIYA ANTIGENIC GROUP. Isolated from a bird *Sylvia curruca* in Egypt. Probably also present in Europe since the bird was viraemic on arrival in Egypt on its way south. Not reported to cause disease in humans.

Burkitt's lymphoma virus Synonym for human (gamma) herpesvirus 4.

burst size In a ONE-STEP GROWTH CURVE, the burst size is the average number of progeny virus particles produced per infected cell.

busatin *See* methisazone.

Bushbush virus A species in the genus BUNYAVIRUS belonging to the CAPIM ANTIGENIC GROUP. Isolated from mosquitoes in Trinidad, and Belem, Brazil. Not known to cause disease in humans.

Bussuquara virus A species in the genus FLAVIVIRUS. Isolated from man, sentinel howler monkeys *Alouatta*, sentinel mice, and *Culex* sp. in Colombia, Panama, and Para, Brazil. A case of febrile disease in man has been reported.

Button willow virus A species in the genus BUNYAVIRUS, belonging to the SIMBU ANTIGENIC GROUP. Isolated from rabbits, hares, and *Culicoides* sp. in Kern County, California, also New Mexico and Texas, U.S.A. Probably present in other parts of the U.S.A. Not reported to cause disease in humans.

734 B virus A species in the genus TYPE B ONCOVIRUS GROUP. Present in MCF-7 cells, a line derived from a pleural effusion from a patient with disseminated mammary adenocarcinoma. No antigenic relationship with TYPE C ONCOVIRUSES, but some cross-reaction with MOUSE MAMMARY TUMOUR VIRUS.

B virus of monkeys Synonym for cercopithecid herpesvirus 1.

Bwamba virus A species in the genus BUNYAVIRUS. With PONGOLA VIRUS forms the Bwamba antigenic group. Isolated from 9 cases of fever in humans in Bwamba, Uganda. Also from *Anopheles funestus*. Present also in Nigeria and the Central African Republic.

Cacao virus An unclassified ARBOVIRUS morphologically like BUNYAVIRUS but not serologically related to members of that genus. Belongs to the PHLEBOTOMUS FEVER ANTIGENIC GROUP. Isolated from *Lutzomyia* sp. in Panama. Not reported to cause disease in humans.

Cache Valley virus

Inverson J.O. *et al.* (1979) *Canad. J. Microbiol.* **25**, 760

A species in the genus BUNYAVIRUS, belonging to the BUNYAMWERA ANTIGENIC GROUP. Isolated in N. Dakota, Maryland, Virginia, Indiana, U.S.A. and in Jamaica. Mosquito-borne. Antibodies are found in man, monkeys, horses, cattle and wild rodents. Not reported to cause disease in humans.

Caimito virus An unclassified ARBOVIRUS. Morphologically like BUNYAVIRUS but antigenically unrelated to members of that genus. Belongs to the PHLEBOTOMUS FEVER ANTIGENIC GROUP. Isolated from the fan fly *Lutzomyia ylephilator* in central Panama. Not reported to cause human disease.

Calf diarrhoea virus *See* neonatal calf diarrhoea coronavirus *and* calf rotavirus.

Calf rotavirus A species in the genus ROTAVIRUS. Causes acute enteritis with diarrhoea in calves. Antibodies are found in many herds. The virus is antigenically related to other rotaviruses. Can be replicated in calf cell culture. A similar disease is caused by NEONATAL CALF DIARRHOEA CORONAVIRUS.

Caliciviridae

Burroughs J.N. & Brown F. (1974) *J. gen. Virol.* **22**, 281

Cooper P.D. *et al.* (1978) *Intervirology* **10**, 165

Studdert M.J. (1978) *Arch. Virol.* **58**, 157

A family of RNA viruses, 35–40 nm in diameter, with typical surface structures, sometimes described as hollows or cups, hence the name from Latin: *calyx* = cup. Non-enveloped, ether-resistant, variable stability at pH 5, unstable at pH 3, probably ICOSAHEDRAL SYMMETRY with 32 CAPSOMERES. GENOME consists of SINGLE-STRANDED RNA of mol. wt. $2{\cdot}6$–$2{\cdot}7 \times 10^6$. There is one VIRION protein of mol. wt. 60,000–70,000. Replicates in the cytoplasm. Species are VESICULAR EXANTHEMA OF PIGS VIRUS, very similar to SAN-MIGUEL SEA-LION VIRUS and FELINE CALICIVIRUS. Morphologically similar virus particles have been seen in the faeces of human infants and calves with diarrhoea.

Calicivirus Formerly a genus in the family PICORNAVIRIDAE. Now raised to the status of a family CALICIVIRIDAE.

California antigenic group viruses

Hubalek Z. *et al.* (1979) *J. gen. Virol.* **42**, 357

Twelve serologically related viruses in the genus BUNYAVIRUS.

California encephalitis* (C)	Lumbo (C)
Inkoo* (C)	Melao (C)
Jamestown Canyon† (C)	San Angelo† (A)
Jerry Slough (C)	Snowshoe hare (L,C)
Keystone† (C,A,R)	Tahyna*† (C,A,H)
La Crosse*† (C,H)	Trivittatus (C,R)

* *Can cause disease in man.*

† *May be regarded as subtypes of* CALIFORNIA ENCEPHALITIS VIRUS.

Isolated from:

(C) Culicine mosquitoes	*(R) Rodents*
(A) Anopheline mosquitoes	*(Ba) Bats*
(H) Humans	*(L) Lemmings, Hares*

California encephalitis virus A species in the genus BUNYAVIRUS belonging to the CALIFORNIA ANTIGENIC GROUP. Isolated from mosquitoes in California, Utah, New Mexico and Texas, U.S.A. Has been associated with a few cases of encephalitis in humans. Antibodies to other group members cross-react so that presence of antibodies does not prove presence of a specific virus.

California rabbit fibroma virus A species in the genus LEPORIPOXVIRUS. Antigenically similar to MYXOMA VIRUS and RABBIT FIBROMA VIRUS. Causes fibromas in its natural host *Sylvilagus bachmani* in California, and experimentally in other *Sylvilagus* sp. In European rabbits it causes a fatal disease without the typical swellings of myxomatosis.

Callitrichid herpesvirus 1 So named because of its original isolation from marmosets (Callitrichid monkeys). Synonym for cebid herpesvirus 1.

Calovo virus A species in the genus BUNYAVIRUS belonging to the BUNYAMWERA ANTIGENIC GROUP. Isolated from mosquitoes in Czechoslovakia, Austria and Yugoslavia. Can cause a febrile illness in man.

Camel pox virus

Al Falluji M.M. *et al.* (1979) *J. Hyg. Camb.* **83**, 267

Davies F.G. *et al.* (1975) *J. Hyg. Camb.* **75**, 381

A species in the genus ORTHOPOXVIRUS. Causes pustules around the lips and nose, and sometimes keratitis. Usually mild but may be severe, causing abortions. Incubation period 4–15 days. Epidemics occur every 3–5 years in camels in the Middle East, N. Africa, Pakistan and southern U.S.S.R. May cause lesions on the hands of camel drivers. Lesions produced on the CAM are very similar to those caused by VARIOLA VIRUS but in cell cultures giant cells are produced. Has a very limited host-range.

SYN: photo-Shootur virus

Canadian vomiting and wasting disease of pigs virus Synonym for porcine haemagglutinating encephalitis virus.

Canary pox virus A species in the genus AVIPOXVIRUS. Similar to FOWL POX VIRUS. Causes a fatal infection in canaries, with pneumonia and exudate over serous membranes. Sparrows are susceptible, chickens usually not.

Candiru virus An unclassified ARBOVIRUS morphologically like BUNYAVIRUS but not serologically related to members of that genus. Belongs to the PHLEBOTOMUS FEVER ANTIGENIC GROUP. Isolated from a man with febrile illness in Para, Brazil. Not found to replicate in mosquitoes experimentally.

Canid herpesvirus 1 A species in the family HERPESVIRIDAE. A natural infection in dogs, often silent but may cause necrotising rhinitis and pneumonia, frequently fatal in new-born

puppies. May cause tracheo-bronchitis (KENNEL COUGH) in older animals but this condition can also be caused by an adenovirus. Replicates in dog kidney cell cultures with CPE. No CPE in human, bovine or porcine cell cultures.
SYN: canine herpesvirus; canine tracheo-bronchitis virus; kennel cough virus.

Canine adeno-associated virus
Ishihara C. & Yanagawa R. (1975) *Jap. J. vet. Res.* **23**, 95
A species in the genus ADENO-ASSOCIATED VIRUS. Antibodies are commonly present in dogs in Japan. No evidence of pathogenicity.

Canine adenovirus
Wright N.G. (1976) *J. small Anim. Pract.* **17**, 25
Emery J.B. *et al.* (1978) *Am. J. vet. Res.* **39**, 1778
A species in the genus MASTADENOVIRUS. There are at least 2 serotypes. A natural infection of dogs, often silent, but in puppies there is often fever, vomiting and diarrhoea with up to 25% mortality. There is cutaneous oedema, ascites, haemorrhages into the viscera and hepatitis. Also a cause of laryngotracheitis (KENNEL COUGH). In foxes there is acute encephalitis and haemorrhage into the brain. Spread of infection is from the respiratory tract and urine. Experimentally, dogs and foxes may be infected by any route. Coyotes, wolves and raccoons are susceptible. Virus replication with CPE occurs in cultures of dog, ferret, raccoon and pig cells. Haemagglutination is reported.
SYN: canine hepatitis virus
canine laryngotracheitis virus
fox encephalitis virus
hepatitis infectiosa canis virus
infectious canine hepatitis virus
kennel cough virus
Rubarth's disease virus

Canine coronavirus
Cartwright S. & Lucas M. (1972) *Vet. Res.* **91**, 571
Keenan K.P. *et al.* (1976) *Am. J. vet. Res.* **37**, 247
A species in the genus CORONAVIRUS. Causes vomiting and diarrhoea in dogs. Antigenically related to PORCINE TRANSMISSIBLE GASTROENTERITIS VIRUS, which can be transmitted to dogs.
SYN: gastro-enteritis virus of dogs.

Canine dermal papilloma virus Synonym for canine papilloma virus.

Canine hepatitis virus Synonym for canine adenovirus.

Canine herpesvirus Synonym for canid herpesvirus 1.

Canine laryngotracheitis virus Synonym for canine adenovirus.

Canine oral papillomavirus
Chambers V.C. (1960) *Cancer Res.* **20**, 1083
A species in the genus PAPILLOMAVIRUS. A natural infection of dogs causing papillomas on the lips, which spread inside the mouth. Do not produce skin papillomas.

Canine papilloma virus A species in the genus PAPILLOMAVIRUS. A natural infection of dogs causing skin papilloma. Probably distinct from CANINE ORAL PAPILLOMA VIRUS.
SYN: canine dermal papilloma virus.

Canine parvovirus Synonym for minute virus of canines.

Canine rhinotonsillitis A disease closely related to distemper.

Canine tracheo-bronchitis virus Synonym for canid herpesvirus 1.

Cape Wrath virus A species in the genus ORBIVIRUS, belonging to the KEMEROVO ANTIGENIC GROUP. Isolated from a female tick *Ixodes uriae*, found under rocks at Cape Wrath, Scotland. Not reported to cause disease in humans.

Capim antigenic group viruses Six serologically related viruses in the genus BUNYAVIRUS. Reported only from N. and S. America.

Acara (C,R)
Bushbush (C)
Capim (C,R,M)
Guajara (C,R)
Juan Diaz
Moriche (C)

Isolated from:
(C) Culicine mosquitoes
(R) Rodents
(M) Marsupials

Capim virus A species in the genus BUNYAVIRUS. A member of the CAPIM ANTIGENIC GROUP. Isolated from a rodent *Proechimys guyannensis oris*, opossums of *Caluromys* sp. and mosquitoes of *Culex* sp. in Para, Brazil. No association with disease in humans reported.

capped terminus

Clemens M.J. (1979) *Nature, Lond.* **279**, 673

An unusual sequence of methylated bases at the 5′ terminus of a mRNA molecule. Such caps are present on many viral and cellular mRNA's. There is evidence that the cap is involved in TRANSLATION, but some viruses, notably PICORNAVIRIDAE, do not have capped termini on their mRNA molecules. Viruses which have a VIRION transcriptase responsible for mRNA synthesis also contain an enzyme function which caps the mRNA.

capping *See* capped terminus.

Caprine herpesvirus 1 Synonym for bovid herpesvirus 5.

caprinized virus Virus adapted to goats. When RINDERPEST VIRUS is adapted to goats it ceases to be virulent for cattle.

Capripoxvirus A genus of the subfamily CHORDOPOXVIRINAE. Viruses of ungulates. The VIRIONS are longer and narrower than vaccinia virions. Infectivity is ether-sensitive. Species show serological cross-reactivity. They produce no haemagglutinin. Mechanical transmission by arthopods occurs. Type species SHEEP POX VIRUS. Other species are GOAT POX VIRUS and LUMPY SKIN DISEASE VIRUS.

SYN: sheep pox subgroup viruses.

capsid A protein shell which surrounds the virus NUCLEIC ACID and its associated protein (the NUCLEOPROTEIN CORE). The capsid usually has ICOSAHEDRAL SYMMETRY but in some cases is helical. Capsid and core together form the nucleocapsid. *See* capsomere.

capsomeres Units from which the CAPSID is built, visible in the EM, and consisting of groups of identical protein molecules (protomers). In icosahedral capsids, the capsomeres at the twelve corners are called pentons because they have five neighbouring capsomeres. All other capsomeres have six neighbours and are called hexons. Each penton contains five protomers, each hexon three or six. Many animal viruses have their capsomeres arranged in ICOSAHEDRAL SYMMETRY.

Caraparu virus A species in the genus BUNYAVIRUS, belonging antigenically to the C GROUP VIRUSES. Mosquito-borne. Isolated from a sentinel *Cebus* monkey and mice in Para, Brazil. Also isolated from bats. Has been associated with a febrile illness in man. Found in Brazil, Panama, Trinidad, French Guiana and Surinam.

Cardiovirus

Cooper P.D. *et al.* (1978) *Intervirology* **10**, 165

A genus of the family PICORNAVIRIDAE. Consists of (a) encephalomyocarditis virus such as Col SK, MM, ME and MENGO VIRUS. (b) mouse encephalomyelitis virus such as TO, FA, GDVII and related strains. Differs from enteroviruses in losing infectivity below pH 4 instead of pH 3 and being unstable at pH 6 in the presence of chloride or bromide ions. Strains of encephalomyocarditis virus are antigenically identical and there is some CROSS-NEUTRALIZATION between TO, GDVII and FA viruses.

Carey Island virus A species in the genus FLAVIVIRUS. Isolated from bats in Malaysia. Not reported to cause disease in humans.

Carnivora pox virus

Marennikova S.S. *et al.* (1978) *Arch. Virol.* **56**, 7

A strain of COW POX VIRUS which differs from the reference strain (Brighton) by a low ceiling temperature for pock development on the CAM. Caused an EPIZOOTIC among carnivora in Moscow Zoo. Similar to RODENT (WILD IN TURKMENIA) POXVIRUS.

Carp pox herpesvirus Synonym for cyprinid herpesvirus 1.

Carp virus

Carp R.I. *et al.* (1977) *Lancet* **ii**, 814

Carp R.I. *et al.* (1978) *Prog. med. Virol.* **24**, 158

A transmissible virus obtained from cases of multiple sclerosis. Depresses the number of circulating polymorphonuclear neutrophils within 16–48 hours of inoculation into adult mice. The effect lasts at least 11 months during which time the mice remain normal. The virus passes through membranes of 50 nm average pore diameter but not of 25 nm. Replicates in PAM cells, a line of mouse fibroblasts. The effect in mice can be neutralized by serum from patients with multiple sclerosis. However the mouse test has proved difficult to reproduce and is unreliable. It is possible that these results are an artifact and the virus does not exist.

carrier cultures A type of persistent infection of cell cultures in which only a small proportion of the cell population is infected. These cells release virus and are killed, but the released virus infects a small number of other cells. A carrier culture can be 'cured' of virus infection by adding antiviral antibody. Many different viruses can cause carrier infections. Carrier cultures may arise because most of the cells in it are genetically resistant to the infecting virus, or due to the presence of weak antibody or INTERFERON in the cell CULTURE MEDIUM.

Catarrhal jaundice virus Synonym for hepatitis A virus.

Cat distemper virus Synonym for feline panleucopenia virus.

Cat endogenous type C oncovirus *See* CCC cat endogenous type C oncovirus.

Cat fever virus Synonym for feline panleucopenia virus.

Cat flu virus Synonym for feline Calicivirus.

Cat leukaemia virus

Jarrett W.F.H. (1976). In *Scientific Foundations of Oncology*, p. 393. Ed. Symington T. and Carter R.L. London: Heinemann

Essex M. (1975) *Adv. Cancer Res.* **21**, 175

A species in the subgenus MAMMALIAN TYPE C ONCOVIRUS GROUP. A common infection of urban cats causing leukaemia of various types, sarcomas, anaemia, glomerulonephritis and susceptibility to various infections due to depression of immune system. There are ENDOGENOUS viruses, transmitted vertically, which are XENOTROPIC and may not be leukaemogenic. The EXOGENOUS virus is horizontally transmitted and causes leukaemia in a proportion of infected cats after an interval of months or years. Virus cannot be demonstrated in some cases of leukaemia. The dose of virus and immune response are important. If there is depression of the immune response disease is likely, whereas a good immune response is protective. Antibodies are produced to the feline oncovirus-associated cell membrane antigen (FOCMA). Antibody levels are low in leukaemic animals: disease does not develop in animals with high levels. Protective levels of antibodies can be induced with a vaccine. The virus replicates in cells of feline, human, canine or porcine origin. INTERFERENCE and NEUTRALIZATION TESTS have demonstrated at least three subgroups of exogenous virus designated A, B and C. Strain MAH is subgroup A, strain F4 is subgroup B and strain FL237 is subgroup C. The CAT SARCOMA VIRUS is a DEFECTIVE member of the species, requiring a leukaemia virus as a HELPER to code for the surface proteins of the virus particle as do other sarcoma viruses.

Cat plague virus Synonym for feline panleucopenia virus.

Cat sarcoma virus

Porzig K.J. *et al.* (1979) *Virology* **92**, 91

A species in the subgenus MAMMALIAN TYPE C ONCOVIRUS GROUP. Causes sarcomas in cats.

A DEFECTIVE transforming virus which requires a cat leukaemia virus as a HELPER VIRUS for production of infective particles. NON-PRODUCER CELLS occur naturally in some cat sarcomas from which the viral GENOME can be rescued by superinfection with a CAT LEUKAEMIA VIRUS.

Cat-scratch disease virus

Torres J.R. *et al.* (1978) *J. Am. med. Ass.* **240**, 1628

The disease is thought to be due to a virus or chlamydia, though none has yet been isolated. It is a mild disease, with fever, malaise, and a local lesion which becomes a pustule, and with lymphadenitis in the draining lymph nodes. A skin test has been used to confirm the diagnosis, using pus from a case as antigen. This is prepared by heating to 60 °C for varying periods up to 3 days and there is thus a danger of transmitting hepatitis.

SYN: benign inoculation lymphoreticulosis virus;
non-bacterial regional lymphadenitis virus.

Cattle plague virus Synonym for rinderpest virus.

Cat type C oncovirus Synonym for cat leukaemia virus and cat sarcoma virus.

Catu virus A species in the genus BUNYAVIRUS, belonging to the GUAMA ANTIGENIC GROUP. Isolated from a young man with a febrile illness, in Para, Brazil. Also isolated from bats, and mosquitoes, and SENTINEL monkeys and mice. Also found in Trinidad and French Guiana.

Cauliflower disease of eels virus

Nagabayashi T. & Wolf K. (1979) *J. Virol.* **30**, 358

A species probably in the family ORTHOMYXOVIRIDAE. Isolated from an European eel *Anguilla anguilla* with stomatopapillomas and is known as EV2. Eels develop lesions with a cauliflower-like appearance, predominantly around the mouth and head and consisting of hyperplastic squamous cells. An icosahedral virus has been isolated from the blood of affected eels, but the relationship of this virus to EV2, and of both to the disease is not clear. EV2 virus is 90–140 nm in diameter and pleomorphic, with surface projections 10 nm long. Concentrated preparations agglutinate chick and sheep erythrocytes. Spontaneous elution occurs at room temperature. Replicates in FHM cells, optimally at 15°, producing syncytia and irregular masses of rounded cells which eventually lyse. Infectivity is ether-sensitive and does not survive much over 3 weeks at 4°. Replication inhibited by ACTINOMYCIN D but not IDOXURIDINE. *See* eel virus.

Caviid herpesvirus 1

Smith M.G. (1959) *Prog. med. Virol.* **2**, 171

Fong C.K.Y. *et al.* (1979) *J. gen. Virol.* **42**, 127

A species in the family HERPESVIRIDAE. A silent infection of guinea pigs: inclusion bodies can be found in cells of the salivary gland ducts. The infection can be passed experimentally by peripheral injection of salivary gland extract. Inoculation i/c causes fatal meningitis. Intratracheal inoculation causes pneumonia. There is replication in primary guinea pig fibroblast culture with the appearance of small foci of enlarged cells in 10 days. Nuclear inclusions appear, and on passage CPE may be seen in 1–2 days. The virus is cell-associated.

SYN: guinea pig cytomegalovirus; guinea pig salivary gland virus; guinea pig submaxillary gland virus.

Caviid herpesvirus 2

Rhim J.S. (1977) *Virology* **82**, 100

A species in the family HERPESVIRIDAE. Isolated from cultures of Strain 2 guinea pig cells which developed focal areas of swollen rounded cells 9–13 days after preparation. No virus was obtained from homogenized guinea pig tissue extracts. Not reported to cause disease in guinea pigs or other animals. Replicates in rabbit kidney cell, mink lung cell and VERO CELL cultures, but not in monkey, hamster, human or fowl CMA cells. Infective virus in rat cells does not kill them all and transformed cells appear which on injection grow into tumours and contain viral antigen. The virus is not neutralized by antiserum to GUINEA PIG CYTOMEGALOVIRUS.

SYN: guinea pig herpesvirus.

CCC cat endogenous type C oncovirus An ENDOGENOUS cat type C oncovirus obtained from a continuous cat cell line CCCa. It does not have the group specific antigen of the exogenous CAT LEUKAEMIA VIRUS but does have that of RD 114 VIRUS. RD 114-related NUCLEIC ACID sequences are found in four closely related species of *Felidae* but not in others, though they are also present in Old World monkeys and apes. It is a XENOTROPIC VIRUS, which can be induced by treatment of CCC cells with IDOXURIDINE.

CCL Abbreviation for CERTIFIED CELL LINE.

Cebid herpesvirus 1

Hunt R.D. & Melendez L.V. (1969) *Lab. Anim. Care* **19**, 221

A species in the family HERPESVIRIDAE. Originally isolated from throat swabs and autopsy material from marmosets *Tamarinus nigricollis* in which it causes a fatal disease. Also isolated from owl monkeys *Aotus* sp. and squirrel monkeys *Saimiri* sp. The latter is probably the natural host and may excrete the virus intermittently for long periods. Only minor disease is caused in spider and squirrel monkeys, but experimental or laboratory contact infection of owl monkeys and marmosets causes a generalized fatal disease. The virus replicates in mouse and chick embryo and rabbit and marmoset kidney cell cultures. Pocks are produced on the CAM. It is pathogenic for rabbits and adult mice given i/c, and for suckling mice and hamsters given i/p.

SYN: Callitrichid herpesvirus; herpesvirus M; herpesvirus platyrrhini; herpesvirus T (tamarinus); marmoset herpesvirus; M virus.

Cebid herpesvirus 2

Deinhardt F.W. *et al.* (1974) *Adv. Cancer Res.* **19**, 167

A species in the family HERPESVIRIDAE. Isolated from squirrel monkeys *Saimiri sciureus* which appears to be the natural host and in which it is either non-pathogenic or very rarely so. The virus is often present in the lymphocytes of healthy squirrel monkeys, though its presence is only demonstrable on culture *in vitro*. Infective virus is present in the throat, and transmission among monkeys is probably via the respiratory tract. Replication occurs in a variety of cell cultures, e.g. monkey kidney, with focal and general CPE. The virus is the cause of malignant lymphoproliferative disease in non-human primates of several species. Certain marmosets (*Saguinus puscicollis or S. nigricollis*) inoculated at any age consistently develop lymphomas, fatal in 3 months. Owl monkeys (*Aotus trivirgatus*) are somewhat less susceptible. New Zealand white rabbits given multiple injections develop lymphomas which are multiclonal and of T-cell origin.

SYN: herpesvirus saimiri; squirrel monkey herpesvirus.

Cebid herpesvirus 3

Deinhardt F.W. *et al.* (1974) *Adv. Cancer Res.* **19**, 167

Falk L. *et al.* (1978) *Internat. J. Cancer* **21**, 652

Luetzeler J. *et al.* (1979) *Arch. Virol.* **60**, 59

A species in the family HERPESVIRIDAE. Originally isolated from a cell culture of kidney tissue from a Guatemalan spider monkey (*Ateles geoffroyi*) which developed characteristic herpes-type CPE. Four isolates from peripheral lymphocytes of Colombian spider monkeys (*Ateles fusciceps robustus*) are antigenically slightly different. The virus appears to be a natural, horizontally transmitted infection of spider monkeys in which it rarely if ever causes disease. It is very similar in behaviour to CEBID HERPESVIRUS 2 causing lymphomatous neoplasms in marmosets, owl monkeys and other species. Marmoset lymphocytes are transformed by it *in vitro* and the transformed cells have T-cell markers.

SYN: herpesvirus ateles; spider monkey herpesvirus.

Cebid herpesvirus 4 (number assigned by us)

Melendez L.V. *et al.* (1971) *Lab. Anim. Sci.* **21**, 1050
Daniel M.D. *et al.* (1976) *Lab. Anim. Sci.* **26**, 1073

Obtained from owl monkey *Aotus trivirgatus* kidney cell cultures. A number of viruses have been isolated. They differ antigenically and in the cell cultures in which they will replicate. The number of species remains to be determined.
SYN: herpesvirus aotus; owl monkey herpesvirus.

cell-associated virus Virus particles which remain attached to or inside the host cell after replication. The amount of cell-associated compared to released virus varies considerably with the virus and/or the host cell involved. CYTOMEGALOVIRUSES are a typical example of cell-associated virus.

cell culture *See* tissue culture.

cell cycle Cytological study identifies only two phases in the cell growth cycle: 1 mitosis, during which the chromosomes become visible and undergo redistribution within the cell which then divides, and 2, interphase, which occupies the majority of the cell growth cycle. Biochemical analysis has resulted in the sub-division of interphase into 3 phases characterised by their metabolic activity, the most prominent of which is the period of DNA synthesis (S), usually lasting 6–8 hours, which occurs in the middle of interphase. The gap between mitosis (M) and the S phase is known as G_1, and the second, between S and M is known as G_2. Thus the cell cycle occurs as M-G_1-S-G_2-M-etc. Most viruses are able to multiply in cells independently of cell division or the stage in the cell cycle at which infection occurs. However, the PARVOVIRIDAE are an exception and require rapidly dividing cells for the establishment of infection.

CELO virus An acronym for *C*hicken *E*mbryo *L*ethal *O*rphan virus.

central dogma

Crick F.H.C. (1970) *Nature, Lond.* **227**, 561

The idea originally proposed by Crick F.H.C. (*Symp. Soc. exp. Biol.* **12** (1958), 137), that genetic information can be perpetuated in the form of NUCLEIC ACID, but cannot be retrieved from the amino-acid sequences of proteins.

centrophyten Minute basophilic particles reported by Lipschütz (1928, *Wien. klin. Wschr.* **41**, 365) to be present in epidermal cells infected with MEASLES VIRUS.

Cercopithecid herpesvirus 1 A species in the family HERPESVIRIDAE. A natural infection of asiatic monkeys. 10% of newly caught rhesus monkeys have antibodies, and the virus is frequently present in kidney cell cultures of this animal. Causes vesicular lesions on the tongue and lips, and sometimes of the skin. Infection of humans by monkey bites or other means leads to ascending myelitis or acute encephalitis: almost all cases are fatal. Mice under 3 weeks old, day-old chicks and guinea pigs can be infected experimentally. Not all strains are antigenically identical. There may be some antigenic relationships to HUMAN (ALPHA) HERPESVIRUS 1 and SUID (ALPHA) HERPESVIRUS 1.
SYN: B virus; herpesvirus simiae.

Cercopithecid herpesvirus 2

Smith K.O. *et al.* (1969) *J. natn. Cancer Inst.* **42**, 489
Malherbe H. & Harwin R.S. (1963) *S. Afr. med. J.* **37**, 407

A species in the family HERPESVIRIDAE, probably a CYTOMEGALOVIRUS. Isolated from vervet monkey *Cercopithecus aethiops pygerythrus* kidney and salivary gland cell cultures. Focal lesions were observed in monolayer cultures. Giant cells and eosinophilic inclusion bodies were seen.
SYN: African monkey cytomegalovirus: SA6 virus.

Cercopithecid herpesvirus 3

Eichberg J.W. *et al.* (1976) *Arch. Virol.* **50**, 255

A species in the family HERPESVIRIDAE. Isolated from vervet *Cercopithecus aethiops* kidneys, and from a baboon *Papio ursinus*. Serologically related to HUMAN (ALPHA) HERPESVIRUS 1. Infant baboons inoculated intratracheally develop fatal pneumonia, but

the virus has not been observed to cause human disease. Infectivity is neutralized by antiserum to CERCOPITHECID HERPESVIRUS 1, though antiserum to cercopithecid herpesvirus 3 will not neutralize cercopithecid herpesvirus 1.
SYN: SA 8 virus.

Cercopithecid herpesvirus 4 (number assigned by us)
Falk L. *et al.* (1976) *Int. J. Cancer* **18**, 798
Rabin H. *et al.* (1977) *Intervirology* **8**, 240
A species in the family HERPESVIRIDAE. Isolated from cell lines established from splenic lymphocytes of a baboon *Papio hamadryas* by CO-CULTIVATION with X-irradiated marmoset or baboon lymphoblastoid cell cultures carrying CEBID HERPESVIRUS 2. The baboon had been injected with blood from another baboon which had been injected with human blood and had a lymphoma. The cell lines have B-lymphocyte characteristics and carry a virus related to, but not identical with EPSTEIN–BARR VIRUS as demonstrated by cross-reactivity of viral CAPSID antigens, but only partial (40%) DNA homology. It can transform other non-human primate cells *in vitro* but its relationship to disease in the baboon is uncertain. It is B-cell tropic like HUMAN (GAMMA) HERPESVIRUS 4, but unlike similar viruses isolated from New World monkeys which are T-cell tropic, e.g. cebid herpesvirus 2.
SYN: baboon lymphotropic herpesvirus, herpesvirus papio.

Cercopithecid herpesvirus 5 (number assigned by us)
Felsenfeld A.D. & Schmidt N.J. (1977) *Infect. Immun.* **15**, 807
Felsenfeld A.D. & Schmidt N.J. (1979) *J. gen. Virol.* **42**, 171
A species in the family HERPESVIRIDAE. A severe, often fatal, exanthematous disease has been observed in captive patas, vervet and macaque monkeys. From these geographically separated but clinically similar outbreaks, herpes viruses have been isolated which have similar biological characteristics, but have not been directly compared. It seems likely they are strains of the same species: cercopithecid herpesvirus 5. Antibodies to the virus are rare among monkeys in the wild but the infection spreads rapidly when they are brought together in captivity. Sub-clinical infections are common but in severe cases there are necrotic haemorrhagic lesions in the lungs, intestine, liver and other organs. Other monkeys, mice and rabbits are resistant to infection. Virus replicates with CPE in patas and vervet monkey kidney cell cultures, also in human thyroid, VERO CELLS and many other cell lines. Produces no pocks on the CAM and does not kill the embryo. The virus is strongly CELL-ASSOCIATED. Antigenically very closely related to HUMAN HERPESVIRUS 3.
SYN: delta herpesvirus; Liverpool vervet monkey virus; macaque monkey virus; Medial Lake macaque herpesvirus; patas monkey virus; simian varicella virus; vervet monkey herpes virus; delta virus.

Cercopithecid herpesvirus 6 (number assigned by us)
Frank A.L. *et al.* (1973) *J. inf. Dis.* **128**, 618, 630
A species in the family HERPESVIRIDAE. Appears to be a common infection of rhesus monkeys but there is no evidence that it causes disease in them. Isolated by CO-CULTIVATION of rhesus blood leukocytes with simian or human fibroblasts such as W1-38 or MRC-5 cells. Causes CPE within 6–8 days, which slowly progresses. On staining with ACRIDINE ORANGE, multiple green inclusions are seen in the nucleus but not in the cytoplasm. More than half the virus infectivity is CELL-ASSOCIATED. Experimental inoculation of mice, hamsters and rabbits caused no obvious disease. Infection of rhesus monkeys resulted in a rise in antibodies. No cross-NEUTRALIZATION could be demonstrated with a range of other human and simian herpesviruses. There appear to be at least 2 antigenic types.
SYN: leukocyte-associated herpesvirus.

Certified Cell Line A line of cells certified by the American Cell Culture Collection Committee. Each cell line is assigned an accession number, e.g. CCL 2 = HeLa, and derivatives are given a decimal notation, e.g. CCL 2·1 = HeLa 229. Information on cell lines can be obtained from the American Type Culture Collection, 12301 Parklawn Drive, Rockville, Maryland 20852, U.S.A.

C group viruses Eleven serologically related viruses in the genus BUNYAVIRUS. Found only in the Western Hemisphere. All save nepuyo and gumbo limbo viruses have been associated with febrile illness in man. They can be divided into three antigenic groups:

(1) Apeu (C,H,M)
Caraparu (C,H,R)
Madrid (C,H,R)
Ossa (C,H,R)

(2) Gumbo limbo (C,H,R)
Marituba (C,H,M)
Murutucu (C,H,R,M)
Nepuyo (C,R,Ba)
Restan (C,H)

(3) Itaqui (C,H,R,M), Oriboca (C,H,R,M)

Isolated from:
(C) Culicine mosquitoes
(H) Humans
(R) Rodents
(Ba) Bats
(M) Marsupials

Chaco virus

Monath T.P. *et al.* (1979) *Arch. Virol.* **60**, 1

A species in the family RHABDOVIRIDAE. With TIMBO VIRUS forms the Timbo antigenic group. Isolated from the lizards *Ameiva ameiva ameiva* and *Kentropyx calearatus* in Para, Brazil. Not isolated from arthropods but considered to be arthropod-transmitted as it will replicate in experimentally infected mosquitoes. Kills new-born mice which are more sensitive than VERO CELLS in which it replicates with CPE at 30°.

Chaffinch papilloma virus Synonym for fringilla papilloma virus.

Chagres virus

Robeson G. *et al.* (1979) *J. Virol.* **30**, 339

An unclassified ARBOVIRUS morphologically like BUNYAVIRUS but serologically unrelated to members of that genus. A member of the PHLEBOTOMUS FEVER ANTIGENIC GROUP. Isolated from a man with a febrile illness in the Canal Zone, Panama. Also isolated from the mosquito *Sabethes chloropterus* and *Lutzomyia* sp. Causes CPE in primary rhesus monkey kidney, human amnion and mouse embryo cell cultures. On injection i/c kills new-born mice.

Chamois contagious ecthyma virus Synonym for contagious ecthyma virus

Chamois papilloma virus Synonym for contagious ecthyma virus

Chandipura virus A species in the genus VESICULOVIRUS. Antigenically related to VESICULAR STOMATITIS VIRUS. Isolated from a man with dengue/chikungunya-like disease, in Nagpar, India. Also isolated from sand flies of *Phlebotomus* sp. and a hedgehog of *Atelerix* sp. in Nigeria.

Chang liver cells (CCL 13) A heteroploid cell line established from non-malignant human liver. One of the original successful attempts in serial propagation of human cells from normal tissues and named after the man who accomplished it.

Changuinola virus A species in the genus ORBIVIRUS which with IRITUIA VIRUS forms the Changuinola antigenic group. Isolated from *Phlebotomus* sp. and small rodents in Panama. Has also been isolated from a mosquito catcher with a febrile illness.

Channel catfish herpesvirus Synonym for silurid herpesvirus 1.

Chargaff's rule In DOUBLE-STRANDED DNA molecules, the proportion of adenine equals that of thymine, and the proportion of guanine equals that of cytosine. This results from the pairing of the bases.

Charleville virus An unclassified ARBOVIRUS. Isolated from sand flies of *Phlebotomus* sp. and the lizard *Gehyra australis* in Charleville and Mitchell River, Queensland, Australia. Not reported to cause disease in humans.

Chelonid herpesvirus 1

Rebell G. *et al.* (1975) *Am. J. vet. Res.* **36**, 1221

Haines H. & Kleese W.C. (1977) *Infect. Immun.* **15**, 756

A species in the family HERPESVIRIDAE. EPIZOOTICS of grey patch disease were observed in green sea-turtles *Chelonia mydas* kept in captivity in the West Indies. Two types of lesion were seen: papules and spreading grey patches 7–8 weeks after hatching. Intranuclear inclusions were present in sections of the lesions and herpesvirus-like particles were present in scrapings from the lesions. The disease could be transmitted between turtles by a cell-free extract.

SYN: green sea-turtle herpesvirus; grey patch disease of turtles virus.

chemotherapeutic index The ratio between the lowest effective antiviral concentration and the highest non-toxic concentration.

Chenuda virus A species in the genus ORBIVIRUS belonging to the KEMEROVO ANTIGENIC GROUP. Isolated from *Argas h. hermanni* ticks in Egypt and Africa. Not reported to cause disease in humans.

Ch1Es(NBL-8) cells (CCL 73) A heteroploid line derived from the trypsinized oesophagus of a male foetus of the goat *Capra hircus*. Developed for study of viruses that affect domestic animals. Has been used in studies of SCRAPIE VIRUS.

Chicken embryo lethal orphan virus

Aghakhan S.M. (1974) *Vet. Bull.* **44**, 531

A species in the genus AVIADENOVIRUS, closely related to QUAIL ADENOVIRUS. Isolated originally from embryonated eggs inoculated with various materials, and in which the embryos died. It became clear that the source of the virus was the eggs and not the injected material. It has been associated with various diseases in chickens, turkeys and pheasants. Oncogenic in new-born hamsters. Replicates with typical adenovirus CPE in chicken cell cultures.

Chicken leukosis sarcoma virus A species in the subgenus AVIAN TYPE C ONCOVIRUS. There are seven subspecies or subgroups designated A to G. They are defined by ENVELOPE properties such as host-range, sensitivity to viral INTERFERENCE and antigenicity. There are (1) strains producing solid tumours, sarcomas, on injection into birds. These sarcoma viruses can transform cells in culture but most of the strains are DEFECTIVE and require a leukaemia virus to provide the genetic information for the viral COAT proteins. The HELPER thus determines the subgroup and host-range of the progeny virus. (2) Strains which *in vivo* transform haematopoietic cells and induce leukaemia on injection into birds and can act as helpers for DEFECTIVE sarcoma viruses. They do not transform cells in culture. There are ENDOGENOUS viruses in chickens and other gallinaceous birds which are transmitted vertically, and do not usually appear as free virus, but can be induced and belong to subgroup E. Birds carrying the endogenous virus give a positive CFT for the avian leukosis gs antigen (COFAL TEST). They are described as gs^+ and are said to have the CHICK HELPER FACTOR (chf). The laboratory strains of sarcoma virus, such as Bryan High Titre strain of ROUS VIRUS, consist of a sarcoma virus and a ROUS ASSOCIATED VIRUS (RAV), which is a helper virus providing information for the virus coat proteins, and thus determining the host-range of the progeny. The sarcoma virus can transform cells alone, but for infective virus production a helper virus is required. If non-virus-producing transformed cells are cloned and passaged in gs^-, chf^- cells they are found by EM to be producing virus particles which cannot be shown to be infectious for any known cells. These virus particles are designated RSV (O). When RSV (O) is propagated in gs^+, chf^+ cells, virus is produced with the aid of the chf which is RAV 60 and belongs to subgroup E. Whether or not gs^- cells contain chf in a repressed form is not clear. Some cells which are COFAL negative support the production of RSV (O). Both gs^+, and gs^- cells appear to contain the viral GENOME. Virus can be induced from both gs^+ and gs^- cells.

Chickenpox virus Name probably derived from Old English *gican*, meaning itch, as this is a characteristic symptom.

Synonym for human herpesvirus 3.

chick helper factor (chf)

Hanafusa H. *et al.* (1970) *Proc. natn. Acad. Sci. U.S.A.* **66**, 314

An ENDOGENOUS avian leukosis virus of subgroup E, present in certain chicken cells. It can act as HELPER for a DEFECTIVE avian sarcoma virus by providing genetic information for the viral surface glycoproteins of the infectious progeny virus. Probably the same as RAV-60. *See* chicken leukosis sarcoma virus.

Chick syncytial virus A strain of AVIAN RETICULOENDOTHELIOSIS VIRUS.

Chikungunya virus

Chanas A.C. *et al.* (1979) *Arch. Virol.* **59**, 231

A species in the genus ALPHAVIRUS. Causes an epidemic disease in man characterized by severe joint and back pains which are so severe the patient is doubled up; hence the name, a native word meaning 'that which bends up'. Incubation period 3–12 days. Onset sudden and the disease biphasic. Following 1–6 days fever the temperature returns to normal for 1–3 days before the second period of fever which lasts a few days. In this phase a maculopapular pruritic rash on the trunk and limbs is common. After 6–10 days recovery is usually complete though rarely joint pains may persist. Haemorrhagic fever-type disease may occur but shock is uncommon. Transmitted by *Aedes africanus* and *A. aegypti.* No vertebrate host is known, but antibodies are present in monkeys, birds and many mammals. Occurs in India, S.E. Asia, eastern, western, central and southern Africa. Strains from Asia and Africa show some antigenic differences. Kills suckling mice on injection i/c: guinea pigs and rabbits show no signs of infection. Replicates with CPE in chick embryo, rhesus kidney and HELA CELL cultures.

Chilibre virus An unclassified ARBOVIRUS morphologically like BUNYAVIRUS but not serologically related to members of that genus. Belongs to the PHLEBOTOMUS FEVER ANTIGENIC GROUP. Isolated from insects of *Lutzomyia* sp. in Canal Zone, Panama. Not reported to cause disease in humans.

Chimpanzee agent Synonym for chimpanzee (gamma) herpesvirus 1.

Chimpanzee coryza agent The original name given to the virus now designated RESPIRATORY SYNCYTIAL VIRUS. Isolated from a throat swab from a chimpanzee with clinical symptoms of coryza at the Walter Reed Army Institute of Research in 1955.

Chimpanzee (gamma) herpesvirus 1

Gerber P. *et al.* (1976) *J. Virol.* **19**, 1090

A species in the subfamily GAMMAHERPESVIRINAE. Antigenically related to HUMAN (GAMMA)HERPESVIRUS 4 and appears to have very similar biological properties. Long-term cultures can be established from lymphoid cells of chimpanzees with antibodies to the human virus, and these cells contain DNA sequences homologous to approximately 35–40% of the GENOME of the human virus.

Chinook salmon virus Synonym for Sacramento River chinook salmon disease virus.

Chlamydia

Moulder J.W. (1966) *Ann. Rev. Microbiol.* **20**, 107

A group of obligate intracellular micro-organisms, once thought to be viruses. However, they are unlike true viruses in several important respects:

(1) they multiply by binary fission;
(2) they have cell walls like bacteria, with muramic acid-containing mucopeptides;
(3) they have a number of enzymes which are metabolically active;
(4) they possess both DNA and RNA, as do bacteria;
(5) unlike viruses, they possess ribosomes;
(6) growth can be inhibited by a number of antibacterial agents, including tetracyclines, chloramphenicol, rifampicin and sulphonamides.

SYN: Bedsonia; miyagawanella; TRIC agent.

Chlamydozoa ribasi

Aragao H.B. (1933) *C. r. Soc. Biol. Paris* **113**, 1271

A name given to the ELEMENTARY BODIES seen in association with cells infected with VARIOLA MINOR.

Chlamydozoa variolae Synonym for PASCHEN BODIES. *See also* Buist bodies.

5-chloro-2-deoxyuridine A halogenated pyrimidine.

1-(*p*-chlorophenyl)-3-(*m*-3-isobutylguanidinophenyl)urea hydrochloride

Swallow D.L. *et al.* (1977) *Ann. N.Y. Acad. Sci.* **284**, 305

A guanidine derivative differing significantly from guanidine hydrochloride in its antiviral properties. Has very high *in vitro* activity against RHINOVIRUSES. Relatively non-toxic to laboratory animals. Studies in man in progress.

SYN: I.C.I. 73602.

Chobar Gorge virus An unclassified ARBOVIRUS. Isolated from ticks of *Ornithodoros* sp. in Nepal. Not reported to cause disease in humans.

CHO cells (CCL 61)

Kao F. & Puck T.T. (1968) *Science, N.Y.* **164**, 312

Lobban P.E. & Siminovitch L. (1975) *Cell* **4**, 167

A cell line derived from Chinese hamster ovary tissue. A range of drug-resistant mutants of these cells has been developed, including lines resistant to α-AMANITIN.

Chordopoxvirinae A subfamily of the family POXVIRIDAE, comprising the poxviruses of vertebrates. Contains six genera: ORTHOPOXVIRUS, PARAPOXVIRUS, AVIPOXVIRUS, CAPRIPOXVIRUS, LEPORIPOXVIRUS and SUIPOXVIRUS.

chromatids Thread-like structures formed from CHROMATIN during the first stage of mitosis (prophase).

chromatin A dispersed network of fibres in the nucleus consisting of NUCLEIC ACID and protein. In eukaryotic cells which are not undergoing mitosis most of the NUCLEOPROTEIN is in the form of chromatin.

chromoneme GENOME of bacteria or viruses: term introduced by H.L.K. Whitehouse (*Towards an Understanding of the Mechanism of Heredity*, London: Edward Arnold, 1969) to distinguish the 'thread-like' structure of bacterial or viral genetic material from the true chromosome of plant and animal cells. *See also* genophore.

chromosomes Structures formed from CHROMATIDS during mitosis. Contain the NUCLEOPROTEIN of the nucleus in an organized form in which it can be divided into two equal parts for division of the genetic information which it contains to the daughter cells.

Chronic progressive pneumonia of sheep virus Synonym for maedi virus.

cinchocaine

Rifkin D.B. & Reich E. (1971) *Virology* **45**, 172

A local anaesthetic which has been found to lyse chick embryo fibroblasts. Cells transformed by CHICKEN LEUKOSIS SARCOMA VIRUS are more sensitive to lysis than normal cells, perhaps because they attain higher intracellular levels of the drug.

Cisternavirus A

Dalton A.J. *et al.* (1975) *J. natn. Cancer Inst.* **55**, 941

A name proposed for a genus in the family RETROVIRIDAE, which would contain the viruses with A-TYPE VIRUS PARTICLES.

cis-trans test

Benzer S. (1955) *Proc. natn. Acad. Sci. U.S.A.* **41**, 344

A genetic complementation test originally used in fine structure genetic mapping of T4 bacteriophage. *See* cistron.

cistron The unit of genetic function. No smaller unit or part of a cistron is functional. It is defined by the cis-trans test: if x^- and y^- are two function-abolishing mutations and they are on the same cistron, then in a mixed infection of x^+y^+/x^-y^- the cis diploid will be functional but x^-y^+/x^+y^- the trans diploid will not function because x and y being on the same cistron cannot function alone. They are indivisible. *See* gene.

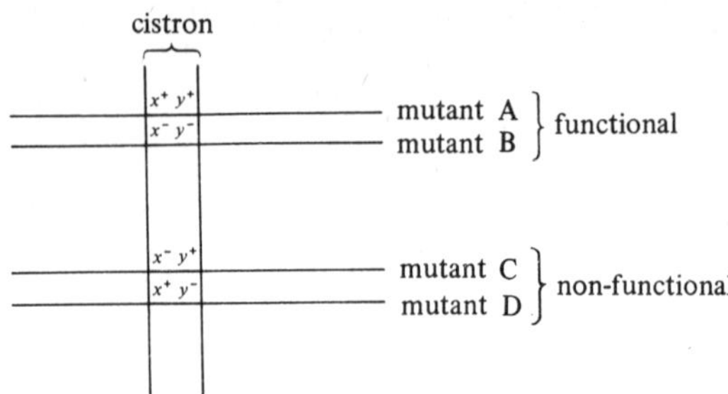

citrullinaemia cells
Mellman W.J. (1967) *Proc. natn. Acad. Sci. U.S.A.* **57**, 829
A human diploid fibroblast cell line derived from skin of a female infant with citrullinaemia.

Clavelée virus Synonym for sheep pox virus

Clo Mor virus An unclassified ARBOVIRUS belonging to the SAKHALIN ANTIGENIC GROUP. Isolated from a tick *Ixodes* (*Ceratixodes*) *uriae* found under rocks in Cape Wrath, Scotland. Not reported to cause disease in humans.

coat The protective protein which surrounds the virus NUCLEIC ACID. Includes the CAPSID, and may consist of a single layer as in the PICORNAVIRIDAE, or several layers as in the POXVIRIDAE.

Cobra herpesvirus Synonym for elapid herpesvirus 1.

Cocal virus Synonym for Indiana 2C strain of vesicular stomatitis virus.

co-cultivation A mixed culture of two or more different types of cell. If one of them is permissive for the replication of a latent virus present in the other cell line, this virus may replicate and become detectable, i.e. be 'rescued'. The cells in which replication takes place are known as 'indicator cells'. The frequency of virus rescue during co-cultivation can often be increased by artificially fusing the cells, with resulting heterokaryon formation. An example of rescue is the recovery of MEASLES VIRUS from the brain tissue of patients with sub-acute sclerosing panencephalitis by co-cultivation with VERO CELLS.

codon A group of three consecutive bases in a NUCLEIC ACID molecule which together specify a particular amino-acid during TRANSLATION from MRNA. Since there are four bases, there are 64 possible codons, but as only 21 amino-acids need to be specified most are coded for by several alternative codons (degeneracy of the code). However, no codon specifies more than one amino-acid. The sequence of bases which makes up a gene are translated as a series of codons, beginning with an initiation codon AUG. This establishes the reading frame within the gene. In some virus nucleic acids there is more than one reading frame, so that up to three different proteins may be specified by a single sequence of bases. Termination of translation is specified by a terminator codon UAG, UAA or UGA except in mitochondria where UGA appears to code for tryptophan. Barrell B.G. *et al. Nature, Lond.* **282**, 189 (1979).

Coe virus An old name for coxsackie virus A21, which can cause a 'common cold'-like disease.

COFAL test A *CO*mplement *F*ixation test for the common group-specific (gs) antigen present in all *A*vian *L*eukosis viruses. *See* chicken leukosis sarcoma virus.

co-formycin Isolated together with FORMYCIN from culture filtrates of *Streptomyces kaniharaensis* and *Nocardia interforma.* A potent inhibitor of adenosine deaminase and used to prevent intracellular conversion of ADENINE ARABINOSIDE to the hypoxanthine. Potentiates the inhibitory action of FORMYCIN B on INFLUENZAVIRUS A HOMINIS in the CAM.

cohesive ends The projecting 5′ SINGLE-STRANDED ends occurring on certain DOUBLE-STRANDED NUCLEIC ACID molecules which, through sequence homology can base pair and thus form a circular molecule. Such structures occur in the GENOME DNA of TEMPERATE BACTERIOPHAGES and facilitiate integration into host DNA.

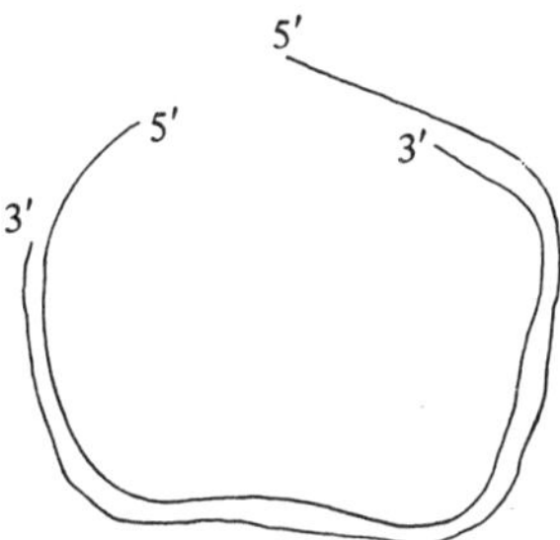

Coital exanthema virus Synonym for equid herpesvirus 3. However, some cases of coital exanthema have been attributed to EQUID (ALPHA) HERPESVIRUS 1, which also causes genital infection.

cold-adapted mutants Mutants which can replicate at temperatures below that at which the WILD TYPE generally replicates or replicates optimally. Influenza virus can be adapted to replicate in eggs at 25° and then has a reduced efficiency of replication at 37°, making it suitable for use as a live virus vaccine.

col factors BACTERIOCINOGENS present in coliform bacteria, which carry genes for colicin production.

colicins BACTERIOCINES produced by *Escherichia coli.*

coliphage A bacteriophage whose host cell is *Escherichia coli.*

Colorado tick fever virus A species in the genus ORBIVIRUS. Causes disease in humans 4–5 days after the bite of an infected tick *Dermacentor andersoni.* There is fever, usually saddle-back type, leucopenia, headache, limb pains and often vomiting. No rash. There may be encephalitis, especially in children. Virus has been isolated from wild rodents but in them infection is inapparent. Hamsters can be infected experimentally i/p and on passage the virus may kill them. Occurs in north-west U.S.A. but does not reach the Pacific coast. Infectivity is acid-sensitive but ether-resistant. The VIRION has two protein shells 80–50 nm in diameter, contains DOUBLE-STRANDED RNA and may also have some SINGLE-STRANDED RNA. Replicates in eggs when injected into the yolk sac, and in cells with CPE. Control depends on protection from ticks. Natural host probably the ground squirrel.

Columbia-SK virus (Col-SK) A strain of ENCEPHALOMYOCARDITIS VIRUS.

Columbid herpesvirus 1

Vindevogel H. *et al.* (1977) *J. comp. Path.* **87**, 597, 605

A species in the family HERPESVIRIDAE. A natural and widespread infection of pigeons, not transmissable to any other species. Causes conjunctivitis, respiratory lesions and focal necrosis of the liver, but can be carried by apparently normal birds. Replicates with CPE in primary chicken embryo fibroblasts. Propagated on the CAM it produces plaques and kills the embryo in 4 days.

SYN: inclusion disease of pigeons virus; pigeon herpesvirus.

Common cold virus *See* human rhinovirus.

complementary strand A single-stranded NUCLEIC ACID molecule complementary in base sequence to the single strand from which it was transcribed. All SINGLE-STRANDED RNA and DNA viruses employ complementary strands as intermediates in their replication. Strands which are complementary to one another can hybridize to form a double strand.

complementation Occurs in doubly infected cells and consists in one of the viruses providing a gene product which the other requires but is unable to make. The genotypes of the infecting viruses are not altered and the progeny virus has the genome of its parent although it may have certain structural proteins such as COAT proteins for example specified by the other virus. There are two types of complementation between mutant viruses: (*a*) nonallelic (intergenic) in which mutants defective in different genes assist each other by providing the missing functions; the assistance is often unequal one virus replicating rapidly and the other very slowly, (*b*) allelic (intragenic) in which mutants defective in the same gene produce a functional gene product by each providing a part of it; this occurs between t_s mutants of T_4 but has not been unequivocally observed among vertebrate viruses.

complementation group A group of mutant viruses with mutations in the same CISTRON. They cannot complement each other. There should be as many complementation groups as cistrons but mutations in some cistrons are not always lethal.

complementation test A test to determine whether two virus mutants are defective in the same CISTRON. A mixed infection with the two viruses is carried out; complementation is positive if the virus yield exceeds the sum of the yields in single infection. If no increase in yield results from the mixed infection, the two viruses are said to be in the same complementation group.

COMUL test *CO*mplement fixation test for *MU*rine *L*eukaemia virus antigens.

concatemeric forms of DNA Long DNA molecules made by continual repetition of a certain basic DNA chain sequence. Can be formed during DNA replication involving a circular intermediate molecule.

concatenates Long molecules made by continuously repeating one basic molecular unit.

conditional lethal mutants Mutants which will not replicate under conditions in which the wild type replicates, but will replicate under permissive conditions, such as in another cell line, at a different temperature, or as a component of a mixed infection: COMPLEMENTATION.

congenital infections

Waterson A.P. (1979) *Br. med. J.* **ii**, 564

Infection occurring before birth. May follow a number of viral infections and is sometimes lethal. May produce foetal abnormalities, e.g. RUBELLA VIRUS and HUMAN (BETA) HERPESVIRUS 5. Some viruses affect particular organs depending on the stage of foetal development at which infection occurs, while others which are noncytocidal may infect every cell in the embryo and persist throughout adult life, e.g. LYMPHOCYTIC CHORIOMENINGITIS VIRUS in mice.

Congo antigenic group viruses There are three viruses in this group: CONGO, HAZARA and CRIMEAN HAEMORRHAGIC FEVER VIRUS. They are tick-borne and have been isolated from ixodid ticks. Congo virus has caused a few cases of human disease in Africa but it is serologically similar or identical to Crimean haemorrhagic fever virus which has caused disease in many humans in the U.S.S.R. They are morphologically like BUNYAVIRUS but unrelated antigenically to members of that genus.

Congo virus An unclassified ARBOVIRUS morphologically like BUNYAVIRUS but serologically not related to members of that genus. The first member of the CONGO ANTIGENIC GROUP. Isolated from febrile patients in 1956 in what was then the Belgian Congo. It is widespread in East and West Africa. Similar to viruses isolated from cattle and probably transmitted by ticks. In man causes a febrile disease with mortality of 16–19 per cent. On the 3rd to 5th day of illness there is a purpuric rash and haemorrhages into lungs, gastrointestinal tract and kidneys, shock and renal insufficiency.
SYN: Crimean haemorrhagic fever virus.

conservative replication A model for NUCLEIC ACID replication which does not occur in nature. The original or parent double strand is preserved intact and the progeny molecule has both strands newly synthesized. In nature a semi-conservative method takes place.

contact inhibition

Abercrombie M. (1979) *Nature, Lond.* **281**, 259

When normal cells come into contact their movements cease. Cell division is also inhibited, but since this is dependent on other factors as well the term 'contact inhibition' is used to imply loss of movement only. *See* density-dependent inhibition.

Contagious ecthyma virus

Renshaw H.W. & Dodd A.G. (1978) *Arch. Virol.* **56**, 201

A species in the genus PARAPOXVIRUS. Causes lesions similar to those produced by GOAT POX VIRUS, but the lesions are primarily round the lips and mouth, and infrequently on the udder, thighs, anus, nostrils and eyes. Antigenically different from goat pox virus and the two do not cross-protect. An important cause of disease in sheep, and a live vaccine is used. As virus remains active in scabs for a long period the vaccine is used annually. Occurs in many parts of the world.

SYN: chamois contagious ecthyma virus, chamois papilloma virus.

Contagious pustular dermatitis of horses virus Synonym for horse pox virus.

Contagious pustular dermatitis of sheep virus Synonym for orf virus.

Contagious pustular stomatitis of horses virus Synonym for horse pox virus.

Contagious pustular stomatitis of sheep virus Synonym for orf virus.

continuous cell lines Cells of uniform morphology which are capable of indefinite propagation *in vitro*. They originate by TRANSFORMATION of primary cell cultures, frequently of tumour tissue. Often aneuploid in chromosome number and on injection into an immunologically compatible animal may grow into a tumour. Most do not show CONTACT INHIBITION.

contour length The length of a NUCLEIC ACID strand measured by EM.

core The central part of the VIRION enclosed by the CAPSID and consisting of protein and the viral NUCLEIC ACID GENOME. The core of REOVIRUS, for example, can be isolated by removing one of the two capsid protein shells, leaving a single-shelled particle which is transcriptionally active.

Cormorant herpesvirus 1 Synonym for phalacrocorid herpesvirus 1.

Coronaviridae

McIntosh K. (1974) *Curr. Topics Microbiol. Immunol.* **63**, 85

Tyrrell D.A.J. *et al.* (1978) *Intervirology* **10**, 321

Pedersen N.C. *et al.* (1978) *Arch. Virol.* **58**, 45

A family of SINGLE-STRANDED RNA viruses. Only one genus has been created: CORONAVIRUS. Type species AVIAN INFECTIOUS BRONCHITIS VIRUS. The VIRIONS are pleomorphic, approximately spherical, 80–160 nm in diameter (average 100 nm) covered with petal-like projections (PEPLOMERS) 20 nm long and arranged in a characteristic fringe giving the appearance of a crown from which the family name is derived. Virus is assembled in the cytoplasm and matures by budding through the endoplasmic reticulum. NUCLEIC ACID consists of one single strand of mol. wt. 9×10^6. There are at least 6 virus-specific polypeptides, 2 or more of which are glycosylated. Some species have haemagglutinin and receptor-destroying enzyme which is not NEURAMINIDASE. Inactivated by lipid solvents.

Coronavirus

Davies H.A. & MacNaughton M.R. (1979) *Arch. Virol.* **59**, 25

The only genus in the family CORONAVIRIDAE. May require subdivision when more data is available on the species which cause disease in a wide range of birds and mammals. Type species is AVIAN INFECTIOUS BRONCHITIS VIRUS (IBV). Other species are:

human coronavirus (HCV)
murine hepatitis (MHV)
porcine transmissible gastroenteritis (TGEV)
porcine haemagglutinating encephalitis (HEV)
turkey bluecomb disease (TBDV)
neonatal calf diarrhoea coronavirus (NCDCV)
feline infectious peritonitis (FIPV)
canine coronavirus (CCV)

rat coronavirus (RCV) | gastroenteritis of foals coronavirus
sialodacryoadenitis virus of rats (SDAV) | (GEFC)

Only two species agglutinate erythrocytes: human coronavirus (OC-43 and OC-38) and porcine haemagglutinating encephalitis virus. IBV is not antigenically related to any other coronavirus. There are two groups of antigenically related viruses which are distinct from each other: MHV, HEV, NCDC, HCV strain OC43, and FIPV, TGEV, CCV, HCV strain 229E.

Corriparta virus

Carley J.G. & Standfast H.A. (1969) *Am. J. Epidemiol.* **89**, 583

A species in the genus ORBIVIRUS, isolated from culicines and birds in northern Australia. With ACADO VIRUS it forms the Corriparta antigenic group. Not known to cause disease in humans.

Coryza virus *See* human rhinovirus.

Cotia body

Ueda Y. *et al.* (1978) *J. gen. Virol.* **40**, 263

Inclusion body seen late in infection with COTIA VIRUS. Eosinophilic when stained with haematoxylin and eosin, but appears as a reddish-purple ring with an inner pale blue area when stained with Giemsa. Morphologically different from those of COWPOX and other poxviruses.

Cotia virus

Ueda Y. *et al.* (1978) *J. gen. Virol.* **40**, 263

A species of the family POXVIRIDAE. Isolated from sentinel mice and mosquitoes in Sao Paulo. Isolated from a man in French Guiana, but not reported to be a significant cause of disease in humans. Replicates in human embryo lung cells as well as in several other cell lines. Shares some antigens with VACCINIA VIRUS but not neutralized by antisera to vaccinia, FOWL POX, GOAT POX, MYXOMA or TANAPOX VIRUSES. Cannot yet be assigned to a genus.

Cotton-tail herpesvirus Synonym for leporid herpesvirus 2.

councilman bodies Collections of eosinophilic necrotic hyaline cells in the livers of yellow fever patients.

co-vidarabine (*R*)-3-(2-deoxy-β-D-*erythro*-pentofuranosyl)-3,6,7,8-tetrahydroimidazo-[4,5-*d*][1,3]diazepin-8-ol. A fermentation product of *Streptomyces antibioticus* and a powerful inhibitor of adenosine deaminase. Protects ADENINE ARABINOSIDE from enzymatic deamination to the very much less active hypoxanthine. Plaque formation by HUMAN HERPESVIRUS 1 and 3, and by VACCINIA VIRUS, was markedly prevented by the two drugs in combination compared to adenine arabinoside alone. Increased survival rate or highly significant increase in life span of moribund virus-infected mice treated with both drugs was observed when compared to adenine arabinoside given alone.

Cowbone ridge virus A species in the genus FLAVIVIRUS. No known arthropod vector. Isolated from a cotton-rat in Florida. Not reported to cause disease in humans.

Cowdry type A inclusion bodies

Cowdry E.V. (1934) *Arch. Path.* **18**, 527

Intranuclear acidophilic inclusions as seen in HUMAN (ALPHA) HERPESVIRUS 1 and 2 infected cells. Cowdry described a second type of inclusion (type B), also acidophilic and intranuclear, but the basophilic chromatin of the nucleus is not marginated. This type was found in poliomyelitis, borna disease and rift valley fever, but the term is no longer used.

Cow pox virus

Baxby D. (1977) *Brit. med. J.* **i**, 1379

A species in the genus ORTHOPOXVIRUS. Causes papules, developing into vesicles on a firm inflamed base. Crusting follows and may not clear for several weeks. Lesions appear on teats and udders of cows. May infect the hands of milkers who then may spread the infection among cattle. Transmission from man to man is rare. A number of infections of man have been reported in which there was no obvious contact with cattle. It is likely that the natural host is a small mammal rather than cattle. Rabbits, guinea pigs, mice and monkeys are also susceptible. Pocks on the CAM are intensely haemorrhagic and smaller at 48 hours than those caused by VACCINIA VIRUS. Pocks not produced above 40 °C. Variant strains may produce white pocks. Lesions produced in rabbit skin are large and indurated, with a purple-black centre. Replicates in many cell lines, some of which e.g. RK 13 may be more sensitive than CAM. Outside Europe lesions in the cow are usually due to vaccinia virus.

Coxsackie virus Species in the genus ENTEROVIRUS. Named after a small town in New York state from where the first one came. They are divided on biological characters into two groups: A and B. In suckling mice group A viruses produce a flaccid paralysis due to an acute necrotic myositis: group B viruses produce a spastic paralysis due to encephalitis. Serologically there are 24 viruses in group A and 6 in group B. Newly recognized enteroviruses (from type 68) are no longer assigned to the coxsackievirus or echovirus species but are given the next enterovirus number. Type A 7 agglutinates erythrocytes from fowls whose erythrocytes are agglutinated by VACCINA VIRUS Types A 21 and B 3 agglutinate human O erythrocytes. Type B viruses replicate readily in primary monkey kidney cell cultures with CPE. Only a few A viruses will replicate in tissue culture. All coxsackieviruses are pathogenic for suckling mice. Both types A and B are frequent, often silent, human infections though A viruses may cause herpangina and aseptic meningitis, and B viruses epidemic pleurodynia or myalgia (BAMBLE DISEASE), orchitis, aseptic meningitis, and myocarditis.

Coxsackie virus A 7

Grist N.R. & Roberts G.B.S. (1966) *Arch. ges. Virusforsch.* **19**, 454

Causes paralysis on injection into monkeys, cotton-rats and new-born mice. Has been associated with outbreaks of aseptic meningitis with paralysis in man. Sometimes called poliomyelitis virus type IV.

Coxsackie virus A 9 Resembles the ECHOVIRUSES in being inhibited by 2-(α-hydroxybenzyl) benzimidazole. Has caused many cases of aseptic meningitis sometimes with an exanthem. Has some antigenic relationship to COXSACKIE A23-ECHO 9. Replicates in rhesus monkey kidney cell cultures with CPE and causes myocarditis in mice.

Coxsackie virus A 10

Steigman A.J. *et al.* (1962) *J. Pediat.* **61**, 331

Associated with a distinct syndrome, lymphonodular pharyngitis.

Coxsackie virus A 14 More neurotropic than other coxsackie A viruses on injection into monkeys.

Coxsackie virus A 16

Hagiware A. *et al.* (1978) *Microbiol. Immunol.* **22**, 81

A species in the genus ENTEROVIRUS. The commonest cause of hand, foot and mouth disease in humans. Shares an antigen with ENTEROVIRUS 71 but there is no cross-NEUTRALIZATION. The first coxsackie virus to be associated with hand, foot and mouth disease and probably the most common cause.

Coxsackie virus A 21 Serologically identical to COE VIRUS.

Coxsackie virus A 23 Probably identical to ECHO 9 VIRUS. Some strains may be isolated in suckling mice, others in cell cultures and adapted to mice.

Creutzfeldt-Jakob disease virus

Matthews W.B. (1977) *Recent Adv. Clin. Virol.* **1**, 51

Gajdusek D.C. *et al.* (1977) *New Eng. J. Med.* **297**, 1253

Gibbs C.J. *et al.* (1978) *Proc. natn. Acad. Sci. U.S.A.* **75**, 6268

One of the subacute spongiform encephalopathy viruses. Causes a progressive degeneration of the CNS in man, with dementia in the early stages. There may be myoclonus

and typical ECG changes. Onset between 35 and 65 years. Occurs sporadically all over the world, but small clusters of cases are reported. Some cases have familial history but verticle transmission is not certain. Has been transmitted in humans by corneal graft when the incubation period was 18 months. Mode of natural transmission in man is not known. There is no evidence of increased risk of developing the disease in health care workers. However, post mortems should be conducted with extreme care. Disease can be transmitted to Old World and New World monkeys, cats, hamsters, guinea pigs and mice. Morphology of the virus unknown, probably because of its small size; indicated by extreme resistance to irradiation. Very heat-resistant, some infectivity surviving 100 °C. Not inactivated by formalin, alcohol, or ether. For disinfection, autoclaving is best, though sodium hypochlorite, iodine or phenolic disinfectants can be used.
SYN: transmissible virus-dementia virus.

Cricetid herpesvirus 1
Melendez L.V. *et al.* (1973) *Lab. Animal Sci.* **23**, 385
A species in the family HERPESVIRIDAE. Isolated from new-born field mouse *Microtus pennsylvanicus* cell culture which showed spontaneous CPE. Replicates in a wide variety of cell lines, including VERO CELLS, with CPE. Some antigenic relationship to HUMAN HERPESVIRUS 1.

Cricetid herpesvirus 2 (number assigned by us)
Luis V. *et al.* (1976) *Lab. Animal Care* **17**, 302
A species in the family HERPESVIRIDAE, isolated from a laboratory colony of Egyptian sand rats *Psammomys obesus* in which there had been numerous deaths. Post mortem examination was inconclusive, and the virus was isolated in primary rabbit kidney cell cultures from throat swabs of live animals. CPE appeared after 8 days and progressed to confluence by 11 days. Type A intranuclear INCLUSION BODIES are produced. Replicates with CPE in HELA, human amnion, sand rat and squirrel monkey cells. Not pathogenic for 5 day old mice or rats. Probably not pathogenic for sand rats.
SYN: sand rat nuclear inclusion virus.

Cricetid herpesvirus 3 (number assigned by us)
Tomita Y. & Jonas, A.M. (1968) *Am. J. vet. Res.* **29**, 445
A species in the family HERPESVIRIDAE. Isolated from a Syrian hamster *Mesocricetus auratus* with a regional enteritis which has been considered a neoplastic disease. Replicates in hamster embryo fibroblast cell cultures with CPE in 14–16 days. Ether-sensitive. 100–200 nm in diameter by filtration. Replication inhibited by 5-BROMO-2′-DEOXYURIDINE. Non-pathogenic on injection into adult hamsters and mice, but fatal for suckling hamsters.

Crimean–Congo haemorrhagic fever group viruses *See* Congo antigenic group viruses

Crimean haemorrhagic fever virus An unclassified ARBOVIRUS morphologically like BUNYAVIRUS, but serologically not related to members of that genus. A member of the CONGO ANTIGENIC GROUP VIRUSES. Recognized when it caused an epidemic of acute severe haemorrhagic fever in 1944 and 1945 in the western Crimea. Isolated from patients and from the tick *Hyalomma marginatum marginatum*. A similar disease had been known for many years in the central Asian republics of the U.S.S.R. and has since been observed on the borders of the Black and Caspian Seas, and in Bulgaria and Yugoslavia. It is closely related or identical to CONGO VIRUS.

cross-reactivation *See* reactivation.

Croup-associated virus Synonym for parainfluenza virus type 2.

CR 326 virus
Carmine C. *et al.* (1973) *Proc. Soc. exp. Biol. Med.* **142**, 276, 1257
Provost P.J. *et al.* (1975) *Proc. Soc. exp. Biol. Med.* **148**, 532
A strain of HEPATITIS A VIRUS. Isolated from patients in Costa Rica by the injection of

serum or extracts of clotted blood into white moustached marmosets *Saguinus mystax*. Can be serially passed in marmosets, causing hepatitis. Human convalescent serum neutralises the virus.

cryptogram

Gibbs A.J. *et al.* (1966) *Nature, Lond.* **209**, 450

In virology this is a cipher used to record certain basic properties of viruses. Each cryptogram consists of four pairs of symbols with the following meanings:

1st pair: type of NUCLEIC ACID and strandedness.

2nd pair: mol. wt. of nucleic acid in millions and percentage in infective particle.

3rd pair: outline of particle and shape of NUCLEOCAPSID.

4th pair: kind of host infected and kind of vector.

e.g. HUMAN POLYOMAVIRUS = D/2:3·4/13:S/S:V/O.

cryptovirogenic Having the potential to produce infective virus particles after derepression of the viral GENOME present within the cell. Analogous to the term lysogenic used for bacterial cells.

C type virus particles

Bernard W. (1960) *Cancer Res.* **20**, 712

Dalton A.J. (1972) *J. natn. Cancer Inst.* **49**, 323

A term used originally by electron microscopists to describe a morphologically defined group of enveloped RNA virus particles, often seen outside the cells in leukaemic tissues. The leukaemogenic viruses are C-type particles as are many ENDOGENOUS viruses with no known biological function. They are never seen inside the cytoplasmic matrix, but within cytoplasmic vacuoles or at the cell surface from which they bud. Just after budding they are described as immature C-type particles or enveloped A-type particles, because some people believe intracytoplasmic A type particles can become C-type particles by budding through the cell membrane. The immature C-type particle resembles an A-type particle with an outer unit membrane derived from the cell with surface structures. They mature rapidly, the CORE seems to collapse and become more electron dense. They have a diameter of 90 to 110 nm and the core is centrally located. There is a lipo-protein ENVELOPE covered with knobs 8 nm in diameter, but devoid of prominent projections. The core appears to have cubic symmetry and to consist of an outer layer of ring-like subunits 6 nm in diameter forming a hexagonal pattern and an inner membrane 3 nm thick. Within this is a tubular structure which usually appears as a ring but may fill the core and may have helical symmetry. *See* type C oncovirus group.

culture medium A liquid or semi-solid mixture which supplies the physical conditions and substances necessary for cell growth or maintenance. All culture media must provide:

(1) The correct osmotic pressure. This is largely due to the concentration of sodium chloride, but other ions and glucose also contribute.

(2) The correct pH. This is usually obtained with bicarbonate buffer, with up to 5% carbon dioxide in the closed head-space above the medium.

(3) The necessary inorganic ions: sodium, potassium, calcium, magnesium, iron, carbonate, phosphate and sulphate.

(4) Carbohydrate, usually glucose.

(5) Amino acids. About 12 are necessary.

(6) Vitamins and growth factors. These may be provided either in the form of pure substances or as undefined products such as yeast or embryo extract.

(7) Peptides and proteins. Some cells will grow in completely defined media, but for most tissue cultures a supply of serum and peptides is necessary.

Most culture media contain phenol red to give visual indication of change of pH. Antibiotics are virtually always included to maintain sterility, though neither phenol red nor antibiotics are required for cell metabolism. *See also* tissue culture.

curing Conversion of a LYSOGENIC bacterial culture to a non-lysogenic state. Can occur spontaneously, or can be induced, for example, by heating the culture briefly or by exposure to irradiation.

C value The amount of DNA in the haploid GENOME of a eukaryotic cell.

CV-1 cells (CCL 70) A heteroploid cell line derived from the kidney of an adult male African green monkey *Cercopithecus aethiops* for use in TRANSFORMATION studies on ROUS SARCOMA VIRUS.

cyanophage

Padan E. & Shilo M. (1973) *Bact. Rev.* **37**, 343

Viruses which replicate in blue-green algae.

cybrid Result of the fusion of a cell with a cytoplast. The cytoplast can transmit cytoplasmic components which may not be under the control of the cell GENOME. For example, intracisternal A TYPE VIRUS PARTICLES can be transmitted to a cell which does not contain them by fusion of the cell with a cytoplast which does. The result of the fusion is a cybrid.

cycloheximide 3-[2-(3,5-dimethyl-2-oxocyclohexyl)-2-hydroxyethyl]glutarimide. A glutarimide antibiotic isolated from the beers of streptomycin-producing strains of *Streptomyces griseus*. A potent reversible inhibitor of protein synthesis but does not affect

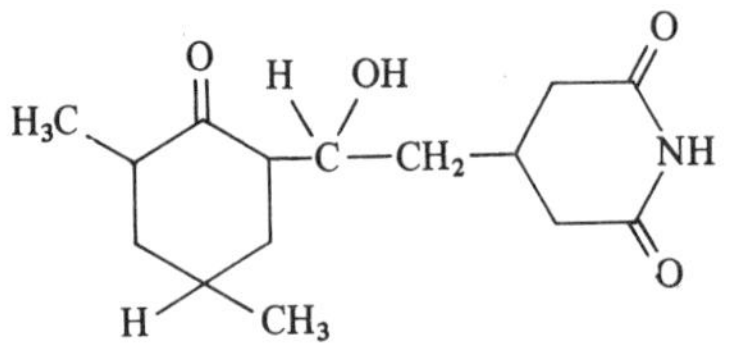

O H OH
H_3C C—CH_2— NH
O
H CH_3

the maturation of ribosomes. Active against a wide range of eukaryotic cells but does not inhibit prokaryotic systems.

SYN: actidione.

cyclo-octylamine A compound structurally related to AMANTADINE which inhibits INFLUENZA VIRUS replication in cell cultures.

Cyprinid herpesvirus 1

Grutzner L. (1956) *Zentbl. Bakt. ParasitKde 1. Abt. Orig.* **165**, 81

A species in the family HERPESVIRIDAE. Isolated from epithelioma of carp. Produces specific CPE in cell cultures of a warm water aquarium fish *Lebistes reticulatus*.

SYN: carp pox herpesvirus; epithelioma of carp virus.

cyprinid rhabdoviruses

(1) Rhabdovirus carpio
(2) Swim-bladder inflammation virus
(3) Grass carp rhabdovirus

Cysternaviridae A name proposed but not adopted for the family CORONAVIRIDAE.

cytarabine hydrochloride 1-β-D-arabinofuranosylcytosine hydrochloride. An antiviral and antileukaemic agent. The antiviral properties are an aspect of its ability to inhibit

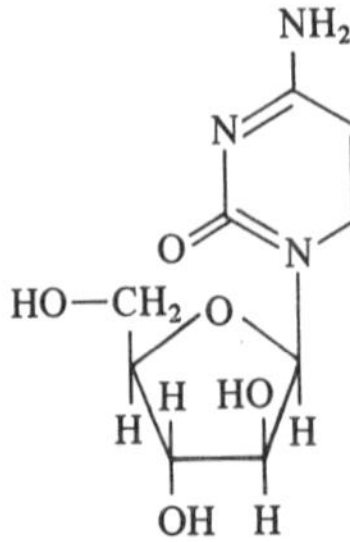

NH_2
N
O N
HO—CH_2 O
H HO
H H
OH H

Cytarabine

DNA synthesis. In the body the drug is converted to the corresponding NUCLEOTIDE, when it is able to inhibit both DNA POLYMERASE and NUCLEOSIDE reductase. Its antiviral spectrum resembles that of IDOXURIDINE but some of the HERPESVIRUSES are more sensitive to cytarabine. Rapidly inactivated *in vivo*. Has been used with some success in the treatment of herpes keratitis and severe generalised herpes infection. Apparently not effective in the treatment of herpes zoster. Side effects include nausea, vomiting, ulceration of the mouth, conjunctivitis, keratitis and depression of the bone marrow. Available as 100 mg vials, with 5 ml water as solvent (contains 0·9% benzyl alcohol).

SYN: Cytosar (Upjohn)

cytocidal Causing cell death.

Cytomegaloviruses

Weller T.H. (1971) *New Eng. J. Med.* **285**, 203, 267

Plummer G. (1973) *Prog. med. Virol.* **15**, 92

A group of species in the family HERPESVIRIDAE, distinguished by their slow growth-rate, narrow host-range and high degree of cell-association. They can often be isolated from the kidney, and with particular frequency from the salivary glands. It is likely that viruses of this group might be found in all mammalian species were adequate search to be made. They have already been demonstrated in man, mouse and guinea pig. Other probable cytomegaloviruses are found in various primates, rats and pigs.

Cytomegalovirus group Synonym for Betaherpesvirinae.

cytopathic effect (CPE) Alteration in the microscopic appearance of cells in culture following infection with a virus. May consist of rounding up, cell-detachment, cell fusion, production of INCLUSION BODIES, etc. NEUTRALIZATION of CPE is widely used in serological identification of viruses.

cytoplasmic amphibian viruses Synonym for icosahedral cytoplasmic deoxyviruses of amphibians.

Cytoryctes variolae The name originally applied by Guarnieri to the INCLUSION BODIES which now take his name, under the impression that they were protozoa.

Cytosar Trade name for cytarabine hydrochloride.

cytosine arabinoside hydrochloride *See* cytarabine hydrochloride.

cytosis A general term for pinocytosis and phagocytosis.

cytotoxic Harmful to cells. A property of certain chemicals (drugs) and viruses. The viruses may be toxic without replicating, or as a result of replicating in the cell.

Dabney's grippe or **grip** Synonym for Bamble disease.

dactinomycin Synonym for actinomycin D.

Da Fano bodies Minute basophilic intracytoplasmic INCLUSION BODIES found in cells infected with HUMAN HERPESVIRUS 1 or 2.

D'Aguilar virus A species in the genus ORBIVIRUS, belonging to the PALYAM ANTIGENIC GROUP. Isolated from *Culicoides brevitarsis* in S.E. Queensland, Australia. Antibodies are present in cattle and sheep. Not reported to cause disease in humans.

Dakar bat virus A species in the genus FLAVIVIRUS with no known arthropod vector. Isolated from insectivorous bats of *Scotophilus* sp. in Senegal, Nigeria, Uganda and Central African Republic. Not known to cause disease in humans.

Dandy fever virus Synonym for dengue virus.

Dane particle The original name for the complete human hepatitis B virus particle.

Da virus

Hsiung G.D. (1959) *Virology* **9**, 717

A strain of PARAINFLUENZA VIRUS TYPE 5. Isolated from post mortem blood from a case of infectious hepatitis. Antigenically identical to SIMIAN VIRUS SV5 and SA VIRUS.

Deer fibroma virus

Tajima M. *et al.* (1968) *Am. J. vet. Res.* **29**, 1185

A species in the genus PAPILLOMAVIRUS. A natural infection of deer in U.S.A. producing tumours which are histologically fibromas. Not transferable to calves, rabbits, guinea pigs or sheep.

defective interfering (DI) virus

Huang A.S. (1973) *Ann. Rev. Microbiol.* **27**, 101

Virus generated by growth at high multiplicity of infection which can interfere with the replication of normal virus (known as 'STANDARD' VIRUS) and may modify the outcome of disease. The term does not include virus particles in which the complete GENOME is missing. DI virus has four main properties: defectiveness (inability to grow in the absence of HELPER VIRUS); dependence (ability to be complemented by and to replicate in the presence of helper virus); INTERFERENCE (causing a decrease in yield of standard virus); and enrichment (ability to increase the proportion of its own yield). Originally discovered with INFLUENZA VIRUS (*see* von Magnus phenomenon), it now appears that any virus is liable to generate defective interfering particles if passaged at high multiplicity. In all cases examined, the defective virus is found to lack a part of the genome NUCLEIC ACID, but the factors leading to the generation of DI virus are not completely understood.

defective virus

Huang A.S. (1973) *Ann. Rev. Microbiol.* **27**, 101

Virus which is unable to replicate because it is abnormal in some way. In all virus preparations there are many defective particles and they may interfere with the replication of complete particles. When viruses are passed at high multiplicity the proportion of defective particles may increase. *See* von Magnus Phenomenon. Some defective viruses can replicate in a mixed infection with a HELPER VIRUS. The helper often provides the coat proteins. *See* phenotypic mixing.

degeneracy of the code *See* codon.

Delta herpesvirus

Ayres J.P. (1971) *Lab. Animal sci.* **21**, 685

Allen W.P. *et al.* (1974) *Lab. Animal Sci.* **24**, 222

Synonym for cercopithecid herpesvirus 5.

denaturation Of virus: synonym for inactivation. Of NUCLEIC ACID: dissociation of double-stranded molecules into single strands. Caused by high temperature or extremes of pH.

Dendrid Trade name for IDOXURIDINE eye drops.

Dengue virus

Miles J.A.R. (1978) *Asian J. inf. Dis.* **2**, 1

A species in the genus FLAVIVIRUS. There are 4 serotypes. Double diffusion tests reveal a common antigen and specific antigens. Type 1 occurs in S.E. Asia from India to Japan and Hawaii, with temporary spread to Greece, S. Africa and Australia. Type 2 occurs in S.E. Asia, central America and the Caribbean. Types 3 and 4 occur in Thailand and the Philippines. In man dengue is an acute febrile illness. Incubation period 5–8 days. The disease lasts about 10 days with severe headaches, back and limb pains. Often there is a scarlatiniform or maculopapular rash. Haemorrhagic fever with shock may result from infection with one type in persons immune to another. An antigen/antibody reaction occurs in the tissues. The haemorrhagic type of disease has not yet appeared in the Caribbean. Replication occurs in HELA CELLS with CPE, and in suckling mouse brain. Virus can be adapted to eggs and other cell types. Adapted experimentally to mice it causes flaccid paralysis of the limbs. Chimpanzees and most monkeys have an inapparent infection following experimental infection. Control is by elimination of *Aedes aegypti*, and there is an effective vaccine.

SYN: breakbone fever virus; dandy fever virus; polka fever virus.

dense virus particles

Rowlands D.J. *et al.* (1975) *J. gen. Virol.* **29**, 223

Wiegers K.J. *et al.* (1977) *J. gen. Virol.* **34**, 465

The VIRIONS of PICORNAVIRIDAE which band at a density of 1·44 g/ml compared to 1·34 g/ml at which standard particles band. Dense and standard virions are probably two configurations of the virion structure.

density-dependent inhibition Inhibition of cell division in tissue cultures due to the presence of neighbouring cells, though other factors are involved. For example, if cell metabolism has rendered the medium acid, restoration of an alkaline pH will temporarily restore growth. Addition of serum or other growth factors may also have a similar effect. *See* contact inhibition.

density gradient centrifugation Centrifugation in a supporting column of fluid whose density is lowest at the top of the tube, and increases towards the bottom where it is greatest. This technique is particularly useful for the study of viruses. *See* rate zonal centrifugation and isopycnic gradient centrifugation.

Densovirus A genus of the family PARVOVIRIDAE. Arthropod viruses which replicate without a HELPER VIRUS. The VIRIONS contain single-stranded DNA which is either a POSITIVE or a NEGATIVE STRAND. They are COMPLEMENTARY and on extraction anneal to form double-stranded DNA.

(*R*)-3-(2-deoxy-β-D-*erythro*-pentofuranosyl)-3,6,7,8-tetrahydroimidazo-[4,5-*d*] [1,3]diazepin-8-ol *See* co-vidarabine.

deoxyribonucleic acid (DNA)

Watson J.D. & Crick F.H.C. (1953) *Nature, Lond.* **171**, 737

Diagrammatic representation of the DNA molecule

A. Part of the polynucleotide chain.
B. Pairing of the bases in two polynucleotide chains.
C. Arrangement of the chains as a double helix.

A polymer of deoxyribonucleotides. A very large molecule mol. wt. 10^6–10^{10}. Adenine, cytosine, guanine and thymine are the four bases characteristic of DNA. However, in certain types of viral DNA other bases occur e.g. in T_2, T_4 and T_6 BACTERIOPHAGES cytosine is replaced by 5-hydroxymethylcytosine. In DOUBLE-STRANDED DNA, the adenine and thymine are present in equimolecular amounts, as are guanine and cytosine (*see* Chargaff's rule). There is pairing between adenine and guanine on one strand and thymine and cytosine on another to form the double strand (see G+C content). The two strands are of opposite polarity, the 5′ end of one chain being opposite the 3′ end of the other, and exist as a double helix. The two helices are both right-handed. The exact conformation and number of residues per turn depends on the physical conditions, and three structures A, B and C are described. SINGLE-STRANDED DNA molecules are rare in nature, but are found to constitute the GENOME of some viruses such as PARVOVIRIDAE and bacteriophage $\phi X174$.

Deoxyriboviruses DNA-containing viruses.

Dera Ghazi Khan antigenic group viruses A group of 5 unclassified tick-borne viruses. DERA GHAZI KHAN VIRUS has been isolated from ixodid ticks, the remainder from argasid ticks. They have not been isolated from other arthropods or from vertebrates. Not reported to cause disease in humans.

Abu Hammad
Dera Ghazi Khan
Kao Shuan
Pathum Thani
Pretoria

Dera Ghazi Khan virus An unclassified ARBORVIRUS, and the first member of the DERA GHAZI KHAN ANTIGENIC GROUP. Isolated from a tick *Hyalomma dromedarii* in Pakistan. Not reported to cause disease in humans.

Dermovaccinia virus Strains of VACCINIA VIRUS less virulent than others. Produce opaque white pocks on the CAM.

Detroit-6 cells (CCL 3) A heteroploid cell line developed from sternal marrow taken from a human male adult with carcinoma of the lung.

Detroit-98 cells (CCL 18) A heteroploid cell line developed from sternal marrow taken from a human male adult with no history of malignancy.

devil's clutch Synonym for Bamble disease.

devil's grip or grippe Synonym for Bamble disease.

dexamethasone 9α-fluoro-16α-methylprednisolone. A synthetic glucocorticoid which, when added to certain lines of mammary tumour cells in culture, stimulates the rate of production of MOUSE MAMMARY TUMOUR VIRUS. Probably acts by increasing cell gene TRANSCRIPTION.

Dhori virus

Sokhey J. *et al.* (1977) *Indian J. med. Res.* **66**, 726

An unclassified ARBOVIRUS. Isolated from a tick *Hyalomma dromedarii* in India, Egypt, and the Volga river delta in U.S.S.R. Antibodies are frequently found in sera from camels in India. Not reported to cause disease in humans.

D.H.S.S. Department of Health and Social Security.

DI Abbreviation for deaminase inhibitor. *See* co-vidarabine. Also an abbreviation for DEFECTIVE INTERFERING. *See* interference.

3,8-diamino-5-ethyl-6-phenylphenanthridinium bromide *See* homidium bromide.

Diarrhoea virus of bovines Synonym for pestivirus diarrhoea virus.

dibucaine hydrochloride Synonym for cinchocaine.

2,7-bis-[2-(diethylamino)ethoxy]-fluoren-9-one hydrochloride *See* tilorone hydrochloride.

***N*-*N*-dimethylamino-2-propanol *p*-acetamidobenzoate** *See* inosiplex.

3-[2-(3,5-dimethyl-2-oxocyclohexyl)-2-hydroxyethyl]glutarimide *See* cycloheximide.

dimethyl sulphoxide A very hygroscopic liquid with a slightly bitter taste and exceptional solvent properties for both inorganic and organic chemicals. Its penetrative properties have been used to aid the absorption of topically applied drugs such as IDOXURIDINE. Widely used experimentally as a solvent for substances administered to cells in tissue culture.

diphasic milk fever Synonym for tick-borne encephalitis virus (Central European subtype)

Diplornavirus (double-stranded RNA) A name once proposed for the family REOVIRIDAE.

Distemper virus

Appel M.J.G. & Gillespie J.H. (1972) *Virology Monograph 11*. Berlin: Springer-Verlag.

A species in the genus MORBILLIVIRUS. A natural infection of dogs, foxes, wolves, raccoons and mink. The infection is endemic in dogs and usually attacks the young, causing fever, nasal and ocular discharge and sometimes skin eruptions, after an incubation period of 4–5 days. The fever subsides to rise again, this time with vomiting, diarrhoea and often pneumonia. The disease may be mild, especially in puppies, but signs of CNS involvement, particularly fits, may occur. The virus also causes hard-pad, and probably canine rhinotonsillitis. The disease is spread by air-borne droplets and is highly infectious. The virus is antigenically closely related to MEASLES and RINDERPEST viruses. The roughly spherical VIRION is 100–250 nm in diameter. The helical NUCLEOCAPSID has a diameter of 15–18 nm. BUOYANT DENSITY in CsCl 1·25 g/ml. Lacks NEURAMINIDASE. Chick and guinea pig erythrocytes are agglutinated irregularly. Distemper virus replicates in ferret, dog and monkey (Vero) cell cultures and can be adapted to eggs. Giant cell and cytoplasmic inclusions are produced. May be related to rare demyelinating disease in man. *See* Cook S.D. *et al.* (1978), *Ann. Neurol.* **3**, 141.

SYN: hundestaupe; maladie de jeune age.

Ditchling virus

Appleton H. *et al.* (1977) *Lancet* **i**, 409

Very similar or identical to WOLLAN VIRUS. Observed by EM in 7 or 8 faecal specimens collected during an outbreak of acute epidemic gastroenteritis in a school at Ditchling, Sussex, U.K.

DMSO *See* dimethyl sulphoxide.

DNA Deoxyribonucleic acid.

DNA-dependent RNA polymerase A TRANSCRIPTASE mediating the transference of the information encoded in the base sequence in DNA to an analogous base sequence in mRNA. The bases are transcribed thus:

DNA ⟶	RNA
G	C
C	G
T	A
A	U

The RNA chain is initiated at a specific site on the DNA, the 'promoter region', and TRANSCRIPTION is terminated at another specific site, the 'terminator region'. These are specific signals in the DNA template recognised by the transcription apparatus. In animal cells, three distinct DNA-dependent RNA polymerases are found, known usually as forms I, II and III (though sometimes as forms A, B and C) which mediate the synthesis from DNA of ribosomal RNA, mRNA and tRNA respectively. Only form II, and to a minor extent form III, are inhibited by α-AMANITIN, which binds to the enzymes. ACTINOMYCIN D inhibits the function of all three enzymes by binding to the DNA template. Some viruses, notably the poxviruses, contain a VIRION-bound DNA-dependent RNA polymerase which mediates the synthesis of virus-specific mRNA early in infection.

DNA gyrase

Denhardt D.T. (1979) *Nature, Lond.* **280**, 196

DNA ligase

An enzyme present in bacteria which introduces negative superhelical twists into relaxed closed circular DNA molecules. Several DNA phages require the action of this enzyme during replication of their DNA.

DNA ligase

Lehman I.R. (1974) *Science, N.Y.* **186**, 790

An enzyme involved in DNA synthesis, and in repair of single-stranded breaks introduced by ENDONUCLEASES. Catalyses the formation of a phosphodiester bond between the 5′-phosphate end of one OLIGONUCLEOTIDE and the 3′-OH group of another. Ligases are

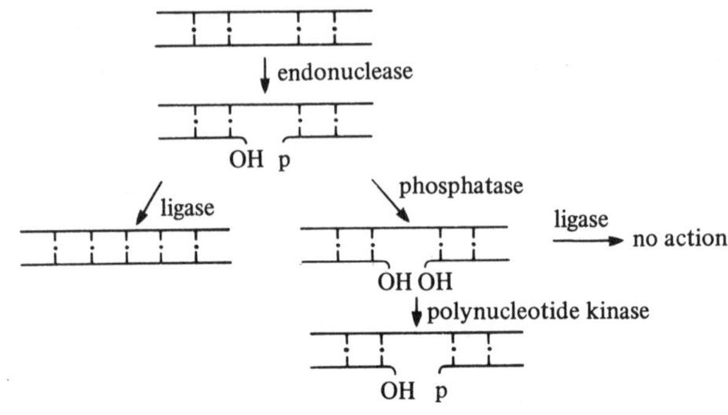

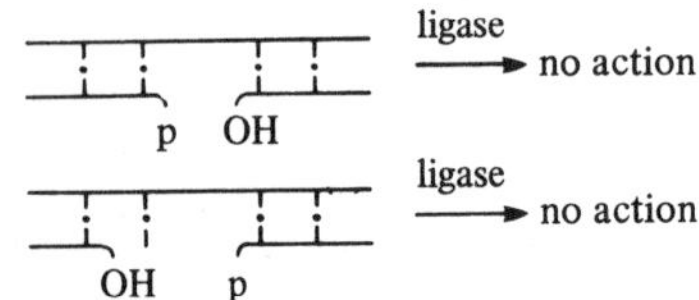

present in both animal and plant cells, including bacteria. Cf. DNA polymerase, and *see* semi-conservative replication.

DNA polymerase

Wickner S.H. (1978) *Ann. Rev. Biochem.* **47**, 1163

H H
O H
O=P—OH
O
5′
CH_2 O Thymine
H H
H H ← Growing end (Primer)
3′
O H
O=P—OH ← Phosphodiester bond
O
5′
CH_2 O Guanine
H H
H H ← Nucleotide (5′ monophosphate nucleoside)
OH H

An enzyme involved in DNA replication which catalyzes the addition of deoxyribonucleotide units to a DNA chain by forming a phosphodiester bond between the 3′-OH group on the growing end of the DNA molecule (known as the primer strand) and the 5′-phosphate on the incoming deoxyribonucleotide. The reaction requires a TEMPLATE (DNA or sometimes RNA), all four deoxyribonucleoside triphosphates, and a primer with a free 3′-hydroxyl group. The primer can be an uncompleted DNA strand, but is more usually a short RNA strand.

Three types of DNA polymerase have been described in prokaryotes. DNA polymerase I has a 5′–3′ nuclease activity as well as polymerase activity and is involved in repair synthesis of DNA. DNA polymerases II and III possess a 3′–5′ nuclease activity but lack the 5′–3′ nuclease activity. DNA polymerase III appears to be the true DNA replicating enzyme in E. coli; the role of DNA polymerase II is uncertain.

Little is known regarding DNA polymerases which function in eukaryotic cells. Many viruses stimulate new DNA polymerase activity upon infection, and a template-dependent DNA polymerase complex has been isolated from adenovirus-infected cells (Challberg M.D. & Kelly T.J. (1979) *Proc. N.A.S.* **76**, 655). RETROVIRIDAE contain a different type of DNA polymerase which is RNA template-dependent (*see* reverse transcriptase).

DNase Deoxyribonuclease. *See* nucleases

DNA transcriptase Synonym for DNA-dependent RNA polymerase.

Don cells (CCL 16) Diploid cells from a normal 8-month-old adult male Chinese hamster *Cricetulus griseus*.

double-stranded *See* deoxyribonucleic acid.

double-stranded viruses RNA-containing viruses: Reoviridae.
DNA-containing viruses: Adenoviridae, Herpesviridae, Papovaviridae, Poxviridae.

Downie body Large acidophilic cytoplasmic INCLUSION BODIES found in COW POX VIRUS lesions.

D.P.A.G. Dangerous Pathogens Advisory Group.

Driving sickness virus Synonym for Jaagsiekte virus.

D type virus particles

Dalton A.J. *et al.* (1974) *Intervirology* **4**, 201

Colcher D. *et al.* (1977) *Proc. natn. Acad. Sci. U.S.A.* **74**, 5739

Fine D. & Schochetman G. (1978) *Cancer Res.* **38**, 3123

A term used originally to describe the 30 nm unenveloped particles seen in large numbers in the nuclei in POLYOMA VIRUS-infected mice and hamsters. They proved to be polyoma virus particles and the term passed out of use. However in their proposed classification of RETROVIRIDAE Dalton *et al.* suggested a genus Oncornavirus D, with MASON–PFIZER MONKEY VIRUS as the type species. This has resulted in the Mason-Pfizer virus and morphologically similar viruses being described as having type D morphology. There are at least three such primate viruses: Mason-Pfizer monkey virus, SQUIRREL MONKEY RETROVIRUS and LANGUR RETROVIRUS.

Duck enteritis virus Synonym for anserid herpesvirus 1.

Duck hepatitis virus

Asplin F.D. (1961) *Bull. Off. int. Epizoot.* **56**, 793

A species in the genus ENTEROVIRUS. There are 2 serotypes. A widespread infection of ducks causing disease in ducklings. There is haemorrhagic necrosis of the liver and high mortality. Older birds are immune. Virus is present in the excreta. Birds hatched from the eggs of immune birds resist infection. Virus replicates in hens' eggs, killing the embryo, but becomes attenuated on passage and may be used as a vaccine for ducklings. Multiplies without CPE in chick cell cultures, with CPE in duck cell cultures. Experimentally, other birds and mammals are resistant.

Duck/HongKong/D3/75

Alexander D.J. *et al.* (1979) *Arch. Virol.* **60**, 105

A species in the genus PARAMYXOVIRUS. An AVIAN PARAMYXOVIRUS isolated from chickens, ducks and geese in Hong Kong. Unrelated antigenically to NEWCASTLE DISEASE VIRUS and the other avian paramyxoviruses.

Duck infectious anaemia virus A strain of avian reticuloendotheliosis virus.

Duck-plague herpesvirus Synonym for anserid herpesvirus 1.

Duck spleen necrosis virus A strain of avian reticuloendotheliosis virus.

Dugbe virus An unclassified ARBOVIRUS morphologically like BUNYAVIRUS but not serologically related to members of that genus. Belongs to the NAIROBI SHEEP DISEASE ANTIGENIC GROUP. Isolated from cattle and ticks in Nigeria, Central African Republic and Senegal. Has been isolated from humans with a febrile illness.

Duovirus Synonym for rotavirus. Name refers to the double-shelled construction of the virus particle.

duplex Having two parts. Often used to describe the double strand of NUCLEIC ACID.

Duvenhage virus

Meredith C.D. *et al.* (1971) *S. Afr. med. J.* **45**, 767

A species in the genus LYSSAVIRUS. First isolated in S. Africa from the brain of a man who had been bitten by a bat and died after a rabies-like illness. NEGRI BODIES were present in the patient's brain tissue and in the brain of experimentally infected mice, but rabies antigen was not demonstrable in the brain tissue by immunofluorescence. Antigenically related to RABIES VIRUS and resembles laboratory or 'FIXED' strains of the virus. Can be distinguished by *in vivo* NEUTRALIZATION and cross-challenge tests in mice, or less easily by CF and fluorescent antibody tests. In mice after a short incubation period there is inflammatory infiltration of brain parenchyma and small intraneuronal inclusion bodies.

Eastern equine encephalomyelitis virus A species in the genus ALPHAVIRUS. Maintained in the wild as a harmless infection of birds, small rodents, reptiles and amphibia. Man and horses are infected by mosquito bites. In horses there is VIRAEMIA and fever followed by involvement of the CNS. Strains vary in virulence but mortality can be 90%. In man the disease is similar, with high mortality. Most survivors show paralytic or mental sequelae. Outbreaks with high mortality occur in pheasants. The virus is found in eastern U.S.A., the Caribbean, Central America and eastern S. America. Mice, guinea pigs, goats, chicks, snakes and turtles can be infected experimentally. In birds the virus infects the viscera (liver) rather than the CNS. Virus can be propagated in eggs and a variety of tissue cultures in which it causes CPE. An active virus vaccine has been used.

Ebb virus Synonym for human (gamma) herpesvirus 4.

EBNA *E*pstein–*B*arr virus-induced *N*uclear *A*ntigen is associated with the CHROMATIN of lymphoblastoid cells carrying the viral GENOME.

Ebola virus

Dres P. (1978) *Bull. W.H.O.* **56**, 245

Ellis D.S. *et al.* (1978) *Brit. J. exp. Path.* **59**, 584

Report of W.H.O. Internat. Study Team (1978) *Bull. W.H.O.* **56**, 247 and 271

An unclassified RNA virus morphologically indistinguishable from MARBURG VIRUS, but immunologically different. The name comes from a small river in Zaire near which the virus was first isolated. Causes a severe and often fatal haemorrhagic fever. An epidemic involving at least 570 cases and 400 deaths occurred in the Sudan and Zaire in 1976. Incubation period is 7–14 days. There is headache, limb and back pains, diarrhoea, vomiting and extensive internal bleeding. Recovery is slow. The disease was less severe in the Sudan than in Zaire, and the virus isolated from Sudanese patients produced a lower mortality rate in rhesus monkeys than did virus from patients in Zaire. In other characteristics the viruses were indistinguishable. Immune plasma may be of therapeutic value. Transmission requires very close contact with body fluids. Rodents may be the reservoir of infection. Isolated in the laboratory by inoculation of patients' sera into guinea pigs or VERO CELLS.

EBTr (NBL-4) cells (CCL 44) A heteroploid bovine cell line derived from minced whole trachea of a male foetus of *Bos taurus*. Excellent for isolation, replication and quantitation of PESTIVIRUS DIARRHOEA VIRUS, BOVID HERPESVIRUS 1 and PARAINFLUENZA VIRUS TYPE 3. Cells decline beyond the 55th passage.

EBV Abbreviation for Epstein–Barr virus. *See* human (gamma) herpesvirus 4.

ECBO European Cell Biology Organization.

Ecboviruses (*E*nteric *C*ytopathic *B*ovine *O*rphan viruses) Synonym for bovine enteroviruses.

Echino viruses A name proposed for the group of syncytial or FOAMY VIRUSES in the family SPUMAVIRINAE. They have many properties in common, and it is likely that they will form a genus within this family. The name refers to the presence of long projections or spines on the surface of the virus particle.

Echovirus (*E*nteric *C*ytopathic *H*uman *O*rphan virus) A species in the genus ENTEROVIRUS. There are 34 numbered serotypes. Frequently isolated from faecal specimens in primary monkey kidney cell cultures but some strains replicate better in human amnion cells. Originally thought to be non-pathogenic, they may rarely cause ASEPTIC MENINGITIS, encephalitis, respiratory disease, exanthem, gastrointestinal symptoms, pericarditis and myocarditis. Do not produce disease in suckling mice. Newly recognized enteroviruses, from type 68, are no longer assigned a COXSACKIE or echovirus number. Many strains of types 3, 6, 7, 10, 11, 12, 13, 19, 20, 21, 29, 30 and 33 agglutinate human 0 erythrocytes at 4°. A strain of type 9 has been adapted to suckling mice and causes a disease similar to that produced by a coxsackie A virus. Focal lesions can occasionally be produced by some strains on inoculation into the brain or spinal cord of monkeys. Types 4, 6, and 9 have been associated with outbreaks of aseptic meningitis. Types 8, 11, 22 and 25 have been associated with respiratory illness. Type 18 was recovered from infants with diarrhoea. Type 16 caused the 'Boston exanthem', fever with a maculopapular rash. Type 10 is now classed as a REOVIRUS. Type 28 is now classed as a RHINOVIRUS. Data on the history of various strains is available in 'Strains of Human Viruses' by Majer M. and Plotkin S.A. (1972) Publ. S. Karger, Basel.

Echo 4 virus

Chin T.D.Y. *et al.* (1957) *Am. J. Hyg.* **66**, 76

Johnsson T. (1957) *Lancet* **i**, 590

Has caused outbreaks of ASEPTIC MENINGITIS with gastro-intestinal symptoms in about 70% of cases.

Echo 6 virus

Kibrick S. *et al.* (1957) *Ann. N.Y. Acad. Sci.* **67**, 311

Causes outbreaks of ASEPTIC MENINGITIS in children and adults. Gastrointestinal symptoms are uncommon. Localized muscle weaknesses and maculopapular rashes have been observed in some outbreaks. Resembles COXSACKIE VIRUS in causing BAMBLE DISEASE and carditis in humans, and in being pathogenic for suckling mice.

Echo 8 virus

Rosen L. *et al.* (1958) *Am. J. Hyg.* **67**, 300

Isolated from patients with respiratory and intestinal symptoms.

Echo 9 virus Caused widespread epidemic ASEPTIC MENINGITIS in Europe in 1955 and 1956, and in America in 1957. There was often a maculopapular rash. Unlike the prototype strain, many isolates can be adapted to produce coxsackie A type disease in new-born mice. Antigenically identical to COXSACKIE A23 VIRUS.

Echo 10 virus A strain of reovirus type 1.

Echo 11 virus

Nagington J. *et al.* (1968) *Lancet* **ii**, 725

When it causes disease it is usually in infants or young children. Meningeal symptoms are most common, but fever, respiratory or gastro-intestinal symptoms may occur. Sometimes associated with BAMBLE DISEASE. *See* U virus.

Echo 16 virus

Neva F.A. & Enders, J.F. (1954) *J. Immunol.* **72**, 307

Caused the 'Boston exanthem': an outbreak of fever, ASEPTIC MENINGITIS and a maculopapular rash which did not appear until the fever was over.

Echo 18 virus

Eichenwald, H.F. (1958) *J. Am. med. Ass.* **166**, 1563

Viruses isolated from 2 outbreaks of gastroenteritis and designated N_5 and D-3 proved to be Echo 18. Probably a cause of gastroenteritis in infants. Infection often associated with skin rashes.

Echo 19 virus

Cramblett H.G. *et al.* (1962) *Archs intern. Med.* **110**, 574

Isolated originally from an infant with diarrhoea and later from the CSF of an adult male patient. Has been associated with cases of mild respiratory disease and diarrhoea mainly in children.

Echo 20 virus

Buckland F.E. *et al.* (1961) *Brit. med. J.* **i**, 397

Isolated from the stools of children with fever, coryza and diarrhoea. In adult volunteers infection caused mainly constitutional symptoms, but some had 'colds' or gastro-intestinal symptoms.

SYN: JVI virus.

Echo 22 virus

Berkovitch S. & Pangan, J. (1958) *Bull. N.Y. Acad. Med.* **44**, 377

Has been associated with outbreaks of respiratory disease in young children. Has some of the characteristics of COXSACKIE A VIRUSES which it resembles in its reaction to 2-α-hydroxybenzyl benzimidazole and the nuclear changes produced in infected cell cultures.

Echo 23 virus Like echo 22 virus it has some of the properties of COXSACKIE A VIRUSES.

Echo 25 virus

Kasel J.A. *et al.* (1965) *Proc. Soc. exp. Biol. Med.* **118**, 381

Has been associated with rashes in infants. Infection of human volunteers has caused fever, pharyngitis and cervical adenitis.

Echo 28 virus Now designated HUMAN RHINOVIRUS strain 1A. Isolated in a primary rhesus monkey cell culture at the Naval Medical Research Unit No. 4, Great Lakes, Illinois, U.S.A. from a nasal washing from a young man with a mild respiratory infection.

Echo 34 virus An antigenic variant of COXSACKIE A 24.

eclipse period

Doermann A.H. (1952) *J. gen. Physiol.* **35**, 645

The time between the disappearance of the infecting virus and the appearance of new intracellular virus infectivity. The infecting virus loses its infectivity soon after PENETRATION and for some time no infective virus can be demonstrated. *See also* latent period.

Ecmoviruses (*E*nteric *C*ytopathic *M*onkey *O*rphan viruses) Synonym for simian enteroviruses.

Ecotropic murine type C virus

Bryant M.L. *et al.* (1978) *Virology* **88**, 389

A subspecies of MOUSE TYPE C ONCOVIRUS. Infects and replicates in cultures of mouse and rat cells only, unlike the AMPHOTROPIC MURINE TYPE C VIRUS which will also replicate in non-murine cells.

SYN: mouse-tropic strain. Cf. Xenotropic murine type C viruses.

Ecpoviruses (*E*nteric *C*ytopathic *P*orcine *O*rphan viruses) Synonym for porcine enterovirus.

Ecsoviruses (*E*nteric *C*ytopathic *S*wine *O*rphan viruses) Synonym for porcine enterovirus.

Ecthyma contagiosum of sheep virus Synonym for orf virus.

Ectromelia virus A species in the genus ORTHOPOXVIRUS. Similar to VACCINIA VIRUS. A latent infection, endemic in many mouse stocks, activated by stress. Injection i/p causes death from hepatitis. Injection into the skin of rabbits, guinea pigs and cotton rats produces local lesions which can be prevented by immunization with vaccinia. Replicates slowly on the CAM, with small, white, irregularly shaped pocks appearing in 72 hours. Pocks are not produced above 39°. Replication occurs in a number of cell cultures, but the plaques produced are smaller and appear more slowly than those due to vaccinia, COW POX or MONKEY POX VIRUSES.

SYN: mouse pox virus; pseudo-lymphocytic choriomeningitis virus.

E. Derm (NBL-6) cells (CCL 57) A heteroploid cell line initiated from a biopsy of dermis of an approximately 4-year-old quarter-horse *Equus caballus*. Has finite life-expectancy.

Edge Hill virus A species in the genus FLAVIVIRUS. Isolated from mosquitoes in Queensland, Australia. No known association with disease in man or other animals.

EEE virus Abbreviation for eastern equine encephalomyelitis virus.

Eel virus

Schwantz-Peitzner I. (1976) *Prog. exp. Tumor Res.* **20**, 101

An unidentified virus isolated in Europe from the blood of eels with skin papillomas. Diameter of virus particles 46–54 nm. Replicates with CPE in RTG-2 or FHM monolayer cell cultures. Virus particles are present in clusters in the cytoplasm. Injection into eels has not produced any lesions or disease. *See* cauliflower disease of eels virus.

efficiency of plating (EOP) A term introduced by E.L. Ellis & M. Delbrück in 1939 (*J. gen. Physiol.* **22**, 365) to quantify the relative efficiencies with which different cells could be infected and support viral replication. It is obtained by dividing the plaque count by the total number of VIRIONS in the inoculum. For animal viruses it ranges from 10^{-1} to 10^{-6} or less.

Egg drop syndrome 1976–associated virus

Todd D. & McNulty M.S. (1978) *J. gen. Virol.* **40**, 63

A disease involving depressed egg production in broiler breeder flocks has been recognized in recent years in western Europe. A number of serologically indistinguishable viruses have been isolated, one of which, isolate 127, has been further studied. It replicates in the nuclei of infected chick embryo liver cells in culture, is inhibited by IDOXURIDINE and is insensitive to chloroform. Similar in size to an adenovirus, but does not have the classical morphology. Agglutinates fowl erythrocytes. In virus preparations 3 particles with densities of 1·32, 1·30 and 1·28 g/ml were separated on CsCl gradients and named B1, B2 and B3. B1 and B2 were infective and could be labelled with ^{3}H-thymidine but differed morphologically. B2 and B3 aggultinated erythocytes. B3 are probably empty particles. Seven of the polypeptides in B1 and B2 had counterparts in fowl adenovirus type 1. 127 virus is probably a duck adenovirus.

Egtved virus

Robin J. & Rodrigue A. (1977) *Canad. J. Microbiol.* **23**, 1489

A species in the genus VESICULOVIRUS which causes a severe and often fatal haemorrhagic septicaemia in European salmonids, both young and sexually mature fish. Named after a village in Denmark where the disease was first recognised. Rainbow trout are the chief natural host but other trout are susceptible to inoculation. They lose appetite, become apathetic or swim abnormally. Abdomen is swollen, gills pale, with haemorrhages in the gill filaments, around the eyes and at fin bases. Can be propagated in cultures of trout ovarian cells: best at 12–14° and not above 22°.

SYN: haemorrhagic septicaemia virus of fish; viral haemorrhagic septicaemia of trout virus.

EID$_{50}$/HA ratio The ratio between the infective titre measured in eggs (see ID$_{50}$) and the haemagglutinating (HA) titre of a virus preparation. It gives a measure of the proportion of DEFECTIVE VIRUS particles present.

Elaphe virus

Lunger P.D. *et al.* (1974) *J. natn. Cancer Inst.* **52**, 1231

Lunger P.D. & Clark H.F. (1978) *Adv. Virus Res.* **23**, 159

A species in the subgenus REPTILIAN TYPE C ONCOVIRUS. Observed to be associated with the cells of an embryonal rhabdomyosarcoma in a corn-snake *Elaphe guttata*. Primary heart and kidney cells and a cell line derived from a rattlesnake fibroma could be infected with a cell-free extract of the original tumour. Productive infection could not be demonstrated in mammalian, chick embryo, piscine or non-ophidian reptilian cells.

Elapid herpesvirus 1

Monroe J.H. *et al.* (1968) *J. natn. Cancer Inst.* **40**, 135

Dimari S.J. *et al.* (1975) *Biochem. biophys. Acta* **393**, 320

A species in the family HERPESVIRIDAE. Herpesvirus-like particles were present in the venom of a cobra *Naja naja*.

SYN: cobra herpesvirus.

elementary bodies Small, round, stainable, extracellular aggregates of virus or viral products, seen in large numbers by light microscopy in the vesicle fluid or scrapings from skin lesions of smallpox, vaccinia, varicella and zoster.

Elephantid herpesvirus 1

McCully R.M. *et al.* (1971) *Onderstepoort J. vet. Res.* **38**, 225

A species in the family HERPESVIRIDAE. Routine PM examination of 50 elephants *Loxodonta africana* killed in the Kruger National Park revealed lymphoid nodules in the lungs of 37 of them (74%). There were from 1 to 6 greyish-white nodules present, with diameters varying from 3 mm to 30 mm. COWDRY TYPE A INTRANUCLEAR INCLUSIONS were present in epithelial cells of the nodules, and EM demonstrated particles of HERPESVIRUS morphology.

ELISA *E*nzyme-*l*inked *I*mmuno*s*orbent *A*ssay.

El Tifu Negro (black typhus) A local name for MACHUPO VIRUS infection.

elution of virus Release of virus particles from association with a cell surface or other solid support such as an ion-exchange column. The elution of ORTHOMYXOVIRIDAE by the action of NEURAMINIDASE from erythrocytes to which they have been adsorbed constitutes an effective purification method.

EMBO European Molecular Biology Organization.

empty particles Virus particles containing no NUCLEIC ACID.

Encephalitozoon rabei

Manouelian Y. & Viala J. (1924) *Ann. Inst. Pasteur* **38**, 258

Name given to a supposed protozoan aetiological agent of rabies. The structure is now known as the NEGRI BODY.

Encephalomyocarditis virus A species in the genus CARDIOVIRUS. A natural infection of wild rodents in which it probably rarely causes disease. Has been isolated from blood and stools of man, from captive lower primates, pigs, squirrels and other animals. May cause febrile illness with CNS involvement in man. Many animals can be infected experimentally. Mice and hamsters often die with CNS involvement after infection by any route. All strains are identical when compared by NEUTRALIZATION, CFT or HAI, but many show differences in biological behaviour. Agglutinates sheep erythrocytes in the cold. Replicates with CPE in cell cultures of chick, mouse, man, monkey, hamster and cattle.

endemic pneumonia of rats *See* pneumonia of rats.

Endo-epidemic haemorrhagic fever virus Synonym for junin virus.

endogenote *See* heterogenotes.

endogenous virus

Aaronson S.A. & Stephenson J.R. (1976) *Biochim. biophys. Acta Rev. Cancer* **458**, 323

A virus whose GENOME is present in the DNA of normal cells. It is thus genetically transmitted from generation to generation. The gene sequences which can code for virus production are VIROGENES and are normally repressed, but may be activated by intrinsic factors (e.g. hormones) or extrinsic factors (e.g. radiation, chemicals). The DNA sequences which code for endogenous C TYPE VIRUSES should be distinguished from EXOGENOUS viral information which may be added to an animal's genome during infection with an oncovirus. Once integrated into the DNA, the virogenes, both endogenous and exogenous, are subject to the same pressures of selection and mutation as other genes. Endogenous viruses can be recovered from most species, e.g. mice, cats, pigs, baboons etc. They often have a limited host range (N or B tropic) or may not replicate in the species from which they were isolated. Such viruses are XENOTROPIC or 'S'-tropic. The role of endogenous C type viruses in the production of spontaneous tumours is not yet clear.

endonuclease *See* nucleases.

endosymbiotic infection

Fernandes M.V. *et al.* (1964) *J. exp. Med.* **120**, 1099

General term coined to describe infection of cells by viruses in which replication occurs without CPE. The term was employed to distinguish this type of persistent infection from a CARRIER CULTURE, in which only a proportion of the cell population is infected at any one time.

engulfment Synonym for viropexis.

enhancement An increased yield of one virus in cells infected by another. A term used when the mechanism of the process is not clear. Cf. complementation and interference.

Entebbe bat virus A species in the genus FLAVIVIRUS with no known arthropod vector. Isolated from the salivary glands of a pool of bats of *Tadarida* sp. in Uganda. Not reported to cause disease in humans.

Enteritis of mink virus Synonym for feline panleucopenia virus.

Enterovirus

Grist N.R. *et al.* (1978) *Prog. med. Virol.* **24**, 114

Cooper P.D. *et al.* (1978) *Intervirol.* **10**, 165

A genus of the family PICORNAVIRIDAE distinguished from RHINOVIRUS by (1) being resistant to low pH, (2) having a density of 1·32–1·35 g/ml and (3) the disease produced in man or experimental animals. Many species have enteroviruses which tend to be species-specific. Transmission is horizontal by faecal contamination. Food and water are often involved, arthropods may play a minor role. The type species is HUMAN POLIOVIRUS 1. The first 67 human enteroviruses were divided into 4 species (3 poliovirus, 6 coxsackie B, 24 coxsackie A and 34 echoviruses) but the later isolates have not been alloted to a species and are called enterovirus 68 and so on. Other species are simian enteroviruses 1 to 18, PORCINE ENTEROVIRUSES 1 to 8 and BOVINE ENTEROVIRUSES 1 to 7. Enteroviruses have been isolated from several other species e.g. horse, sheep, buffalo and dog.

Enterovirus 68

Schieble J.H. *et al.* (1967) *Am. J. Epidem.* **85**, 297.

A species in the genus ENTEROVIRUS. Isolated from patients with pneumonia and bronchiolitis in California.

Enterovirus 69

Melnick J.L. *et al.* (1974) *Intervirology* **4**, 369

A species in the genus ENTEROVIRUS. Isolated from a rectal swab of a healthy 4-year-old child in Toluca, Mexico in 1959. Few strains have since been detected. Not reported to cause disease in humans. Prototype strain Toluca-1.

Enterovirus 70

Melnick J.L. *et al.* (1974) *Intervirology* **4**, 369

Yoshii T. *et al.* (1977) *J. gen. Virology* **36**, 377

Enterovirus 71

A species in the genus ENTEROVIRUS. Isolated in 1971 from epidemics of acute haemorrhagic conjunctivitis in Japan, Singapore and Morocco. These outbreaks were part of a pandemic involving millions of humans in Africa, southeast Asia, Japan, India and England during 1969–1971. The virus can adsorb *in vitro* to cells from a wider range of species than most Enteroviruses. In some it produces no CPE, but in others such as RK 13 (rabbit cells) and BK 1 (bovine cells) it produces virus and CPE. Prototype strain is AHC(J670/71).

Enterovirus 71

Hagiware A. *et al.* (1978) *Microbiol. Immunol.* **22**, 81

Melnick J.L. *et al.* (1979) *Intervirology* **12**, 297

A species in the genus ENTEROVIRUS. Isolated from the brain of a fatal case of encephalitis in California, U.S.A. in 1970. Related strains have been isolated from stools of sporadic cases of meningitis and encephalitis in California and from outbreaks in Australia and Sweden. Associated with an epidemic of meningitis among children in Bulgaria in 1975, in which 21% of cases had paralysis. Has been isolated from cases of hand, foot and mouth disease in Japan. Prototype strain Br Cr. Shares an antigen with COXSACKIE A16, but there is no CROSS-NEUTRALIZATION.

Entomopoxvirinae A subfamily in the family POXVIRIDAE, consisting of one genus ENTOMOPOXVIRUS, containing the poxviruses of insects.

Entomopoxvirus A genus of the subfamily ENTOMOPOXVIRINAE. Consists of viruses of insects. Probably do not replicate in vertebrates.

envelope Used sometimes to refer to the outer coat of large viruses, e.g. POXVIRIDAE. Strictly, the outer lipoprotein coat of viruses which mature by budding through the cell membrane. Such viruses are inactivated by lipid solvents e.g. chloroform or ether.

Env gene One of the genes in the GENOME of the AVIAN TYPE C ONCOVIRUS. Codes for the major glycoprotein found on the surface of the viral *env*ELOPE. Hence the name.

enzootic A disease constantly present in an animal community but affecting only a small number of animals at any one time. Analogous to *endemic*.

Enzootic abortion of ewes virus Not a virus. A chlamydia.

Enzootic bovine leukosis virus Synonym for bovine type C oncovirus.

enzootic bronchiectasis of rats

Nelson J.B. (1946) *J. exp. Med.* **84**, 7, 15

See pneumonia of rats.

Enzyme elevating virus Synonym for lactic dehydrogenase virus.

EOP EFFICIENCY OF PLATING.

Ephemeral fever virus

Della-Porta A.J. & Brown F. (1979) *J. gen. Virol.* **44**, 99

Gaffar Elamin M.A. & Spradbrow P.B. (1978) *J. Hyg. Camb.* **81**, 1

A species of the family RHABDOVIRIDAE, isolated in S. Africa, Australia and Japan from cattle with respiratory symptoms, increased salivation, lacrimation, joint pains, tremors and stiffness. The disease is of short duration. Virus replicates in mice and in cell cultures such as BHK 21. Loses pathogenicity for calves on passage in new-born mice, hamsters or BHK 21 cells. Can be isolated in eggs by inoculation of embryo. In Kenya transmitted by *Culicoides* sp. probably from the reservoir host buffalo and water buck.

SYN: bovine ephemeral fever virus; bovine epizootic fever virus; bovine influenza virus; three day stiff-sickness virus.

Epidemic diarrhoea of infant mice virus (EDIM)

Kraft L.M. (1966) *Natn. Cancer. Inst. Monograph 20*, p. 55

A species in the genus ROTAVIRUS. Attacks chiefly mice 11–15 days old, causing diarrhoea and dirty yellow fur. Not necessarily fatal. Disease is most common in first litters. Replication in cell cultures is in doubt. Infectivity resists ether, chloroform and pH 3. A stock free of virus can be obtained by caesarean section and fostering on disease-free females. Virus morphologically identical and antigenically very similar to human and other ROTAVIRUSES.

Epidemic haemorrhagic fever virus Synonym for Korean haemorrhagic fever virus.

Epidemic jaundice of man virus Synonym for hepatitis A virus.

epidemic myalgia Synonym for Bamble disease.

Epidemic tremor virus Synonym for avian encephalomyelitis virus.

episomes PLASMIDS which can be integrated into the cell GENOME, where they behave as part of a chromosome.

Epithelioma contagiosum virus Synonym for fowl pox virus.

Epithelioma of carp virus Synonym for cyprinid herpesvirus 1.

epizootic A disease temporarily present in an animal community, attacking many animals at the same time, spreading rapidly and becoming widely diffused. Analogous to *epidemic*.

Epizootic cellulitis virus Synonym for equine infectious arteritis virus.

Epizootic haemorrhagic disease of deer virus

Hourrigan J.L. & Klingsporn A.L. (1975) *Aust. vet. J.* **51**, 203

A species in the genus ORBIVIRUS and a member of the BLUE TONGUE ANTIGENIC GROUP. Has caused fatal epizootics in Virginian white-tailed deer *Odocoileus viriginianus*. Mule deer and other species are insusceptible. After an incubation period of 6–8 days there are signs of shock, multiple haemorrhages, coma and death. Virus can be passed i/c in suckling mice and loses virulence for deer. There are eight serotypes. Virus is found in U.S.A. and Canada. Infection does not pass by direct contact and an arthropod vector is suspected, probably a *Culicoides* sp. VIRIONS have a diameter of 62 nm. There may be 42 CAPSOMERES, 11 nm in diameter with an axial hole. ACRIDINE ORANGE staining suggests double-stranded RNA. Infectivity is ether- and desoxycholate-resistant, moderately chloroform-sensitive and destroyed by low pH. Injection into European deer, sheep, goats and cattle leads to a silent infection. Not reported to cause disease in humans.

Epstein–Barr virus Synonym for human (gamma) herpesvirus 4.

equestron

Cooper P.D. *et al.* (1973) *Intervirology* **1**, 1

Name given to a postulated regulatory protein produced during HUMAN POLIOVIRUS replication. It would regulate the suppression of host protein synthesis and control the production of viral RNA and protein. No satisfactory evidence in favour of the existence of this regulator has been forthcoming.

Equid (alpha) herpesvirus 1

Jackson T.A. *et al.* (1977) *Am. J. vet. Res.* **38**, 709

A species in the family HERPESVIRIDAE. A natural infection confined to equines. A common cause of acute respiratory disease in horses during their first two years of life. Natural transmission probably by respiratory route. Usually silent in mares, but abortion may occur especially in 8–10th month of pregnancy. Should not be confused with EQUINE INFECTIOUS ARTERITIS VIRUS which can also cause abortion in mares. Experimental infection during the 3–9th month of gestation may result in encephalitis due to vasculitis. Genital vesicular exanthema or pustular vulvo-vaginitis may be produced. Experimentally, causes abortion in guinea pigs; suckling hamsters infected i/p develop hepatitis. Has been adapted to growth on the CAM, in the yolk sack and amnion. Replicates with CPE in foetal horse cell cultures, also in HELA, human aminon, sheep, pig, cattle, cat and chick cell cultures. Live virus given to non-pregnant mares is safe and gives protection.

SYN: equine abortion virus; equine influenza virus; equine rhinopneumonitis virus; mare abortion virus.

Equid herpesvirus 1 Synonym for equid (alpha) herpesvirus 1.

Equid herpesvirus 2

Plummer G. *et al.* (1969) *J. Virol.* **4**, 738

Studdert, M.J. (1974) *Cornell Vet.* **64**, 94

Dutta S.K. & Campbell D.L. (1978) *Am. J. vet. Res.* **39**, 1422

A species in the family HERPESVIRIDAE. Originally isolated from a horse with catarrh, but usually causes only mild disease or silent infection. Is widespread and can be isolated from infected horses over a prolonged period. A slowly replicating cytomegalo-type virus but is not host cell specific. There are several sero-types, and the viruses numbered by Plummer as types 2, 3 and 4 are probably best regarded as sero-types of EQUID HERPESVIRUS 2. Serologically distinct from EQUID HERPESVIRUS 1 and 3.

SYN: equine cytomegalovirus.

Equid herpesvirus 3

Studdert M.J. (1974) *Cornell Vet.* **64**, 117

A species in the family HERPESVIRIDAE. Isolated from horses during an outbreak of coital exanthema, an acute relatively mild disease in which there are pustular lesions on the external genitalia and vagina. Cross-NEUTRALIZATION TESTS showed it to be distinct from EQUID HERPESVIRUSES 1 and 2. Transmission experiments with this virus produced typical equine coital exanthema, except in one animal which had recently recovered from the disease.

SYN: coital exanthema virus.

equilibrium density gradient centrifugation *See* isopycnic gradient centrifugation.

Equine abortion virus Synonym for equid (alpha) herpesvirus 1.

Equine adeno-associated virus

Dutta S.K. (1975) *Am. J. vet. Res.* **36**, 247

A species in the genus ADENO-ASSOCIATED VIRUS. Obtained from a foal.

Equine adenovirus

Studdert M.J. *et al.* (1974) *Am. J. vet. Res.* **35**, 693

Whitlock R.H. *et al.* (1975) *Cornell Vet.* **65**, 393

Fatemie-Nainie S. & Marusyk R. (1979) *Am. J. vet. Res.* **40**, 521

A species in the genus MASTADENOVIRUS. Isolated from horses with respiratory disease. Often causes death from pneumonia in foals. Isolates in Germany, Australia and U.S.A. are antigenically similar.

Equine arteritis virus Synonym for equine infectious arteritis virus.

Equine cytomegalovirus Synonym for equid herpesvirus 2.

Equine encephalosis virus

Verwoerd D.W. (1970) *Prog. med. Virol.* **12**, 192

A species in the genus ORBIVIRUS, isolated from horses in S. Africa.

Equine infectious anaemia virus *See* infectious anaemia of horses virus.

Equine infectious arteritis virus A species in the family TOGAVIRIDAE. Horses are the only susceptible species. The probable cause of EPIZOOTICS, highly contagious, infecting mainly young animals via the respiratory tract. Causes fever, conjunctivitis, rhinitis, oedema of the legs and trunk, enteritis and colitis. In pregnant mares the foetus may become infected and abortion occurs. Bronchopneumonia and pleural effusions occur in fatal cases. There is medial necrosis of small arteries and when the intima is involved, thrombosis. The VIRION is 50–70 nm in diameter with a CORE 20–30 nm in diameter, enveloped, inactivated by lipid solvents and low pH. Replicates in horse kidney cell cultures with CPE. Virus becomes attenuated on passage in tissue culture and can be used as a vaccine.

SYN: epizootic cellulitis virus, equine influenza virus; fièvre typhoide du cheval virus, infectious arteritis of horses virus; pferdestaupe virus; pink eye virus.

Equine influenza virus A poor term because it has been used for three different viruses, viz.: EQUID (ALPHA) HERPESVIRUS 1; EQUINE INFECTIOUS ARTERITIS VIRUS and INFLUENZA VIRUS A EQUINE.

Equine papilloma virus

Cook R.H. & Olson C. (1957) *Am. J. Path.* **27**, 1087

A species in the genus PAPILLOMAVIRUS. A natural infection of horses causing papillomas on the nose and lips, but can be transferred to the skin. Causes papillomas experimentally in horses, but not in other species.

Equine rhinopneumonitis virus Synonym for equid (alpha) herpesvirus 1.

Equine rhinovirus

Burrows R. (1970) *Proc. 2nd Int. Conf. Inf. Dis. Paris*, p. 154. Basèl: Karger.

A species in the genus RHINOVIRUS. Two serotypes. Replicates with CPE in cell cultures of horse, monkey, man and rabbit tissue. Does not require low temperature or low bicarbonate. World-wide infection causing rhinits and pharyngitis, often with fever. Incubation period 3–7 days. Rabbits, guinea pigs, monkeys and man can be infected. Spreads readily in stables: virus may persist in pharyngeal secretions for up to a month.

ERC group viruses Synonym for human rhinovirus.

Erosive stomatitis of cattle virus Synonym for bovine papular stomatitis virus, though other viruses may cause the same clinical picture.

Erythroblastosis of mice virus Has been used as a synonym for KIRSTEN LEUKAEMIA VIRUS, but erythroblastosis occurs to some degree with other leukaemia viruses such as FRIEND LEUKAEMIA VIRUS.

Erythroblastosis virus Synonym for avian erythroblastosis virus.

erythrodermatitis of carp The chronic form of infectious dropsy. Not caused by RHABDOVIRUS CARPIO. The aetiological agent has not yet been identified.

Ethidium Ethidium bromide. Trade name. *See* homidium bromide.

Eubenangee antigenic group Consisted of the EUBENANGEE, IBARAKI, PATA and TILLIGERRY VIRUSES. These are now included in the BLUE TONGUE ANTIGENIC GROUP.

Eubenangee virus A species in the genus ORBIVIRUS and a member of the BLUE TONGUE ANTIGENIC GROUP. Isolated in northern Australia from mosquitoes. Antibodies found in wallabies and kangaroos. Not reported to cause disease in humans.

EUMS European Union of Medical Specialities.

European ground squirrel cytomegalovirus Synonym for sciurid herpesvirus 1.

Everglades virus A species in the genus ALPHAVIRUS. Isolated from the cotton mouse, rat and *Culex* sp. in the Everglades National Park. Three cases of infection, with fever and headache, have been reported in humans.

EV virus Abbreviation for ENTEROVIRUS. Usually followed by the species number e.g. EV 70.

excisionase A viral enzyme which removes integrated viral DNA from chromosomal DNA.

exogenote *See* heterogenotes.

exogenous virus A virus originating from some source external to the cell in which it is found. Cf. endogenous virus.

exon

Gilbert W. (1978) *Nature, Lond.* **271**, 501

A region of the GENOME NUCLEIC ACID of a virus or a cell which is expressed in mature mRNA. *See also* intron, splicing.

exonuclease *See* nucleases.

Eyach virus

Rehse-Kupper B. *et al.* (1976) *Acta Virol. Prague* **20**, 339

A species in the genus ORBIVIRUS antigenically related to COLORADO TICK FEVER VIRUS. Isolated from ticks, *Ixodes ricinus* collected near the village of Eyach in the Neckar Valley, Federal Republic of Germany. Passed through a 200 nm filter but not a 100 nm filter. Infectivity resisted treatment with ether or deoxycholate but was sensitive to chloroform at room temperature for 30 minutes.

eye disease caused by viruses

Locatcher-Khoraze D. & Seegal B.C. (1972) *Microbiology of the eye*. St Louis, U.S.A.: Mosby

Viruses from 8 families can cause ocular disease in man. In most cases infection spreads from the upper respiratory tract or skin.
1. ADENOVIRIDAE: human species cause (*a*) epidemic keratoconjunctivitis; (*b*) pharyngo-conjunctival fever and (*c*) acute follicular conjunctivitis.
2. PAPILLOMAVIRIDAE: human species causes papillomas on the lids.
3. HERPESVIRIDAE: human types 1 and 2 cause keratoconjunctivitis. In chicken pox about 4% of cases have some corneal or conjunctival involvement. In shingles vesicles may occur on the cornea and result in scarring. In congenital CYTOMEGALOVIRUS infection the virus can be demonstrated in the retina at post mortem. Ocular involvement is a rare complication of infectious mononucleosis.
4. POXVIRIDAE: 4 species may affect the eyes *viz.*: VARIOLA VIRUS, VACCINIA VIRUS, ORF VIRUS and MOLLUSCUM CONTAGIOSUM VIRUS.
5. TOGAVIRIDAE: RUBELLA VIRUS infection during pregnancy is an important cause of congenital eye disease. Certain ARBOVIRUSES notably DENGUE and YELLOW FEVER often cause severe deep pain behind the eyes.
6. MYXOVIRIDAE: In some influenza epidemics conjunctivitis may be a common complication.
7. PARAMYXOVIRIDAE: In measles photophobia is a characteristic symptom. MUMPS VIRUS may rarely cause blindness due to nerve damage. NEWCASTLE DISEASE VIRUS can cause conjunctivitis.
8. PICORNAVIRIDAE: Paralysis of oculomotor nerves can occur in poliovirus infection. COXSACKIE VIRUS A 24 causes epidemic conjunctivitis, and ENTEROVIRUS 70 causes acute haemorrhagic conjunctivitis. Conjunctivitis is common in RHINOVIRUS infections.

faecal viruses unclassified

Tyrell D.A.J. (1976) *Ciba Foundation Symposium 42*, p. 261

EM permits many morphologically different virus particles to be seen in faeces. Some are morphologically CORONAVIRUSES and some are adenoviruses. It has been suggested that others should be called unclassified faecal viruses types I, II and so on.

Type no.	Original designation	Particle size
IA	Norwalk virus	27 nm
IB	Hawaii virus	27 nm
IC	Wollan or W. virus	—
II	Reo-like virus, orbivirus, duovirus, rotavirus, infantile gastroenteritis	65 nm
III	Possible parvovirus (Pover *et al.* (1973), *Lancet* **i**, 237)	22 nm
IV	Vellore virus-like particles	Enveloped particle similar to influenza

ASTROVIRUSES would be included if evidence of association with disease were found.

Far East Russian encephalitis virus Synonym for tick-borne encephalitis virus (Eastern subtype).

fat head minnow cells *See* FHM cells.

FA virus A strain of mouse poliovirus.

FBJ osteosarcoma virus

Finkel M.P. & Biskis, B.O. (1968) *Prog. exp. Tumor Res.* **10**, 72

Levy J.A.P. *et al.* (1973) *J. natn. Cancer Inst.* **51**, 525

Levy J.A.P. *et al.* (1978) *J. Virol.* **26**, 11

A naturally occurring strain of MOUSE SARCOMA VIRUS (Mu SV). Isolated from a spontaneous osteosarcoma in the thoracic spine of a CF1 mouse. It induces parosteal sarcomas in mice after a short latent period (3 weeks). In cell cultures produces foci of altered cells, different in morphology from those produced by other strains of mouse sarcoma virus. It is accompanied by a HELPER leukaemia virus. Unlike other strains of Mu SV it transforms mouse embryo cells into autonomously replicating cells. It thus produces plaques without having to produce infective virus. Produces osteosarcomas on injection into new-born Syrian hamsters.

FEBS Federation of European Biochemical Societies.

Felid herpesvirus 1

Bistner S.I. *et al.* (1971) *J. Am. vet. med. Ass.* **159**, 1223

A species in the family HERPESVIRIDAE. Cats which have recovered from infection with this virus may still carry it and infect kittens in which it causes nasal discharge, lacrimation and fever. Virus replicates in the mucous membranes of the nose, larynx and trachea, also in the conjunctiva, and can infect the genital tract. Focal lesions are produced in cell cultures from cat kidney, lung and testis. There is no CPE in cultures of bovine, human or monkey cells. Not antigenically related to HUMAN HERPESVIRUS 1, EQUID HERPESVIRUS 1–4, BOVID HERPESVIRUS 1 or SUID HERPESVIRUS 1.

SYN: feline herpesvirus 1, feline rhinotracheitis virus.

Felid herpesvirus 2

Fabricant C.G. & Gillespie J.H. (1974) *Infect. Immun.* **9**, 460

A species in the family HERPESVIRIDAE, probably a CYTOMEGALOVIRUS. Isolated by culture of cat tissues. Virus titres in culture medium are low, most of the virus being CELL-ASSOCIATED. Induces formation of syncytia and nuclear changes. Intracellular and extracellular crystals are formed, some of which are cholesterol. Replicates in cat and bovine embryo cells. Antigenically distinct from FELID HERPESVIRUS 1 and other HERPESVIRUSES.

Feline agranulocytosis virus Synonym for feline panleucopenia virus.

Feline calicivirus

Zwillen L.O. & Burki F. (1966) *Arch. ges. Virusforsch.* **19**, 373

Wardley R.C. & Povey R.C. (1977) *Res. vet. Sci.* **23**, 7 and 15

A species in the family CALICIVIRIDAE. Several serotypes are described. Most strains have been isolated from the respiratory tract but some may be associated with the gastro-intestinal tract. Experimental exposure to aerosol of virus caused rhinitis, conjunctivitis, oral ulceration and pneumonia. Infection most often seen in catteries, may be mild or severe, even fatal. Replicates in cultures of feline cells more readily than RHINOVIRUS. An attenuated strain is used as a vaccine, given intranasally or i/m.

SYN: cat flu virus, feline rhinotracheitis virus.

Feline enteritis virus Synonym for feline panleucopenia virus.

Feline herpesvirus 1 Synonym for felid herpesvirus 1.

Feline infectious aleukocytosis virus Synonym for feline panleucopenia virus.

Feline infectious enteritis virus Synonym for feline panleucopenia virus.

Feline infectious peritonitis virus

Starks B.W. *et al.* (1976) *Am. J. vet. Res.* **37**, 335

Pedersen N.C. *et al.* (1978) *Arch Virol.* **58**, 45

Horzinek M.C. & Osterhous A.D.M.E. (1979) *Arch. Virol.* **59**, 1

A species in the genus CORONAVIRUS. Antigenically related to PORCINE TRANSMISSIBLE GASTROENTERITIS VIRUS but infection with transmissible gastroenteritis virus does not give immunity to infectious peritonitis. Cats of any age, leopards and other large cats are susceptible. Causes a gradual loss of appetite, wasting and abdominal distension due to fibrinous peritonitis. Fatal in a few weeks. There is often pleurisy and necrotic inflammatory lesions in many organs. Infective virus is present in ascitic fluid and organ extracts. There is hypogammaglobulinaemia and there may be meningo-encephalitis and panophthalmitis.

Feline panleukopenia virus

Johnson R.H. *et al.* (1974) *Arch. Virol.* **46**, 315

A species in the genus PARVOVIRUS. A natural infection of all *Felidae*: domestic cats, lions and tigers, but in zoos usually the smaller species, raccoons and mink. Chiefly seen as a severe febrile illness, with vomiting and some times blood-stained diarrhoea in young cats though older cats may be attacked when virus is first introduced to a previously virus-free group. Subclinical and mild cases probably occur and give immunity. Infected animals may excrete virus for a year, and virus contaminating the environment may remain infectious for months. Kittens infected before 9 days of age may suffer damage to the developing cerebellum and at 3–4 weeks show ataxia and tremors. Cats, mink and newborn ferrets can be infected experimentally. After an initial leucocytosis there is a progressive fall in circulating lymphocytes and polymorphs, with lethargy and anorexia. Virus replicates in kitten kidney cell cultures. CPE may be transient. Virus replicates best in rapidly dividing cells. Some strains have weak haemagglutinins for pig erythrocytes at 4°. An attenuated virus vaccine gives protection.

SYN: ataxia of cats virus; cat distemper virus; cat fever virus; cat plague virus; enteritis of mink virus; feline agranulocytosis virus; feline enteritis virus; feline infectious aleukocytosis virus; feline infectious enteritis virus; feline parvovirus; show fever virus.

Feline parvovirus Synonym for feline panleucopenia virus.

Feline pneumonitis virus Not a virus. A chlamydia.

Feline respiratory viruses The clinical picture of acute upper respiratory disease in the domestic cat may be caused by a number of different viruses: FELID HERPESVIRUS 1, FELINE CALICIVIRUS, FELINE PANLEUKOPENIA VIRUS, and by feline pneumonitis agent which is a chlamydia.

Feline rhinotracheitis virus Synonym for felid herpesvirus 1.

Feline syncytial virus

Chiswell D.J. & Pringle C.R. (1979) *J. gen. Virol.* **44**, 145

Chiswell D.J. & Pringle C.R. (1978) *Virology* **90**, 344

A species in the sub-family SPUMAVIRINAE. Has been isolated from normal cats and from cats with various diseases. Not known to cause disease. Replicates in feline embryo cell cultures. Infected cells contain infectious proviral DNA of mol. wt. 6×10^6. Late in the course of the infection the PROVIRUS is integrated into the host cell GENOME.

FEMS Federation of European Microbiological Societies.

Fer-de-lance virus

Clark H.F. *et al.* (1979) *J. gen. Virol.* **44**, 405

Lunger P.D. & Clark H.F. (1978) *Adv. Virus Res.* **23**, 159

A species in the genus PARAMYXOVIRUS. Isolated from the lungs of fer-de-lance tropical American pit vipers *Bothrops atrox*, from a snake farm in Switzerland where there was an outbreak of lethal respiratory disease among the snakes. Replicates with CPE in a wide variety of reptilian, piscine and mammalian cells at 30°. The CPE varies in different cell types; in some syncytia are a prominent feature. Infected cells haemadsorb guinea pig erythrocytes. Replicates in hens' eggs at 27°; at first only on injection into the amniotic cavity but adapts to the allantoic cavity. Agglutinates chicken and guinea pig erythrocytes and has NEURAMINIDASE activity. No antigenic relationship demonstrable by CF test to other paramyxoviruses.

Feulgen stain One of the few staining methods specific for DNA. Other methods are (1) photography in u.v. light, as NUCLEIC ACIDS absorb avidly at 260 nm, and (2) staining after treatment with specific enzymes.

FHM cells (CCL 42) A heteroploid cell line derived from tissue posterior to the anus, exclusive of the caudal fin, of normal adult fat head minnows *Pimephales promelas* of both sexes. Supports growth of INFECTIOUS PANCREATIC NECROSIS VIRUS and FROG VIRUS 1. ECHO 11 VIRUS will multiply in these cells but CPE is not extensive.

Fibroma virus *See under* host animal species.
Fiebre amarilla virus Synonym for yellow fever virus.
Field mouse herpesvirus Synonym for cricetid herpesvirus 1.
Fièvre typhoide du cheval virus Synonym for equine infectious arteritis virus.
filipin

Majuk Z. *et al.* (1977) *J. Virol.* **24**, 883

A polyene antibiotic which interacts with sterols in liposomes and biological membranes, producing alterations in the lipid bilayer structure. Exposure of VESICULAR STOMATITIS VIRUS to the drug led to change in the permeability barrier of the virus ENVELOPE. Morphological changes could also be induced in the envelopes of RAUSCHER LEUKAEMIA VIRUS and INFLUENZA VIRUS, but were different from those seen in vesicular stomatitis virus.

fish viruses

Wolf K. (1966) *Adv. Virus Res.* **12**, 35

Wolf K. (1972) *Diseases of Fish*, Symposia of the Zoological Society of London no. 30, p. 305. London: Academic Press.

Cyprinid herpesvirus 1
Cyprinid rhabdoviruses
Hydrocephalus of pike
Infectious pancreatic necrosis
Lymphocystis
Pike fry rhabdovirus
Salmonid rhabdoviruses
Silurid herpesvirus 1

fixed virus Attenuated RABIES VIRUS.
FL amnion cells (CCL 62) A heteroploid cell line derived from normal human amnion cells.
Flanders virus

Murphy F.A. *et al.* (1966) *Virology* **30**, 314

A species in the genus VESICULOVIRUS. With HART PARK VIRUS forms the Flanders Hart Park Antigenic Group. Isolated from mosquitoes *Culiseta melanura* and *Culex pipiens*, and from an ovenbird, *Seiurus aurocapillus* in New York State, U.S.A. Serologically similar viruses have been isolated from mosquitoes in Texas, California, Washington, a number of S.E. states of U.S.A. and Canada. Replicates in and kills new born mice on i/c injection but multiplies poorly if at all in embryonated eggs and cell cultures. Not known to be pathogenic in the wild.

Flavivirus A genus in the family TOGAVIRIDAE. All antigenically related but unrelated to other Togaviridae. Some multiply in mosquitoes and some in ticks with transovarial transmission, but others have no known arthropod host. Some replicate in eggs producing pocks on the CAM and in mouse embryo and HELA CELL cultures, but CPE is not invariably seen. Produce encephalitis on i/c injection in mice and most are pathogenic on i/c injection in rhesus and cynomolgus monkeys. The type species is YELLOW FEVER VIRUS. They can be subdivided according to their principal vectors.

(1) The mosquito-borne species are:

Alfuy (C,B)
Benzi* (C,H)
Bouboui (C,A)
Bussuquara* (C,H,R)
dengue-1* (C,H)
dengue-2* (C,H)
dengue-3* (C,H)
dengue-4* (C,H)
Edge Hill (C,A)
Ilheus* (C,H,B)
Japanese encephalitis* (C,A,H,B,Ba)
Jugra (C,Ba)
Kokobera (C)
Kunjin* (C,H,B)
Murray Valley encephalitis* (C,H)
Ntaya (C)
Sepik* (C)
St Louis encephalitis* (C,A,H,B,Ba)
Spondweni* (C,H)
Stratford (C)
Tembusu (C,A)
Uganda S (C,B)
Usutu (C,A,H,R)
Wesselsbron* (C,A,H,R)

West Nile* (C,A,I,Ag,H,R,B,Ba)
Yellow fever* (C,H,M)
Zika* (C,H)

(2) *The tick-borne species are:*
Absettarov*† (I,H)
Hanzalova*† (I,H)
Hypr*† (I,H,R,B,Ba)
Kadam (I)
Karshi (Ag)
Kumlinge*† (I,H,R,B)
Kyasanur forest disease* (I,Ag,H,R,B,Ba)
Langat (I)
Louping-ill* (I,H,R,B)
Negisli* (H)
Omsk haemorrhagic* (I,H,R)
Powassan* (I,H,R)
Royal Farm (Ag)
Russian spring–summer encephalitis* (I,H,R,B)
Tyuleniy (I)

(3) *The species never isolated from wild-caught arthropods:*
Apoi* (R)
Batu Cave (Ba)
Carey Island (Ba)
Cowbone Ridge (R)
Dakar bat (Ba)
Entebbe bat (Ba)
Israel–Turkey meningoencephalitis (B)
Jutiapa (R)
Koutango (R)
Modoc (R)
Montana myotis leukoencephalitis (Ba)
Negishi* (H)
Phnom-Penh bat (Ba)
Rio Bravo* (Ba)
Saboya (R)
Sokuluk (Ba)

* *Can cause disease in man.*

† *These 4 viruses are very closely related antigenically though differing in virulence and epidemiology. They may be regarded as strains of a single species – tick-borne encephalitis virus (central European subtype).*

Isolated from:
(*C*) *Culicine mosquitoes*
(*I*) *Ixodid ticks*
(*H*) *Man*
(*R*) *Rodents*
(*B*) *Birds*
(*Ba*) *Bats*
(*M*) *Marsupials*
(*A*) *Anopheline mosquitoes*
(*Ag*) *Argasid ticks*

floxuridine *See* fluorodeoxyuridine.

flumidin A pharmacological preparation of ABOB combined with methatropine nitrate and methscopolamine nitrate.

fluorodeoxyuridine A pyrimidine analogue and a reversible inhibitor of DNA synthesis. Phosphorylated by cellular THYMIDINE KINASE and thus becomes an analogue of thymidylic acid. Brings about chromosome breaks. Absorption after ingestion is unpredictable and incomplete, so the drug is usually given i/v.
SYN: floxuridine.

9α-fluoro-16α-methylprednisolone *See* dexamethasone.

Flury HEP virus A strain of RABIES VIRUS derived from FLURY LEP VIRUS by further passage in chick embryos. HEP stands for high egg passage, *viz.* more than 180 times. It is avirulent for adult laboratory mammals but causes death in suckling mice. Used as vaccine. Can be propagated in human diploid cell lines, chick embryo fibroblasts and BHK/21 cells.

Flury LEP virus A strain of RABIES VIRUS. Isolated in 1939 from a girl named Flury who contracted the disease in Georgia, U.S.A. Brain tissue was injected into day-old chicks, subsequently passaged in chick brain and later in eggs. LEP stands for low egg passage, *viz.* less than 80 times. Has been used as live vaccine for dogs but is insufficiently ATTENUATED for use in cats and cattle. Can be propagated in human diploid cell lines and in BHK/21 CELLS.

Foamy virus

Hooks J.J. & Gibbs C.J. (1975) *Bact. Rev.* **39**, 169

Viruses which cause a foamy appearance of the cells in which they replicate. Often found in primary tissue cultures especially following prolonged passage. Usually cause persistent infections in their natural host. There are simian and hamster species similar to the syncytial viruses of cattle, cats and man. Members of the sub-family SPUMAVIRINAE.

FOCMA *F*eline *O*ncovirus-associated *C*ell *M*embrane *A*ntigen.

Foot and mouth disease virus Synonym for aphtho virus.

formycin 7-amino-3-(β-D-ribofuranosyl)-pyrazolo[4,3-*d*]pyrimidine. A NUCLEOSIDE antibiotic and a cytotoxic analogue of adenosine. Isolated together with CO-FORMYCIN from culture filtrates of *Streptomyces kaniharaensis* and *Nocardia interforma*. Inhibits INFLUENZAVIRUS A HOMINIS on the CAM, but this action is not potentiated by co-formycin.

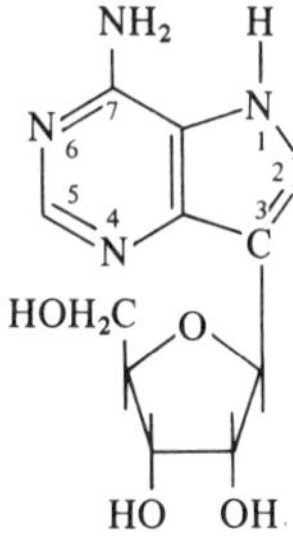

formycin B 3-(β-D-ribofuranosyl)-pyrazolo [4,3-*d*]-6(H)-7-pyrimidone. A NUCLEOSIDE antibiotic and a structural analogue of inosine. Isolated from culture filtrates of *Streptomyces lavendulae* and *Nocardia interforma*. Also produced by conversion of FORMYCIN by adenosine deaminase. Inhibits INFLUENZA VIRUS A HOMINIS on the CAM, an action potentiated by CO-FORMYCIN.
SYN: laurusin.

Fowl diphtheria virus Synonym for fowl pox virus.

Fowl leukaemia virus *See* chicken leukosis sarcoma virus.

Fowl paralysis virus Synonym for gallid herpesvirus 1.

fowl-pest
Barry R.D. *et al.* (1964) *Vet. Rec.* **76**, 1316
A term used in Britain to describe infection with either NEWCASTLE DISEASE VIRUS or fowl plague. *See* influenza virus A avian.

fowl plague (classical) *See* influenza virus A avian.

Fowl pox subgroup viruses Synonym for avipoxvirus.

Fowl pox virus The type species of the genus AVIPOXVIRUS containing a number of strains varying in host-range but otherwise not clearly separable. Resistant to ether but sensitive to chloroform. Haemagglutinin readily separated from VIRIONS. Replicates on CAM producing pocks, and in cell cultures of chick embryo with CPE. The disease caused in fowls has a course of 3–4 weeks. There are proliferative lesions followed by scabbing on the skin, especially of the head, sometimes of feet and vent. Involvement of the trachea is fowl diphtheria. There may be eye lesions. Many species are susceptible. Transmitted by contact and by mosquitoes which may remain infected for 210 days. Vaccine attenuated in eggs is used.
SYN: bird pox virus; epithelioma contagiosum virus; fowl diphtheria virus; poxvirus avium.

Fox encephalitis virus Synonym for canine adenovirus.

frameshift A process by which two or more proteins can be specified by a stretch of viral mRNA which is long enough to code for little more than one of them. The mRNA is translated from different starting points: A ⟶ B and C ⟶ D.

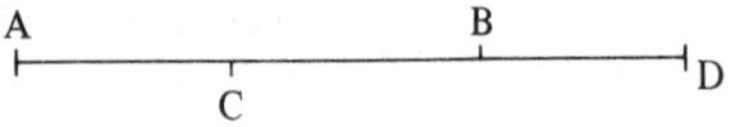

A B
C D

The triplet code is read in a different frame in each case. A stretch of viral GENOME can similarly code for different mRNAs.

Friend leukaemia virus

Steeves R.A. (1975) *J. natn. Cancer Inst.* **54**, 289

Troxler D.H. *et al.* (1977) *Proc. natn. Acad. Sci. U.S.A.* **94**, 4671

Troxler D.H. *et al.* (1978) *J. exp. med.* **148**, 639

A strain of MOUSE TYPE C ONCOVIRUS originally obtained from the leukaemic spleen of a 14-month-old Swiss mouse which had been injected at birth with a cell-free extract of Ehrlich ascites carcinoma cells. Causes a disease not observed to occur spontaneously. Characterized by gross splenomegaly. Adult mice are susceptible and die of the disease in about 3–5 weeks, or longer in a few cases. A number of strains have been isolated: some cause haemorrhage into the spleen and death in 3 weeks, others cause foci of tumour cells in the spleen and a less acutely fatal disease. The virus preparations available appear to be a mixture of two viruses: (1) a LYMPHOID LEUKAEMIA VIRUS which does not produce the erythroleukaemia typical of Friend virus, and (2) a replication-defective RNA tumour virus responsible for the leukaemogenesis. It is designated spleen focus-forming virus (SFFV). Its presence in non-producer cells may be detected by REVERSE TRANSCRIPTASE activity. The GENOME of SFFV consists of two sets of NUCLEIC ACID sequences, one homologous to part of the HELPER leukaemia virus and the other specific to SFFV, but related to sequences in XENOTROPIC mouse leukaemia viruses. Rat passage or passage at end-point dilution results in the separation of the lymphoid leukaemia virus.

Frijoles virus An unclassified ARBOVIRUS, morphologically like BUNYAVIRUS but serologically unrelated to members of that genus. Belongs to the PHLEBOTOMUS FEVER ANTIGENIC GROUP. Isolated from insects of *Lutzomyia* sp. in the Canal Zone, Panama. Not reported to cause disease in humans.

Fringilla papilloma virus

Osterhaus A.D.M.E. *et al.* (1977) *Intervirology* **8**, 351

A species in the genus PAPILLOMAVIRUS. Isolated from papillomas excised from the leg of a chaffinch *Fringilla coelebs*. VIRION diameter 52 nm, SEDIMENTATION COEFFICIENT 300s, and density in CsCl 1·34 g/ml. Composed of 72 morphological units arranged in a skew T = 7d icosahedral lattice. The circular double-stranded GENOME measured 2·6 µm. Protein composition similar to HUMAN PAPILLOMA VIRUS. Papillomas have only been found in two species of *Fringilla*: the chaffinch, and the brambling *F. montifringilla*.

SYN: avian papilloma virus; birds papilloma virus; chaffinch papilloma virus.

Frog adenovirus

Clark H.F. *et al.* (1973) *Virology* **51**, 392

A species in the family ADENOVIRIDAE. Found in a culture of the turtle cell line TH-1 inoculated with cells from a granuloma-bearing kidney of a leopard frog *Rana pipiens*. Replicated with CPE in turtle cells but not in cells from other reptiles, amphibia, fish or mammals. Optimal temperature for virus replication 30 °. Does not have MASTADENOVIRUS group antigen: not neutralized by AVIADENOVIRUS antiserum. Does not cause tumours on injection into nephrogenic ridge of *Rana pipiens* tadpole. Agglutinates rat erythrocytes at 37°.

Frog virus DNA viruses have been isolated from leopard frogs *Rana pipiens*. They have been numbered FV 1, FV 2, etc., or LT 1, LT 2, etc. All are alike antigenically and there is morphological resemblance to the IRIDOVIRUSES. Diameter 120 × 130 nm. These viruses replicate in eggs at 30°, and also in cultures of fish, amphibian, reptile, bird and mammal cells with CPE at 30°. They are lethal on inoculation into tadpoles of several species of

Rana and *Bufo*, but they do not multiply in adult frogs. Herpes-type viruses have also been isolated: *see* ranid herpesviruses 1 and 2.

Frog virus 4 Synonym for ranid herpesvirus 2.

FS (Family Study) virus

Hodges R.G. *et al.* (1956) *Am. J. Hyg.* **64**, 349

A virus isolated from an outbreak of gastroenteritis during the course of the Family Study in Cleveland, U.S.A. Could be passed in humans, and infection gave immunity to infection by MARCY VIRUS. The strain has since been lost and can no longer be identified.

F_3T *See* trifluorothymidine.

FT cells (CCL 41) A heteroploid cell line derived from cells obtained by primary cultivation of normal tongue from an adult female bullfrog *Rana catesbiana.*

FUdR *See* fluorodeoxyuridine.

Fujinami virus An avian sarcoma virus. A subspecies of the species CHICKEN LEUKOSIS SARCOMA VIRUS. Obtained from a transplantable fowl tumour. Similar to ROUS SARCOMA VIRUS. The tumour can be transplanted without difficulty into ducks.

Fujivirus A genus of the family REOVIRIDAE containing species which infect insects.

fusion of cells The formation of multinucleate giant cells known as polykaryocytes or syncytia. Can be caused by a variety of agents including some viruses, notably PARAMYXOVIRIDAE. There are two types of virus-induced fusion. (1) Fusion from without. Not dependent on virus replication or on the synthesis of new proteins. Occurs not more than 1–3 hours after exposure to high multiplicities of most of the large enveloped RNA viruses or certain DNA viruses such as HUMAN (ALPHA) HERPESVIRUS 1 and 2 and VACCINIA VIRUS, even when they have been inactivated by u.v. light or β-propiolactone. May also be caused by viral haemolysin, since treatment which will destroy this enzyme activity without affecting viral infectivity will also prevent the cell-fusing action. (2) Fusion from within. Begins several hours after infection and depends on synthesis of viral macromolecules, though the production of new infectious virus is not necessary. Often most marked after infection at low virus multiplicity. The mechanism may be the same as fusion from without. Fusion from within can be prevented late in infection by anti-viral antibody.

FV 3 virus A species in the family IRIDOVIRIDAE. A member of the group of icosahedral cytoplasmic deoxyviruses which infect amphibia. Enveloped VIRION has a diameter of 165–200 nm. The icosahedral particle is 130–145 nm in diameter. Replicates in the cytoplasm but the nucleus must be functional and the virus will not replicate in u.v.-irradiated cells. At optimal temperature 23–26°, multiplies in cells of all vertebrate classes *in vitro*. ENVELOPE is acquired on budding through plasma membrane. GENOME consists of one molecule of double-stranded DNA of mol. wt. $100–130 \times 10^6$. G+C RATIO 54%. BUOYANT DENSITY (CsCl) 1·287 g/ml. Lethal to tadpoles of several *Rana* and *Bufo* sp. In several toad species they produce haemorrhagic necrosis of kidneys and stomach. Replicates in adult newts but not in frogs. On infection cellular NUCLEIC ACID synthesis is inhibited and viruses such as VACCINIA VIRUS, SV40 and several RNA viruses which were in process of replication in the cell when superinfection by FV_3 occurred have their replication halted, while FV_3 continues to replicate. In mice FV_3 does not replicate but causes acute degenerative hepatitis owing to this blocking of RNA synthesis.

Gag gene

Barbacid M. *et al.* (1976) *Nature, Lond.* **262**, 554

One of the genes in the GENOME of AVIAN TYPE C ONCOVIRUS. Codes for the precursor of all the major internal antigens of the virus, a protein of mol. wt. 76,000.

Gallid herpesvirus 1

Purchase H.G. (1974) *Prog. med. Virol.* **18**, 178

A species in the family HERPESVIRIDAE. A natural infection of fowls, pheasants, turkeys, quails, ducks, swans, geese, pigeons and budgerigars, causing progressive paralysis, usually in 2–8 month old birds. Lymphoid tumours are produced. An acute form of the disease has appeared in Europe and America, characterised by enlargement and lymphocytic infiltration of the liver and other viscera, rather than the nervous system. The virus is cell-associated, but free virus is released from feather follicles and infection is spread by dust and oral secretions. It can be cultivated in chicken kidney cell cultures with production of plaques, but the virus remains CELL-ASSOCIATED. A live ATTENUATED virus vaccine is effective.

SYN: fowl paralysis virus; Marek's disease virus; neurolymphomatosis of fowls virus; phasianid herpesvirus 2.

Gallid herpesvirus 2 A species in the family HERPESVIRIDAE. A CELL-ASSOCIATED virus antigenically related to GALLID HERPESVIRUS 1, and isolated from turkeys. Can cause tumours of various organs in chicks. Replicates in avian cell cultures, but with the exception of hamsters, not in mammalian tissues. It protects fowls against Marek's disease, though the two viruses have only 4% or less DNA homology. It is not released from the feather follicles so that horizontal spread does not occur.

SYN: turkey herpesvirus.

Gallid herpesvirus 3 A species in the family HERPESVIRIDAE. A widespread natural infection of fowls and pheasants, causing haemorrhagic tracheitis with gasping and coughing. Mortality up to 70%. A less virulent strain in Australia and U.S. causes only coughing and sneezing. Ducks, pigeons and turkeys are occasionally infected. No infections of mammals reported. Transmission via the respiratory route, and some recovered birds may excrete virus for long periods. An egg-passage strain can be used as a vaccine, applied to the bursa of Fabricius. On the CAM two types of plaque are formed: (1) large plaques with a necrotic centre due to the more virulent strains, and (2) small non-necrotic ones caused by less virulent strains. Replication with CPE occurs in day-old chick cell cultures, and without CPE in HELA CELL cultures. No serological differences between strains have been reported, but some strains are poorly neutralized by antisera. There is agglutination of fowl erythrocytes.

SYN: avian infectious laryngo-tracheitis virus; phasianid herpesvirus 1.

Gallus-adeno-like virus

Aghakhan S.M. (1974) *Vet. Bull.* **44**, 531

A species in the genus AVIADENOVIRUS. Originally isolated from chicken cell cultures during attempts to isolate CHICKEN LEUKOSIS SARCOMA VIRUS. Replicates with typical adenovirus CPE in chicken cell cultures. In eggs causes the death of the embryo. Not apparently associated with spontaneous clinical disease but on inoculation into chicks causes liver necrosis. Antibodies are common in chickens.

GALV *G*ibbon *A*pe *L*ymphosarcoma *V*irus.

Gal virus *See* gallus-adeno-like virus.

Gamboa virus A species in the genus BUNYAVIRUS. With BERTIOGA VIRUS forms the Gamboa Antigenic Group. Isolated from the mosquito *Aedeomyia squamipennis* in Panama. A similar virus has been isolated in Surinam from mosquitoes of *Aedes* sp. Not reported to cause disease in humans.

Gammaherpesvirinae A subfamily of the family HERPESVIRIDAE. They replicate in lymphoblastoid cells, and some species will also replicate in epithelioid and fibroblastic cells, causing cell lysis. They are specific for either B- or T-lymphocytes. In lymphocytes replication is often incomplete with persistence of the viral GENOME but with minimal expression. Even when replication has caused cell death little or no complete virus may be produced. Latent virus is frequently demonstrable in lymphoid tissues. Several species are associated with tumour formation. Host range narrow, usually limited to species in the same order as the natural host. DNA mol. wt. $85–110 \times 10^6$. Both ends of the DNA molecule have reiterated sequences that are not repeated internally. One genus is identified but has not been named. The type species is HUMAN (GAMMA) HERPESVIRUS 4. Other possible species in the subfamily are CEBID HERPESVIRUSES 2 and 3, GALLID HERPESVIRUS 1 and 2, and LEPORID HERPESVIRUS 1.

SYN: lymphoproliferative herpesvirus group.

Ganjam group viruses A term no longer in use. The two viruses which it contained: GANJAM and DUGBE, are now placed in the NAIROBI SHEEP DISEASE ANTIGENIC GROUP.

Ganjam virus An unclassified ARBOVIRUS morphologically like BUNYAVIRUS but serologically unrelated to members of that genus. Belongs to the NAIROBI SHEEP DISEASE ANTIGENIC GROUP. Isolated from ticks of *Haemaphysalis* sp. in India. Two laboratory infections are reported, one SILENT and the other resulting in mild fever.

Garba virus An unclassified ARBOVIRUS belonging to the MATARIYA ANTIGENIC GROUP. Isolated from birds in Central African Republic. Not reported to cause disease in humans.

Gasping disease virus Synonym for avian infectious bronchitis virus. Not to be confused with GALLID HERPESVIRUS 1.

Gastro-enteritis of dogs virus Synonym for canine coronavirus.

Gastro-enteritis of foals virus

Dichfield W.J.B. (1969) *J. Am. vet. med. Ass.* **155**, 384

Bass E.P. & Sharpee R.L. (1975) *Lancet* **ii**, 822

A species in the genus CORONAVIRUS. Causes acute gastro-enteritis in foals which may be fatal. Neutralizing antibodies are present in some horse sera.

Gastro-enteritis viruses of humans

Holmes I.H. (1979) *Prog. med. Virol.* **25**, 1

Madeley C.R. (1979) *J. clin. Path.* **32**, 1

Many viruses such as species of ENTEROVIRUS can be isolated from human faeces but they are rarely the cause of gastro-enteritis. Many other viruses can be seen in faeces with the EM but these are difficult to cultivate *in vitro*. Some of them cause gastro-enteritis:

(1) Acute epidemic gastro-enteritis virus of humans.
(2) Human rotavirus.
(3) Human adenovirus.
(4) Astrovirus.
(5) Human corona virus.
(6) Human calicivirus.
(7) Small round viruses 20–35 nm in diameter. A number have been reported but their classification and pathogenicity are not certain.

Gazdar mouse sarcoma virus

Gazdar A.F. *et al.* (1971) *Nature New Biol.* **234**, 69

A strain of mouse sarcoma virus isolated from a spontaneous tumour arising in a New Zealand white × New Zealand black F_1 mouse. Transforms mouse cells *in vitro* and rapidly induces sarcomas in mice, rats and hamsters. *See* mouse sarcoma virus.

GB virus

Deinhardt F. *et al.* (1967) *J. exp. med.* **125**, 673

A strain of HEPATITIS A VIRUS. Isolated from a patient with hepatitis, by injection of his serum into marmosets of *Saguinus* sp. which then developed the disease. Could be serially passed in marmosets.

G+C content The total guanine (G) and cytosine (C) content of a double stranded DNA is usually expressed as a percentage of the total content of bases. The triple hydrogen bond between G and C is more stable than the double hydrogen bond between adenine (A) and thymine (T). Thus the G+C content effects the physical properties of the DNA: both the melting point and the density of the molecule are proportional to the G+C content. Most mammalian cell DNAs have a G+C content of about 44%, some viral DNA's are similar, but some are as high as 70%.

GD VII virus A strain of mouse poliovirus.

Gecko virus

Stehbens W.E. & Johnston M.R.L. (1966) *J. Ultrastruct. Res.* **15**, 543

A species in the family IRIDOVIRIDAE. The virus has been seen in the erythrocytes of reptiles *Gehyra variegata.* Their diameter was 220 nm and they had a CORE of 120–160 nm. Transmission between animals has been reported.

gene The shortest length of NUCLEIC ACID which can determine the composition of one protein molecule. A protein of 500 amino acids, each one represented by one CODON of three NUCLEOTIDES in the mRNA, thus requires 1,500 nucleotides of genetic information, a piece of double stranded DNA of mol. wt. 10^6.

genetic reassortment *See* recombinants.

genetic transmission Involves passage of a viral GENOME from one host generation to the next either as a DNA PROVIRUS, or in some other close association with the genome of the gamete. Often used with imprecise meaning. *See* congenital infection.

Genital papilloma virus of pigs

Parish W.E. (1961) *J. path. Bact.* **81**, 331 and **83**, 429

A species in the family POXVIRIDAE. Causes papillomas in the genital region of boars. Incubation period of experimental infection about 8 weeks. Man, calf, rabbit, guinea pig, mouse and embryonated eggs cannot be infected.

genome

Bachrach H.L. (1978) *Adv. Virus Res.* **22**, 163

The genetic information in a cell or virus. In viruses it may be DNA or RNA but not both. DNA viral genomes consist of a single molecule which may be circular or linear and of mol. wt. just over $1–200 \times 10^6$. The base composition of viral DNA is more variable than that of cellular DNA, the G+C CONTENT being 35–74%. RNA viral genomes may be linear or circular, of mol. wt. $2–15 \times 10^6$, and consist of a single molecule or be fragmented into several pieces. Viral genomes can be classified into 6 groups according to genome structure and method of TRANSCRIPTION into mRNA.

Group	Virus family	Nucleic acid
1	Papovaviridae	D-S DNA, closed circle with supercoiling unless one strand is broken.
	Adenoviridae	D-S DNA, linear with inverted terminal repeats.
	Herpesviridae	D-S DNA, linear with terminal repeats and inverted internal repeats of the termini.
	Poxviridae	D-S DNA, linear with the strands covalently linked at their ends so that on denaturation a huge S-S loop is formed.
2	Parvoviridae	S-S DNA, linear with repetitions at the ends which facilitate loop formation.
3	Reoviridae	D-S RNA, linear in 10–12 segments.
4	Picornaviridae	S-S RNA, linear POSITIVE STRAND.
	Caliciviridae	S-S RNA, linear positive strand.
	Togaviridae	S-S RNA, linear positive strand, two different sizes of mRNA are made.
	Coronaviridae	S-S RNA, linear positive strand.
5	Rhabdoviridae	S-S RNA, linear unsegmented NEGATIVE STRAND.
	Paramyxoviridae	S-S RNA, linear unsegmented negative strand.
	Orthomyxoviridae	S-S RNA, linear negative strand in 8 segments.
	Arenaviridae	S-S RNA, linear negative strand in 2 segments.
	Bunyaviridae	S-S RNA, linear negative strand in 3 segments.

6	Retroviridae	S-S RNA, linear positive strand diploid consisting of 2 identical haploid molecules, each terminally redundant, and linked near their 5′ ends.

D-S = Double-strand
S-S = Single-strand

genomic masking *See* phenotypic mixing.

German measles virus Synonym for rubella virus.

Germiston virus A species in the genus BUNYAVIRUS, belonging to the BUNYAMWERA ANTIGENIC GROUP. Isolated from culicine mosquitoes, man and rodents in S. Africa, Zimbabwe, Uganda and Mozambique, where it causes fever in humans. Mosquito-borne. Natural hosts are sheep, goats and cattle.

Getah virus

Yoshinaka Y. *et al.* (1979) *Microbiol. Immunol.* **23**, 95

A species in the genus ALPHAVIRUS. Isolated in Malaya, Japan, Campuchia and Australia from mosquitoes. No known association with disease. Causes VIRAEMIA in chicks. Antibodies found in pigs, horses, men and birds.

GF cell line A permanent cell line established from a marine teleost, the blue-striped grunt, *Haemulon sciurus*. Grows in Eagle's Basal Medium with 0·196 M-sodium chloride and both human and calf serum. Incubation at 20°. Used to isolate enteric fish viruses.

giant bacteriophages Aberrant forms of certain enterobacteria phages in which the heads are up to 44 times longer than normal. These forms usually contain greater than unit length of DNA and are infectious. *See also* lollipops.

Giant-cell pneumonia virus Synonym for human (beta) herpesvirus 5.

Gibbon ape leukaemia virus (GaLV) *See* gibbon ape type C oncovirus.

Gibbon ape lymphosarcoma virus Synonym for the complex of SIMIAN SARCOMA VIRUS and its HELPER, the SIMIAN SARCOMA-ASSOCIATED VIRUS.

Gibbon ape type C oncovirus

Reitz M.S. *et al.* (1979) *Virology* **93**, 48

A species in the subgenus MAMMALIAN TYPE C ONCOVIRUS GROUP. Seen by EM in a disseminated lymphosarcoma in a gibbon, *Hylobates lar*. The tumour cells in culture grew as free-floating cells, releasing virus particles. It is non-transforming *in vitro* but in gibbons induces leukaemia and is often called the gibbon ape leukaemia virus, GaLV. Antigenically related to the SIMIAN SARCOMA-ASSOCIATED VIRUS. Several strains have been isolated and their origins are indicated by suffixes, thus: -H for Hall's Island near Bermuda; -SF for San Francisco; -Br for brain extract from gibbons injected with extract of human brain from kuru patients; -SEATO for Seato laboratory, Bangkok.

Girardi heart cells (CCL 27) A heteroploid cell line established from the right atrial appendage of a 41-year-old human male in 1956. The cells grew as fibroblasts at first, but after about 18 weeks they became epithelial-like.

Glandular fever virus Synonym for human (gamma) herpesvirus 4.

gliotoxin

Miller P.A. *et al.* (1968) *Science* **159**, 431

A common fungal metabolite with the structure:

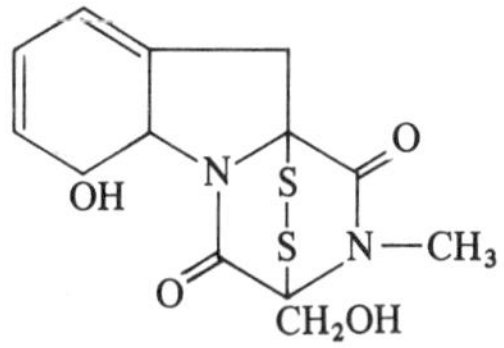

Inhibits viral RNA-dependent RNA synthesis without effect on DNA-dependent RNA synthesis. Thus prevents HUMAN POLIOVIRUS replication in HELA CELLS.

Glugea lyssae

Levaditi C. *et al.* (1924) *C. r. Acad. Sci. Paris* **178**, 256

Name given to a supposed protozoan aetiological agent of rabies. The structure is now known as the NEGRI BODY.

glycyrrhizic acid

Pompei R. *et al.* (1979) *Nature, Lond.* **281**, 689

An antiviral agent derived from the roots of the liquorice plant *Glycyrrhiza glabra.* The ammonium salt completely inhibited growth and CPE of VACCINIA, HUMAN (ALPHA) HERPESVIRUS 1, NEWCASTLE DISEASE and VESICULAR STOMATITIS VIRUSES when grown in cultures of HEP-2 CELLS. There was no effect on HUMAN POLIOVIRUS TYPE 1. In addition to the inhibitory action, there is irreversible inactivation of human (alpha) herpesvirus 1, though not of the other viruses tested. The mode of action of glycyrrhizic acid is not understood, but it is not thought to be mediated through damage to host cells.

GMAG Genetic Manipulation Advisory Group.

Goat and sheep papilloma virus A species in the genus PAPILLOMAVIRUS. A natural infection of some herds but not common. Papillomas produced by this virus may become malignant.

Goat herpesvirus Synonym for bovid herpesvirus 5.

Goat pox virus

Renshaw H.W. & Dodd A.G. (1978) *Arch. Virol.* **56**, 201

A species in the genus CAPRIPOXVIRUS. Causes focal epidermal lesions which proceed through papule, vesicle and pustule stages to scab formation. Lesions are usually on the udder, teats, scrotum, inside of the thighs, and less frequently around the eyes and mouth, whereas in contagious ecthyma, the lips and mouth are primarily involved. Antigenically distinct from CONTAGIOUS ECTHYMA VIRUS and there is no cross-protection. Replicates on the CAM producing opaque pocks, and in cell cultures of lamb and kid kidney tissue with CPE. Transmissible to sheep, and allegedly to calves and rabbits. Experimental vaccines have been used, but a commercial vaccine is not presently available. Occurs in many parts of the world.

Golden pheasant leukosis virus

Fujita D.J. *et al.* (1974) *Virology* **60**, 558

A strain of subgroup G CHICKEN LEUKOSIS SARCOMA VIRUS. An ENDOGENOUS VIRUS found in normal golden pheasant *Chrysolophus pictus* cells, and giving group G host range specificity to virus particles in which it provides the information for the ENVELOPE.

Gomboro disease virus Synonym for infectious bursal disease virus.

Gomoka virus An unclassified ARBOVIRUS. Isolated from mosquitoes and birds in Central African Republic. Not reported to cause disease in humans.

Goose hepatitis virus

Kisary J. (1976) *Acta microbiol. Acad. Sci. Hung.* **23**, 205

A species in the genus PARVOVIRUS. Causes severe and epidemic disease in goslings and young Muscovy ducks. Older birds may show acute or chronic haemorrhagic disease. Injection of 2- to 3-day-old goslings i/m causes haemorrhagic liver disease and pericarditis after a latent period of 5–7 days and death in 5–10 days. Widespread in N. America and Europe. Replicates on inoculation into allantoic cavity of goose and Muscovy duck eggs. In goose embryo fibroblast cell cultures replicates with CPE.

SYN: goose parvovirus.

Goose influenza virus Synonym for infectious myocarditis of goslings virus.

Goose parvovirus Synonym for goose hepatitis virus.

Gordil virus An unclassified ARBOVIRUS morphologically like BUNYAVIRUS but not serologically related to members of that genus. A member of the PHLEBOTOMUS FEVER ANTIGENIC GROUP. Isolated from striped grass mouse and gerbil in Central African Republic. Not reported to cause disease in humans.

Gosling hepatitis virus A species in the genus ENTEROVIRUS. Causes hepatitis and death in goslings.

Gossas virus An unclassified ARBOVIRUS. Isolated from a bat of *Tadarida* sp. in Senegal. Not reported to cause disease in humans.

Graffi leukaemia virus A strain of MOUSE TYPE C ONCOVIRUS obtained by injecting extracts of several transplantable mouse tumours into new-born Agnes Bluhm strain mice. Causes a chloroleukaemia. The cell type may be granulocytic, lymphocytic or histiocytic depending on the mouse strain, age and hormonal status.

Grand Arbaud virus An unclassified ARBOVIRUS morphologically like BUNYAVIRUS but serologically not related to members of that genus. A member of the UUKUNIEMI ANTIGENIC GROUP. Isolated from a tick *Argas reflexus* in southern France. Not reported to cause disease in humans.

Grass carp rhabdovirus

Ahne W. (1975) *Arch. Virol.* **48**, 181

A species in the genus VESICULOVIRUS. Isolated from a moribund grass carp *Ctenopharyngodon idella in* FHM CELLS in which it produces CPE. Optimal temperature for virus replication 16 to 23°. Infectivity not neutralized by antiserum to RHABDOVIRUS CARPIO or SWIM-BLADDER INFLAMMATION VIRUS. Common carp *Cyprinus carpio* appear to be resistant to the virus, but grass carp are easily infected from the water they are in, and die in 8 to 9 days with haemorrhagic inflammation in scale bases and other tissues.

Grease or grease-heel virus Often considered to be the same as HORSE POX but this is not certain. Vesicles appear on flexor surfaces of lower parts of legs, later becoming pustules and crusts.

Great Island virus A species in the genus ORBIVIRUS belonging to the KEMEROVO ANTIGENIC GROUP. Isolated from ticks and sea birds on Great Island, Newfoundland, Canada.

Green lizard papillomavirus

Raynaud A. & Adrian M. (1976) *C. r. hebd. séanc. Acad. Sci.* **283**, 845

A species in the genus PAPILLOMAVIRUS. Seen by EM in skin lesions which were most prevalent in the genital areas in the green lizard *Lacerta viridis*. Successful experimental transmission of the disease with virus extracts was not accomplished.

Green monkey virus Synonym for Marburg virus.

Green sea turtle herpesvirus Synonym for chelonid herpesvirus 1.

Grey lung disease virus

Andrewes C.H. & Glover R.E. (1945) *Brit. J. exp. Path.* **26**, 379

Probably a Mycoplasma. *See* pneumonia of rats.

Grey patch disease of turtles virus Synonym for chelonid herpesvirus 1.

Gross leukaemia virus The first strain of MOUSE TYPE C ONCOVIRUS isolated. Obtained from AKR mice. Also known as passage A virus. Causes lymphoid leukaemia on injection into new-born mice, usually after a latent period of at least 2–3 months. The virulent passage A virus is transmitted in the milk.

Ground squirrel cytomegalovirus Synonym for sciurid herpesvirus 1.

Ground squirrel herpesvirus Synonym for sciurid herpesvirus 2.

Grunt fin agent

Clem L.W. *et al.* (1965) *Ann. N.Y. Acad. Sci.* **126**, 343

Isolated from a culture of GF CELL LINE showing spontaneous CPE. Replicates in primary grunt fin cells and fish cell lines such as GF, but not in KB, HELA or chick embryo. Does not cause disease on injection into adult grunts *Haemulon sciurus* or new-born mice. Ether-sensitive. Oval particles 120–140 nm diameter with dense CORE.

Guajara virus A species in the genus BUNYAVIRUS and a member of the CAPIM ANTIGENIC GROUP. Isolated from SENTINEL mice in Amapá and Para, Brazil. Not reported to cause disease in humans.

Guama antigenic group viruses Six serologically related viruses in the genus BUNYAVIRUS. Isolated only in the Western Hemisphere.

bertioga
bimiti (C,R)
catu (C,A,H,R,Ba,M)
guama (C,H,R,Ba,M)
mahogany hammock (C,R)
moju (C,R,M)

Isolated from:

(*C*) *Culicine mosquitoes*
(*A*) *Anopheline mosquitoes*
(*H*) *Humans*
(*R*) *Rodents*
(*Ba*) *Bats*
(*M*) *Marsupials*

Catu and Guama viruses can cause disease in man.

Guama virus A species in the genus BUNYAVIRUS and member of the GUAMA ANTIGENIC GROUP. Isolated from SENTINEL monkeys and mice, rodents and bats. Mosquito-borne. Found in Brazil, Trinidad, Surinam, French Guiana and Panama. Can cause a febrile illness with arthralgia in humans.

guanidine hydrochloride

Sergiescu D. *et al.* (1972) *Prog. med. Virol.* **14**, 138

Selectively inhibits replication of small RNA viruses in tissue culture. Antiviral activity is directed against GENOME-coded viral RNA polymerase. Picornaviruses become completely resistant after only a few passages in the presence of the drug. It has no activity *in vitro*.

guanylate transferase An enzyme which adds guanosine 5′ monophosphate from guanosine 5′ triphosphate to the 5′ terminus of nascent RNA chains. Present in VIRIONS of REOVIRIDAE, and involved in formation of the 5′ terminal cap structure on mRNA.

guanyloribonuclease *See* ribonuclease T_1.

Guaratuba virus A species in the genus BUNYAVIRUS.

Isolated from SENTINEL mice and hamsters, birds and mosquitoes in São Paulo, Brazil. Not reported to cause disease in humans.

Guarnieri bodies Intracytoplasmic acidophilic INCLUSION BODIES found in cells infected with certain POXVIRIDAE: VARIOLA, VACCINIA and COW POX VIRUSES.

Guaroa virus A species in the genus BUNYAVIRUS and member of the BUNYAMWERA ANTIGENIC GROUP. Isolated in Colombia, Brazil and Panama. Mosquito-borne, probably by *Anopheles* sp. Causes a febrile illness in humans. Antibodies frequently found in humans in the Amazon region.

Guillain–Barré syndrome

Hughes R.A.C. (1978) *Brit. J. Hosp. Med.* **20**, 688

Guillain, Barré and Strohl described two cases of paralysis, muscular tenderness, areflexia and slight sensory disturbance. Recovery was complete. CSF protein was raised but cell count was normal. Landry had described a similar clinical picture in 1856. Cases occur sporadically with an incidence of about 1·6/100,000 population per year. Cause is probably an immunological reaction started by an antigen, which in some cases is a viral protein.

Guinea pig cytomegalovirus Synonym for caviid herpesvirus 1.

Guinea pig endogenous virus Synonym for guinea pig oncovirus.

Guinea pig herpesvirus Synonym for caviid herpesvirus 2.

Guinea pig leukaemia virus

Rhim J.S. & Green I. (1977) *Fedn. Proc. Fedn. Am. Socs. exp. Biol.* **36**, 2247.

The L_2C transplantable leukaemia is a B cell leukaemia transmissible by cell suspension. It arose spontaneously in 1954 in an old female strain 2 animal. The leukaemic cells are always female even when passed in a male guinea pig. Intracellular and extracellular virus-like particles are seen in the leukaemic tissue. The particles have different morphologies and their relationship to each other and to GUINEA PIG ONCOVIRUS, which can be induced by 5 BROMODEOXYURIDINE treatment is not clear. CAVIID HERPESVIRUS 2 has been isolated from leukaemic cells by CO-CULTIVATION with mink lung cells.

Guinea pig oncovirus

Putman D.L. & Rhim, J.S. (1977) *Fedn. Proc. Fedn. Am. Socs. exp. Biol.* **36**, 2316
Davis A.R. & Nayak D.P. (1977) *J. Virol.* **23**, 263

A species in the subgenus MAMMALIAN TYPE B ONCOVIRUS GROUP. An ENDOGENOUS VIRUS the formation of which can be induced in cell cultures from any strain of guinea pig by treatment with 5-BROMODEOXYURIDINE. Maximal virus release occurs 2–4 days after treatment and falls off rapidly, being negligible again by 7 days. No cell line has been found to support continued virus production. Although this endogenous virus is easily induced no EXOGENOUS VIRUS has been obtained. It appears morphologically to be a B-TYPE VIRUS PARTICLE and to have a DNA POLYMERASE which prefers Mg^{2+} to Mn^{2+}. However it shares no genetic sequences with MOUSE MAMMARY TUMOUR VIRUS or MOUSE TYPE C ONCOVIRUS. The role of the virus in leukaemia is not clear but the virus GENOME appears to be completely expressed in the leukaemic cells. However, the virus particles seen in these cells are morphologically different from the endogenous virus.
SYN: guinea pig endogenous virus, guinea pig retrovirus.

Guinea pig pox virus

Hampton E.G. *et al.* (1968) *J. gen. Virol.* **2**, 205

Possibly a species in the family POXVIRIDAE. EM revealed poxvirus-like particles and INCLUSION BODIES in cell cultures prepared from the thigh tissues of approximately 8 month old guinea pigs. The animals from which the tissue was taken were suffering from a spontaneous fibrovascular proliferation in the muscles, which had brought about an increase in the normal volume of the thigh by as much as six-fold.

Guinea pig retrovirus Synonym for guinea pig oncovirus

Guinea pig salivary gland virus Synonym for caviid herpesvirus 1.

Guinea pig submaxillary gland virus Synonym for caviid herpesvirus 1.

Gumbo limbo virus A species in the genus BUNYAVIRUS and one of the C GROUP VIRUSES. Isolated from mosquitoes in Florida, U.S.A. Not known to cause disease in humans.

Gumboro disease virus Synonym for infectious bursal disease virus. Named after the locality where the first outbreaks were observed in the U.S.A. in 1957.

HADEN virus Sigla from *H*aem*AD*sorbing *EN*teric virus of calves. Synonym for bovine parvovirus 1.

Haemadsorbing enteric virus of calves Synonym for bovine parvovirus 1.

haemadsorption Adsorption of erythrocytes to the surface of virus-infected cells. ORTHOMYXOVIRIDAE, PARAMYXOVIRIDAE and TOGAVIRIDAE, which bud from the cell surface, confer this property on the cell. When erythrocytes are added to the culture medium, adsorption to the infected cells makes it possible to identify cultures which show no other indication of infection.

Haemadsorption virus type 1 An old name for human parainfluenza virus type 3.

Haemadsorption virus type 2 An old name for parainfluenza virus type 1 human.

Haemagglutinating encephalomyelitis virus of pigs Synonym for porcine haemagglutinating encephalitis virus.

Haemagglutinating virus of Japan Synonym for parainfluenza virus type 1 murine.

Haemorrhagic conjunctivitis virus *See* acute haemorrhagic conjunctivitis virus.

Haemorrhagic encephalopathy of rats virus

Nathanson N. *et al.* (1970) *Am. J. Epidem.* **91**, 328
Cole G.A. *et al.* (1970) *Am. J. Epidem.* **91**, 339

A species in the genus PARVOVIRUS very similar to, and perhaps a strain of, LATENT RAT VIRUS, but highly pathogenic on injection i/c into new-born rats. Isolated by i/c injection of new-born rats with brain and spinal chord extracts from Lewis rats which became paralysed after treatment with CYCLOPHOSPHAMIDE. Causes haemorrhage and necrosis in the spinal chord. Injection into new-born hamsters causes an acute fatal infection. Adult

rats, new-born mice, rhesus and cynomolgus monkeys are insusceptible. Agglutinates guinea pig erythrocytes but not chicken, sheep, rhesus monkey or human cells.
SYN: HER virus.

Haemorrhagic enteritis of turkeys virus

Gross W.B. & Moore W.E.C. (1967) *Avian Dis.* **11**, 296

A species in the genus AVIADENOVIRUS. Causes short term depression with bloody droppings, followed by death or recovery. The intestine is filled with blood, and death probably results from blood loss. Incubation period 5–6 days. Intestinal contents are infectious only during the acute phase of disease. Chickens are not susceptible to the disease, but following cloacal inoculation excrete the virus for a few days.

Haemorrhagic fever viruses Synonym for viral haemorrhagic fever viruses of man.

Haemorrhagic fever with renal syndrome virus Synonym for Korean haemorrhagic fever virus.

Haemorrhagic nephroso-nephritis virus Synonym for Korean haemorrhagic fever virus.

Haemorrhagic septicaemia virus of fish Synonym for Egtved virus.

HaK cells (CCL 15) A heteroploid cell line derived from the kidneys of two normal young adult Syrian or Golden hamsters *Mesocricetus auratus*. Used for the isolation and growth of ARBOVIRUSES, and for propagation of COXSACKIE A 4, A 8, B 1, HUMAN (ALPHA) HERPESVIRUS 1 and 2, VARIOLA VIRUS and INFLUENZA VIRUS A HOMINIS.

hamster enteritis

Frisk, C.S. & Wagner, J.E. (1977) *Lab. Animals* **11**, 79

A common disease of laboratory hamsters with high mortality. Characterized by diarrhoea, dehydration and weight loss. Cause doubtful, but both viruses and bacteria have been isolated from cases. Animals under stress are very prone to this disease.

Hamster herpesvirus Synonym for cricetid herpesvirus 3.

Hamster osteolytic viruses LATENT RAT VIRUS and related RODENT PARVOVIRUSES.

Hamster papilloma virus

Scherneck S. *et al.* (1979) *Virology* **96**, 100

Graffi A. *et al.* (1968) *J. natn. Cancer Inst.* **40**, 867

A species in the genus PAPILLOMAVIRUS. A natural infection of Syrian hamsters in which it causes skin papillomas, usually in animals more then 6 months old. *See* latent hamster virus.

Hamster polyoma virus Synonym for latent hamster virus.

Hamster retrovirus

Russell P. *et al.* *J. gen. Virol.* **43**, 317

A species in the sub-genus MAMMALIAN TYPE C ONCOVIRUS GROUP. Appeared spontaneously in a pigmented cell culture established from a hamster melanoma after it had been sub-cultured 104 times. Transforms mouse, rat and hamster cells *in vitro*, but not guinea pig, human or feline cells. Injection of transformed cells into hamsters will produce tumours but injection of the virus into hamsters of any age has no effect. *See* hamster type C oncovirus.

Hamster syncytial virus

Fabisch P.H. *et al.* (1973) *Abstr. Ann. Meet. Am. Soc. Microbiol.* **365**, 255

A species in the family SPUMAVIRINAE.

Hamster type C oncovirus

Steinback W.A. *et al.* (1968) *J. Virol.* **2**, 1115

Kelloff G.J. *et al.* (1971) *J. gen. Virol.* **13**, 289

Somers K.D. *et al.* (1973) *Intervirology* **1**, 11

A species in the subgenus MAMMALIAN TYPE C ONCOVIRUS GROUP. Virus particles can be seen in several transplantable tumours, and the blood of tumour-bearing hamsters contains many mature and immature C TYPE PARTICLES. A non-transforming HELPER VIRUS can be separated from the hamster-specific sarcoma virus. Tumours induced by MOUSE SARCOMA VIRUS in hamsters regularly yield non-transforming viruses. The virus has not been shown to cause leukaemia in hamsters. *See* hamster retrovirus.

hand-foot-and-mouth disease

Higgins P.G. (1969) *Health Trends* **1**, 10

Hagiwar A. *et al.* (1978) *Intervirology* **9**, 60

First recognized as a clinical entity and its association with COXSACKIE A VIRUS established in Canada in 1957. The disease is most common in summer and autumn and children aged 1–5 years are usually affected. Incubation period 3–6 days. The patient may feel unwell for a day before red papules and vesicles appear in the mouth and ulcerate. The skin lesion is a maculopapular rash progressing to vesicles on the feet and hands, extending to other parts of the body. At least 4 types of Coxsackie A virus can cause the disease: A16 most often, but in some cases A5, A9 and A10, and 2 types of Coxsackie B virus *viz.* 2 and 5. Occurs all over the world. In Japan, cases complicated by CNS involvement are reported to be caused by ENTEROVIRUS 71.

Hanzalova virus A species in the genus FLAVIVIRUS. Isolated from the brain of a woman with meningo-encephalitis in Beroun, Czechoslovakia. Also isolated from *Ixodes ricinus.* (the first tick-borne encephalitis strain isolated in Czechoslovakia). Antigenically very similar or identical to HYPR and ABSETTAROV strains of TICK-BORNE ENCEPHALITIS VIRUS (Central European subtype).

hard pad A disease of dogs caused by DISTEMPER VIRUS in which there is tenderness and keratinization of the skin of the feet. Later nervous involvement and death usually occur.

Hare fibroma virus A species in the genus LEPORIPOXVIRUS. Serologically related to MYXOMA VIRUS. Causes fibromas in hares in S. France and N. Italy. Transmissible to rabbits. May be identical to fibrosarcoma virus of hares described by E. von Dungern and A.F. Coca in 1903 in *Z. Immun.-Forsch.* **2**, 391.

Hart Park virus A species in the genus VESICULOVIRUS. With FLANDERS VIRUS forms the Flanders Hart Park Antigenic Group. Isolated from mosquitoes in California, U.S.A. Serologically similar viruses have often been isolated in many parts of the U.S.A. and Canada. Multiplies in new-born mice on i/c injection but poorly or not at all in embryonated eggs or cell cultures. Kills new-born mice on i/c injection but not known to be pathogenic under natural conditions.

Haruna virus Antigenically identical to GETAH VIRUS. Isolated in Japan.

Harvey mouse sarcoma virus

Harvey J.J. & East J. (1971) *Int. Rev. exp. Path.* **10**, 265

The first strain of mouse sarcoma virus isolated. Obtained from a rat injected with MOLONEY LEUKAEMIA VIRUS. Appears to be a recombinant between the MOUSE TYPE C ONCOVIRUS and an ENDOGENOUS rat type C virus which provided the sarcoma-producing capacity. *See* mouse type C oncovirus.

HAT selection Growth of cells in medium containing *h*ypoxanthine, *a*minopterin and *t*hymidine. The presence of aminopterin prevents *de novo* synthesis of purines or pyrimidines, and only cells having functional THYMIDINE KINASE and hypoxanthine-guanine phosphoribosyl transferase enzymes will survive and form colonies.

Hawaii virus

Thornhill T.S. *et al.* (1977) *J. infect. Dis.* **135**, 20

An unclassified FAECAL VIRUS type I observed by EM in the faeces from a family outbreak of gastroenteritis. Probably antigenically different from the NORWALK VIRUS.

Hazara virus An unclassified ARBOVIRUS morphologically like BUNYAVIRUS but serologically not related to members of that genus. A member of the CONGO ANTIGENIC GROUP. Isolated from a tick *Ixodes redikorzevi* in Pakistan. Not reported to cause disease in humans.

H B_c Ag Hepatitis B core antigen.

H B_e Ag Hepatitis B e antigen.

H B_S Ag Hepatitis B surface antigen.

HBV Hepatitis B virus.

HB virus

Toolan H.W. (1964) *Proc. Am. Assoc. Cancer Res.* **5**, 64

Toolan H.W. (1968) *Int. Rev. exp. Path.* **6**, 135

A RODENT PARVOVIRUS of serological group 3. Isolated from a cystadenocarcinoma of the ovary of a 12-year-old girl, one human embryo and two placentas. Serologically unlike either H-1 VIRUS or LATENT RAT VIRUS. Agglutinates guinea pig, hamster and rat erythrocytes, but not human cells.

HD virus

Howley P.M. *et al.* (1979) *J. Virol.* **30**, 400

A species in the genus POLYOMAVIRUS. Isolated from a particular line of VERO CELLS in which it does not produce CPE. The only permissive cell line is RITA. Resembles SV 40 in size and structure. Ether-resistant. Contains superhelical DNA of two size classes of mol. wt. $3{\cdot}45 \times 10^6$ and $3{\cdot}25 \times 10^6$. Both are encapsidated in the virus particles, but the proportions vary in different cell systems. Can transform Vero cells *in vitro*. DNA-DNA HYBRIDIZATION shows it to be unrelated antigenically to other members of the genus Polyomavirus, which share some common base sequences. Antiserum to SV 40 tumour or CAPSID antigen does not cross-react with HD VIRUS-infected Vero cells. It appears to be identical to STUMPTAILED MACAQUE VIRUS.

heart disease caused by viruses At least 18 viruses have been associated with heart disease in man but the significance of most of them is doubtful. RUBELLA VIRUS is an important cause of congenital abnormalities and COXSACKIE VIRUSES may be a cause of myocarditis. *See* review by A. B. G. Lansdown in *Prog. med. Virol.* **24** (1978), 70.

heat-tethered virus Virus whose replication is temporarily interrupted by an increase in temperature. The virus is not inactivated and on return to the permissive temperature the replication process recommences. Seen with certain POXVIRIDAE.

Heine–Medin disease virus Synonym for human poliovirus.

HeLa cells (CCL 2) The first aneuploid epithelial-like cell line to be derived from human tissue and maintained continuously by serial cell culture. Derived from cervical adenocarcinoma of a negro female, *HE*nrietta *LA*x.

helenine

Kleinschmidt W.J. *et al.* (1968) *Nature, Lond.* **220**, 167

A fermentation product of the fungus *Penicillium funiculosum* and a potent INTERFERON inducer. This activity is due to the presence of a DOUBLE-STRANDED RNA viral GENOME. Electron microscopic studies have revealed numerous particles of typical virus morphology some 20–30 nm in diameter, and similar to those seen in STATOLON but serologically distinct from them.

helical symmetry A form of symmetry in which many RNA virus CAPSIDS are constructed. Each CAPSOMERE on the helix consists of a single polypeptide molecule and establishes bonds with two capsomeres on each of the adjacent turns, giving stability to the capsid. The overall length of the helix is determined by the length of the RNA molecule. In all animal viruses with helical symmetry the NUCLEOCAPSID is folded and packed within a lipoprotein ENVELOPE, e.g. ORTHOMYXOVIRIDAE, PARAMYXOVIRIDAE and RHABDOVIRIDAE.

helper virus A virus which, in a mixed infection with a DEFECTIVE VIRUS, provides some factor without which the defective virus cannot replicate. *See* phenotypic mixing.

Henderson–Paterson bodies An old name for the molluscum body produced in epidermal cells of patients infected with MOLLUSCUM CONTAGIOSUM VIRUS. An INCLUSION BODY.

Hepatitis A virus

WHO (1977) *Technical Report Series 602*

Siegl G. & Frosner G.G. (1978) *J. Virol.* **26**, 48

Bradley D.W. *et al.* (1978) *J. med. Virol.* **2**, 175

Probably a species in the genus ENTEROVIRUS. Diameter 27–29 nm. Density in CsCl 1·34 g/ml and sedimenting at 160 S in sucrose. Causes 'short incubation' hepatitis (less than 6 weeks). The virus is present in the faeces during the prodromal phase of the disease but usually disappears about the time jaundice appears. Chronic carriers of the virus are not seen and the virus does not cause progressive liver disease. Epidemics of hepatitis A are usually due to water or food-borne infection. Antibodies may be demonstrated by CFT, immune adherence, haemagglutination and radioimmunoassay. They appear soon after the onset of jaundice and persist. They increase in frequency with age and reach a peak at age 50. Chimpanzees and marmosets are susceptible to experimental infection and the virus can be demonstrated in hepatocytes.

SYN: catarrhal jaundice virus; epidemic jaundice virus of man.

Hepatitis B virus

Zuckerman A.J. *et al.* (1978) *Lancet* **ii**, 652

Robinson W.S. (1977) *Ann. Rev. Microbiol.* **31**, 357

WHO (1977) *Technical Report Series 602*

An unclassified DNA virus. Causes 'long incubation' hepatitis (more than 60 days). Classically, infection results from the inoculation of serum from a carrier during blood transfusion, vaccination, tattooing or ear-piercing with inadequately sterilized instruments. However, non-parenteral routes are also important and many cases result from domestic and sexual contact, especially homosexual practices. The complete virus is a double-shelled particle 42 nm in diameter, but small spherical particles 22 nm in diameter and tubular forms of the same diameter but up to 100 nm long are also present in the plasma of carriers. The viral GENOME has a mol. wt. of 2×10^6. Virus may be detected in the plasma by EM or various tests for viral antigens. There are three viral antigens. (1) Surface antigen (HB_sAg) present on the surface of all three types of virus particle. (2) Core antigen (HB_cAg) which is exposed when the outer membrane of the complete virus is disrupted with a detergent and (3) e antigen (HB_eAg) probably present in the CORE of the complete particles and associated with DNA POLYMERASE. Presence of e antigen in serum suggests high infectivity. The HB_sAg displays antigenic heterogeneity. In addition to a common determinant 'a' all strains possess type-specific determinants (combinations of d, y, w and r). The following virus types are recognized:

ayw1 (a_1yw)	adw2 ($a_2{}^1dw$)
ayw2 ($a_2{}^1yw$)	adw4 (a_3dw)
ayw3 ($a_2{}^3yw$)	adr
ayw4 (a_3yw)	adyw
ayr	adyr

(Previous designations are shown in parentheses)

These determinants behave as two allelic groups: d and y as one group and w and r as the other. However, they are probably not completely independent. The two mixed subtypes are rare.

HB_sAg is present in the blood 4 weeks prior to the development of symptoms and usually disappears 6 weeks after the onset of symptoms. If present beyond 13 weeks it is likely the patient will become a chronic carrier and may develop chronic liver disease. Anti-HB_s does not usually appear until convalescence. HB_c Ag does not appear in the blood. Anti-HB_c appears during the disease and unlike Anti-HB_s persists for years and is a valuable marker of previous infection. HB_e Ag appears during the incubation period but disappears more rapidly than HB_s Ag. Persistence beyond 3–4 weeks may herald a chronic infection. Not all chronic carriers of hepatitis B virus develop chronic liver disease. A few infections result in acute hepatic failure probably due to an antigen antibody reaction. Immune serum globulin (ISG) and hyperimmune globulin (HIG) are effective in providing passive immunity. A vaccine consisting of HB_s Ag is being developed. There is evidence that the virus is involved in aetiology of hepatocellular carcinoma – *see* review by W. Szmuness, *Prog. med. Virol.* **24** (1978), 40.

A variety of non-human primates can be infected and on several occasions zoo primates, especially chimpanzees, have been found to be chronic carriers. The source of their infection is not clear but may be in the wild since some human cases have been associated with contact with wild non-human primates.

SYN: serum hepatitis virus.

Hepatitis C virus

Shirachi R. *et al.* (1968) *Lancet* **ii**, 863

Feinstone S.M. & Purcell, R.H. (1978) *Ann. Rev. Med.* **29**, 359

An unclassified virus which causes a hepatitis which is neither A nor B. Often the cause of post-transfusion hepatitis. The incubation period is often less than 60 days. May be spread non-parenterally. Diameter of VIRION 27 nm. Can infect and cause hepatitis in chimpanzees.

SYN: NANB virus; non-A non-B hepatitis virus.

Hepatitis infectiosa canis virus Synonym for canine adenovirus.

Hepato-encephalomyelitis virus

Stanley N.F. *et al.* (1953) *Aust. J. exp. Biol. med. Sci.* **31**, 147

Prototype strain of REOVIRUS type 3.

hep-2 cells (CCL 23) A heteroploid cell line derived from tumours produced in irradiated and cortisone-treated weanling rats after injection with epidermoid carcinoma tissue from the larynx of a 56-year-old human male.

herpangina A short febrile illness with sore throat in which there are small papules or vesicles around the fauces, which soon break down into shallow ulcers. Classically caused by COXSACKIE A VIRUSES, particularly types 1–6, 8, 10 and 22. Sporadic cases have been associated with coxsackie virus A7, A9, B1–5 and ECHOVIRUS 6, 9, 16 and 17.

Herpes febrilis Synonym for human (alpha) herpesvirus 1 or 2.

Herpes gladiatorum, Herpes rugbeiorum Synonyms for scrum-pox.

Herpes simplex virus There are 2 antigenic types: Herpes simplex type 1 is a synonym for human (alpha) herpesvirus 1; Herpes simplex type 2 is a synonym for human (alpha) herpesvirus 2.

Herpes simplex virus group Synonym for alphaherpesvirinae.

Herpes venatorum Synonym for scrum-pox.

Herpesviridae

Honess R.W. & Watson D.H. (1977) *J. gen. Virol.* **37**, 15

Roizman B. (1979) *Cell* **16**, 481

A family of DNA viruses with characteristic morphology. The VIRION is 120–150 nm in diameter. BUOYANT DENSITY (CsCl) 1·26–1·29 g/ml. Consists of four structural components: (1) the CORE, a protein fibrillar spool on which the DNA is wrapped; (2) the CAPSID, 100–110 nm in diameter, composed of 162 CAPSOMERES arranged with ICOSAHEDRAL SYMMETRY; (3) the TEGUMENT, an amorphous asymmetrical layer between the capsid, and (4) the ENVELOPE, a bilayer membrane with surface projections. The capsomeres are hexagonal in cross section and have a hollow running down half their length. The GENOME consists of linear double-stranded DNA with both terminal reiterations and internal repetitions. G+C CONTENT 32–72%. Mol. wt. $80–150 \times 10^6$. There are more than 20 structural polypeptides, mol. wts. 12,000–220,000. Lipid content is variable and located in the envelope. Carbohydrate is covalently linked to envelope proteins. After ATTACHMENT and PENETRATION the genome reaches the nucleus where the viral DNA is transcribed. mRNA passes to the cytoplasm for TRANSLATION. Viral DNA is replicated in the nucleus and immature NUCLEOCAPSIDS are formed which bud through the inner lamella of the nuclear membrane, acquiring an envelope and becoming infective. Virus particles accumulate between the inner and outer lamellae of the nuclear membrane and in the cysternae of the endoplasmic reticulum from where it is released to the cell surface. Margination of CHROMATIN and intranuclear INCLUSION BODIES are characteristic of herpesvirus-infected cells. There are many species and they are found in most eukaryotic hosts which have been examined in detail, from man to oysters. Some species are CELL-ASSOCIATED and free infective units are scarce. A few are oncogenic. Many cause mild or SILENT INFECTIONS in their natural hosts but severe disease in others. Latent infection in the natural host is common. They replicate with CPE in cell cultures and some species produce pocks on the CAM. There are three subfamilies: ALPHAHERPESVIRINAE, BETAHERPESVIRINAE and GAMMAHERPESVIRINAE. The emphasis in defining the subfamilies and the species assigned to them will be placed on the DNA structure. No genera have yet been named, but when they are they will be defined on a serological basis. As a provisional 'label', species will be named after the taxonomic unit (family or subfamily) to which the primary natural host belongs, and given a number. If the species has been allotted to a subfamily this is indicated in parentheses, e.g. HUMAN (ALPHA) HERPESVIRUS 2, EQUID HERPESVIRUS 3.

Herpesvirus A proposed genus of the family HERPESVIRIDAE, containing viruses of mammals which show a considerable degree of serological cross-reactivity (including NEUTRALIZATION) and some genetic homology with the type species HUMAN (ALPHA) HERPESVIRUS 1. Such species are HUMAN (ALPHA) HERPESVIRUS 2, CERCOPITHECID HERPESVIRUS 1 and CERCOPITHECID HERPESVIRUS 3. No genera in the family HERPESVIRIDAE have yet been created but subfamilies are recognized, e.g. ALPHAHERPESVIRINAE, BETAHERPESVIRINAE, etc.

Herpesvirus aotus Synonym for cebid herpesvirus 4.

Herpesvirus ateles Synonym for cebid herpesvirus 3.

Herpesvirus caprae Synonym for bovid herpesvirus 5.

Herpesvirus cuniculi Synonym for leporid herpesvirus 1.

Herpesvirus hominis Synonym for human (alpha) herpesvirus 1 and/or 2.

Herpesvirus M Synonym for cebid herpesvirus 1.

Herpesvirus papio Synonym for cercopithecid herpesvirus 4.

Herpesvirus platyrrhinae Synonym for cebid herpesvirus 1.

Herpesvirus saguinus

Melendez L.V. *et al.* (1971) *Lab. Anim. Sci.* **21**, 1050

A species of the family HERPESVIRIDAE. Isolated from the cotton-top marmoset *Saguinus oedipus* in which it causes a SILENT INFECTION. A number in the CEBID HERPESVIRUS series has not yet been alotted.

Herpesvirus saimiri Synonym for cebid herpesvirus 2. However, two HERPESVIRUSES have the squirrel monkey as their natural host, and L.V. Melendez *et al.* in *Lab. Anim. Sci.* **21** (1971), 1050, proposed herpesvirus saimiri 1 as the name for herpesvirus T (CEBID HERPESVIRUS 1) and herpesvirus saimiri 2 as the name for herpesvirus saimiri (CEBID HERPESVIRUS 2).

Herpesvirus simiae Synonym for cercopithecid herpesvirus 1.

Herpesvirus suis Synonym for suid (alpha) herpesvirus.

Herpesvirus sylvilagus Synonym for leporid herpesvirus 2.

Herpesvirus T (tamarinus) Synonym for cebid herpesvirus 1.

Herpesvirus varicellae Synonym for human herpesvirus 3.

Herpetoviridae A proposed name for the family now known as HERPESVIRIDAE.

Herpid Trade name for a 5% solution of IDOXURIDINE in DIMETHYL SULPHOXIDE.

Hershey Medical Center virus

Geder L. *et al.* (1978) *J. Virol.* **27**, 713

A HERPESVIRUS found in human cells transformed by CYTOMEGALOVIRUS, and subsequently shown to be BOVID HERPESVIRUS 1. Presumably a contaminant from the foetal calf serum used in the culture medium.

HER virus Abbreviation for *H*aemorrhagic *E*ncephalopathy of *R*ats Virus.

heteroduplex A double-stranded DNA molecule in which the strands do not have completely complementary base sequences. Regions of non-complementarity can often be identified in electron micrographs of the DNA, and used to map their position (heteroduplex mapping).

heterogenotes Bacteria with parts of two PROPHAGES. The first prophage is called the endogenote and the second the exogenote.

heterokaryon Hybrid cell formed by fusion of two cells of different species. *See also* homokaryon.

heterologous interference *See* interference.

heteroploid virus A MULTIPLOID VIRUS in which the GENOMES in a particle are not all the same.

hexons Groups of six protein units on the triangular faces of an icosahedral CAPSOMERE.

Highland J virus A species of the genus ALPHAVIRUS. Isolated from rodents, birds and mosquitoes in U.S.A. No known association with disease.

Hinze virus Synonym for leporid herpesvirus 2.

Hirt supernatant

Hirt B. (1967) *J. molec. Biol.* **26**, 365

The supernatant from a virus-infected cell culture lysed with SODIUM DODECYL SULPHATE (SDS). A method of separating viral from cellular DNA, based on the preferential precipitation of undegraded cellular DNA in the presence of SDS and sodium chloride final concentration 1M.

histones Basic proteins rather more complex than PROTAMINES. They contain tyrosine but little or no tryptophan. Millon's reaction is positive for histones but negative for protamines. Found in cell nuclei in varying amounts in close association with DNA. There are five main classes, differing in their relative content of lysine and arginine.

HIX virus

Fischinger P.J.S. *et al.* (1975) *Proc. natn. Acad. Sci. U.S.A.* **72**, 5150

A murine non-transforming TYPE C ONCOVIRUS with properties of both an eco- and a XENOTROPIC VIRUS.

HL 23V virus

Reitz M.S. *et al.* (1976) *Proc. natn. Acad. Sci. U.S.A.* **73**, 2113

A MAMMALIAN TYPE C ONCOVIRUS from cultured human leukaemic cells (acute myelogenous). It is a mixture of one virus indistinguishable from the WOOLLY MONKEY VIRUS (SSAV-1) and another identical to an ENDOGENOUS VIRUS of the baboon *Papio cynocephalus* (BALV-M7). They are not endogenous human viruses, but are probably horizontally transmitted. Similar isolates have been made from other leukaemic patients.

Hog cholera virus

Enzmann P.J. & Weiland F. (1978) *Arch. Virol.* **57**, 339

A species in the genus PESTIVIRUS. Only pigs are naturally infected. Very contagious and fatal in herds of pigs. Causes fever, apathy, vomiting, eye discharge, diarrhoea and cutaneous haemorrhages. Secondary bacterial infection often occurs. Strains vary in virulence; some are mild, others neurotropic and some are poorly neutralized by antiserum. Disease first reported in mid-western U.S.A. about 1833 and has spread all over the world. The pathological lesion consists of degeneration of small blood vessels causing haemorrhage. Leucopenia. Infection in sows 10–50 days pregnant may result in infection of the foetuses, abortion or congenital tremor due to cerebellar hyperplasia. Hyperimmune serum can be used to give passive immunity and an attenuated vaccine for active immunity. Antigenically related to PESTIVIRUS DIARRHOEA VIRUS. Calves, goats and deer can be infected experimentally, but not wild mice, cotton-tail rabbits, rats or sparrows. Passage in laboratory rabbits, which only show transient fever experimentally, results in attenuation of the virus for pigs. Virus 40 nm in diameter with a CORE of diameter

29 nm and ENVELOPE 6 nm thick. Infectivity more stable at pH 4·8–5·1 than at 7·0. Inactivated on drying in the air and exposure to lipid solvents.

SYN: swine fever virus, pestivirus suis.

homidium bromide

Avery R.J. & Levy J.A. (1979) *Virology* **95**, 277

3,8-diamino-5-ethyl-6-phenylphenanthridinium bromide. A trypanocide used in veterinary medicine. Has two useful virological properties: (1) it binds to DNA, (2) it fluoresces in ultra-violet light. NUCLEIC ACIDS which, for example, have been separated by gel electrophoresis can thus be 'stained' by it and visualized. Circular forms of DNA such as in MITOCHONDRIA bind the drug most strongly. Suppresses acute infection by retroviruses, blocking integration of the viral GENOME. Also blocks induction of MOUSE TYPE C ONCOVIRUS by IDOXURIDINE, and virus production by chronically infected cells. Specific mode of action not known.

homokaryon Hybrid cell formed by fusion of two cells of the same species. *See also* heterokaryon.

homologous interference *See* interference.

horizontal transmission Transmission between animals of any age after birth, usually excluding via the maternal milk.

Horse pox virus A species in the family POXVIRIDAE. Causes papular lesions on lips, buccal mucosa and sometimes in the nose with fever and drooling of saliva. Only a few deaths. Course 10–14 days or 3–4 weeks in severe cases. May be transmissible to man; finger lesions have been reported in those working with horses. Not now present in Britain. *See also* grease heel virus.

SYN: contagious pustular dermatitis of horses virus; contagious pustular stomatitis of horses virus.

host cell A cell in which a virus is replicating.

hot spot A site within a gene at which mutations occur with unusually high frequency.

HT virus A species in the genus PARVOVIRUS. A RODENT PARVOVIRUS of serological group 2. Isolated from a few human embryos and placentas. Antigenically related to but not identical with H 1 VIRUS. Shows equal avidity for guinea pig and hamster erythrocytes, but does not react with those of humans or rats.

Huacho virus A species in the genus ORBIVIRUS and a member of the KEMEROVO ANTIGENIC GROUP. Isolated from the tick *Ornithodoros amblus* in Peru. Not reported to cause disease in humans.

Hughes group viruses Four unclassified tick-borne viruses comprise this antigenic group. All isolated from argasid ticks found in areas frequented by sea birds. HUGHES VIRUS has also been isolated from the blood of a sea bird.

Hughes	Soldado
Panta Salinas	Zirqa

Hughes virus An unclassified tick-borne virus isolated from sea birds in the Atlantic and Pacific and carried by *Ornithodoros* ticks. Not reported to cause disease in humans.

Human adeno-associated virus *See* primate adeno-associated virus.

Human adenovirus

Hierholzer J.C. *et al.* (1975) *J. clin. Microbiol.* **1**, 366

Green M. *et al.* (1979) *Virology* **93**, 481

A species in the genus MASTADENOVIRUS. There are 33 serotypes which can be divided into 3 groups on the basis of agglutination of rhesus monkey and rat erythrocytes. Can be divided into 5 groups (A–E) on DNA GENOME homology. Replication occurs in most primary and continuous human cell cultures. There is an early CPE in heavily infected cultures due to PENTON antigen, and a late CPE associated with virus replication. Some animal cells support productive or ABORTIVE INFECTION. With some types, multiplication

is promoted by concomitant infection with sv40. In mixed infections hybrid particles may be formed. Infection in man may be silent, or respiratory disease of varying severity produced. Types 1, 2, 5 and 6 are particularly likely to cause human disease and these are often found latent in human adenoids. Types 3, 4, 7, 14 and 21 are associated with outbreaks of fever and pharyngitis in army camps and boarding schools. Type 8 is associated with kerato-conjunctivitis. Laboratory animals are generally insusceptible. Most types have some oncogenic potential in new-born hamster, and types 12, 18 and 31 are highly oncogenic. Transmission in humans is mainly airborne but virus is often present in stools and urine. The strains present in faeces may be impossible to cultivate *in vitro* though present in large numbers. However, type 7 has been isolated from children with gastroenteritis (Gardner P.S. *Brit. med. J.* (1960) **i**, 91). A vaccine has been used with success, but the oncogenicity of the viruses indicates caution in its use.
SYN: adenoid degeneration agent; adenoidal-pharyngeal-conjunctival agent.

Human (alpha) herpesvirus 1

Honess R.W. & Watson D.H. (1977) *J. gen. Virol.* **37**, 15

Type species of the first genus in the subfamily ALPHAHERPESVIRINAE. Primary infection is common in young children, often subclinical, but may cause acute stomatitis. The virus can pass along nerves and become latent in ganglia from whence it can be reactivated by non-specific stimuli (fever, sunlight, menstruation) to cause lesions, often around the mouth. Rarely, the virus may cause acute hepatitis, kerato-conjunctivitis or meningo-encephalitis. Vaccination has not been successful but treatment of kerato-conjunctivitis and skin lesions with locally applied IDOXURIDINE is beneficial. Chemotherapy may be life-saving in cases of encephalitis. *See* human (alpha) herpesvirus 2.
SYN: herpes febrilis; herpes simplex type 1; herpesvirus hominis.

Human (alpha) herpesvirus 2 A species of the genus HERPESVIRUS. Very similar to HUMAN (ALPHA) HERPESVIRUS 1 except that it is usually, though not always, transmitted venereally. Infection is therefore uncommon before the age of puberty. The virus usually causes genital lesions and it has been named as a possible cause of carcinoma of the cervix. However, it can also be responsible for any of the lesions characteristic of human (alpha) herpesvirus 1. There is a high level of antigenic similarity between viruses 1 and 2 though each has antigens specific to itself. The respective DNAs show at least 50% homology.
SYN: herpes febrilis; herpes simplex type 2; herpesvirus hominis.

Human (beta) herpesvirus 5

Stern H. (1977) *Recent Adv. Clin. Virol.* **1**, 177

Neff B.J. *et al.* (1979) *Proc. Soc. exp. Biol. Med.* **160**, 32

A species in the family HERPESVIRIDAE. A world-wide infection, common in humans. Usually a chronic silent infection of the salivary glands, but primary infection during pregnancy may lead to infection of the foetus with varying degrees of brain damage. Infection *in utero* or neonatal infection may cause severe and often fatal hepatitis, splenomegaly and anaemia. Patients on immunosuppressive therapy and occasional normal people may develop fatal pneumonia or hepatitis or a form of glandular fever. Virus can often be isolated from the urine of patients, and sometimes from that of normal children. An active vaccine has been made, is safe, and will probably come into use. There is replication in primary human fibroblast cultures with a slowly developing CPE and formation of INCLUSION BODIES. Hamster and human cells are transformed *in vitro*. The virus is CELL-ASSOCIATED. No haemagglutinins. Sensitive to freezing and thawing and to prolonged storage at −70 °. G+C CONTENT 58%.
SYN: giant-cell pneumonia virus; human cytomegalovirus; inclusion body disease virus; visceral disease virus.

Human calicivirus

McSwiggan D.A. *et al.* (1978) *Lancet* **i**, 1215

Virus particles morphologically identical to CALICIVIRUSES have been seen in faeces of infants with diarrhoea.

Human corona virus

Clarke S.K.R. *et al.* (1979) *Postgrad. med. J.* **55**, 135

Bradburne A.F. & Tyrrell D.A.J. (1971) *Prog. med. Virol.* **13**, 373

A species in the genus CORONAVIRUS. Causes acute respiratory disease in man mainly from January to March. Not always easy to isolate; human tracheal organ cultures are probably best method. The corona-like virus particles seen in faeces and associated with diarrhoea are difficult to isolate even in organ cultures. Strains have a common CF antigen but differences in antigenic structure can be demonstrated by NEUTRALIZATION TESTS. Antigenically related to MOUSE HEPATITIS VIRUS. Some strains agglutinate human and monkey erythrocytes at 4 °; chicken, rat and mouse erythrocytes at room temperature or 37 °. Neuraminic acid receptors are not involved. Can be adapted to replicate in suckling mice and will kill them in 2–3 days following i/c injection.

Human cytomegalovirus Synonym for human (beta) herpesvirus 5.

Human foamy virus

Nemo G.J. *et al.* (1978) *Infection and Immunity* **20**, 69

Brown P. *et al.* (1978) *J. infect. Dis.* **137**, 421

Achong B.G. & Epstein M.A. (1978) *J. gen. Virol.* **40**, 175

A species in the family SPUMAVIRINAE. Isolated from a human nasopharyngeal carcinoma explant culture. Can be propagated in a variety of human and animal cell cultures but not in chick embryo cell culture. Antigenically closely similar to SIMIAN FOAMY VIRUS type C, but unlike other foamy viruses. Antibodies have been found in 17 of 97 sera from humans in Kenya, but not in 50 sera from Tunisia, 20 from Singapore or 74 from Great Britain. It has been suggested that it may be a simian foamy virus. Not known to be pathogenic in man or animals.

Human (gamma) herpesvirus 4

Epstein M.A. & Achong B.G. (1977) *Lancet* **ii**, 1270

Epstein M.A. & Achong B.G. (1977) *Ann. Rev. Microbiol.* **31**, 421

A species in the family HERPESVIRIDAE. First isolated from Burkitt tumours of African children. A very widespread human infection, mainly of children, in whom it rarely causes disease, but produces a high level of immunity. However, primary infection of young adults may result in infectious mononucleosis, a febrile condition with enlargement of the lymph nodes and often a sore throat. The PAUL–BUNNELL TEST is positive. The virus is the probable cause of Burkitt tumours and carcinoma of the post-nasal space, but as the infection is universal and these tumours only occur in local areas, some accessory factors must be involved. After infection, the virus probably remains in the body in some latent form. It can be propagated in human cell cultures, but is cell-associated and is difficult to purify. A number of virus-coded antigens have been identified in infected tissues, and antibodies to these are found in man.

SYN: Burkitt's lymphoma virus; Ebb virus; Epstein–Barr virus, glandular fever virus; infectious mononucleosis virus.

Human herpesvirus 1 Synonym for human (alpha) herpesvirus 1.

Human herpesvirus 2 Synonym for human (alpha) herpesvirus 2.

Human herpesvirus 3 A species in the family HERPESVIRIDAE, and the cause of common human infection. Causes chickenpox on primary infection, usually in childhood. Incubation period 14–16 days, rarely up to 21 days. Causes herpes zoster, a painful local condition with skin lesions, usually in adults. The eyes may be involved. May follow exposure to infection but most commonly appears to be a reactivation of latent infection. Encephalitis is a rare complication of chickenpox. Foetal malformations have been reported to follow maternal infection. All strains are antigenically similar. Convalescent serum has no therapeutic use but an attenuated vaccine was used in Japan. Animals appear to be resistant to infection. The virus can be cultivated in HELA and various monkey tissue cells, with CPE in 2–7 days. It remains cell-bound and difficult to separate, and is usually passaged with cellular material.

SYN: chickenpox virus; herpesvirus varicellae; varicella-zoster virus.

Human herpesvirus 4 Synonym for human (gamma) herpesvirus 4.

Human herpesvirus 5 Synonym for human (beta) herpesvirus 5.

Human papilloma virus

Rowson K.E.K. & Mahy B.W.J. (1967) *Bact. Rev.* **31**, 110

Zur Hausen H. (1977) *Current Topics Microbiol. Immunol.* **78**, 1

A species in the genus PAPILLOMAVIRUS. Causes papillomas of the epidermis in man: skin warts (verrucae of various types), genital warts (condylomata acuminata), and laryngeal papillomas. Malignant change is reported in genital and laryngeal papillomata. The role of the virus in carcinoma of the cervix and other tumours remains to be elucidated. Virus is readily extracted from skin warts but less easily demonstrated in genital and laryngeal lesions. Accidental or experimental inoculation of virus into the skin of man results in the development of warts. Does not replicate or produce papillomas on injection into animals. There is one report of virus replication in cell culture of human epithelial cells. When DNA from virus extracted from individual warts is cleaved by RESTRICTION ENDONUCLEASES, the cleavage patterns obtained on gel electrophoresis suggest that there are 4 different virus strains (HPV 1 to 4) and that HPV4 is entirely different from HPV 1, 2 and 3 which have many common cleavage sites. HPV4 does not cross react in CFT with HPV 1, 2 and 3. About 30% of common skin warts are caused by HPV4. The 72 CAPSOMERES are arranged in a right-handed skew lattice.

SYN: human wart virus.

Human papovavirus This term would include HUMAN PAPILLOMA VIRUS and HUMAN POLYOMA VIRUSES.

Human parainfluenza viruses *See* parainfluenza virus types 1–4 human.

Human poliovirus The type species of the genus ENTEROVIRUS. There are three serological types: 1, 2 and 3. Easily isolated from faeces in primary monkey kidney cell cultures or in HELA CELLS. Produces a rapid CPE. A common infection of the human intestinal tract which is usually silent, but the CNS may be invaded with damage to the anterior horn cells and lower motor neurone paralysis. A similar disease may be induced experimentally in chimpanzees and cynomolgus monkeys. Suckling mice are not susceptible. An attenuated virus vaccine given by mouth prevents disease. After 1961, following the wide use of vaccine, it was necessary to characterize virus isolates as virulent or attenuated, vaccine-derived or wild. The monkey neuro-virulence test is the only one capable of assessing virulence. A number of *in vitro* tests are in use to distinguish vaccine from wild strains but they are sometimes difficult to interpret. *See* Nakano J.H. *et al.* (1978) *Prog. med. Virol.* **24**, 178.

Human polyoma viruses

Padgett B.L. & Walker D.L. (1976) *Prog. med. Virol.* **22**, 1

Gardner S.D. (1977) In *Recent Advances in Clinical Virology*, vol. I, p. 93. Ed. Waterson A.P. London: Churchill Livingstone

Isolated from the brains of patients with progressive multifocal leucoencephalopathy (PML) which is probably caused by JC VIRUS, and from the urine of patients with impaired immunity due to disease or therapy. BK VIRUS can often be isolated from renal transplant patients. They appear to be common viruses in human populations but rarely seem to cause disease. There are three main species: JC virus, BK virus and SV40 PML.

Human reovirus-like agent Synonym for human rotavirus.

Human respiratory syncytial virus A species in the genus PNEUMOVIRUS. A common human respiratory virus first isolated from a chimpanzee. An important cause of lower respiratory tract infection in infants which may be more severe if they have a low level of antibody, because this may react with viral antigen in the tissues. This antibody is often maternal. For this reason immunization may have unfavourable consequences. Causes 'colds' in captive chimpanzees. Causes no symptoms in ferrets, and can be serially passaged in them. Freezing of specimens for virus isolation reduces the chance of success. Replicates in human cell lines such as HELA and HEP 2 and less readily in monkey kidney cell cultures. Small syncytia appear and within 1–4 days the whole cell sheet is involved. No demonstrable HAEMADSORPTION. No replication in eggs. VIRION 90–120 nm in diameter and variable in size. Matures at the cell surface by budding. There is a helical NUCLEOCAPSID 12–15 nm in diameter containing single-stranded RNA. Inactivated by lipid solvents. ENVELOPE covered with projections NEUTRALIZATION TESTS reveal some antigenic difference between strains but no cross-reaction with other human respiratory viruses.

SYN: chimpanzee coryza agent; respiratory syncytial virus of humans.

Human rhinovirus

Jackson G.G. & Muldoon R.L. (1975) *J. inf. Dis.* **127**, 328

A species in the genus RHINOVIRUS. The cause of most human 'colds' and some other respiratory tract infections. Does not haemagglutinate. Over one hundred serological types. Strains which replicate in rhesus monkey kidney cell cultures are called M strains; the majority which multiply only in human cells are called H strains. Some strains can only be isolated in organ cultures of respiratory epithelium. Optimal conditions for propagation are sodium bicarbonate concentration not more than 0·35 g/litre, temperature 33°, slow rotation of culture, islands of cells rather than confluent sheet and minimal concentration of serum compatible with maintenance of cells. Best cells for isolation are primary human kidney or lung or diploid human cell lines. CPE may not be seen for 10 days or only on passage. No vaccine available but experiments suggest immunity to an individual strain can be produced. Chimpanzees can be infected but do not have symptoms of a 'cold'.

SYN: common cold virus; coryza virus; ERC group viruses; murivirus; respirovirus; Salisbury virus.

Human rotavirus

Obijeski J.F. *et al.* (1977) *J. gen. Virol.* **34**, 485

Lewis H.M. *et al.* (1979) *Arch. Dis. Childh.* **54**, 339

A species in the genus ROTAVIRUS. A cause of gastroenteritis in infants and less often in older children and adults. In infants diarrhoea is often preceded by respiratory symptoms. Isolations from patients are commonest from November to April. New-born rhesus monkeys, calves and pigs can be infected experimentally. Antibodies to CALF ROTAVIRUS can be used to detect human virus. It may also be detected in faecal extracts by direct EM, or by centrifugation onto monolayers of primary human embryo fibroblasts or LLC-MK2 CELLS followed by overnight incubation and straining with labelled antiserum. Maternal antibodies probably provide some protection from disease and may permit SILENT INFECTION. Infection in maternity hospital nurseries tends to cause mild disease, but in children over 6 months of age infection can cause severe symptoms.

SYN: human reovirus-like agent; infantile gastroenteritis virus.

Human syncytial virus Synonym for human foamy virus.

Human wart virus Synonym for human papilloma virus.

hundestaupe Synonym for distemper.

hundskrankheit (German: = 'dog disease') Synonym for phlebotomus fever. So called because the conjunctivae become so markedly injected that they resemble the eyes of a bloodhound. *See* phlebotomus fever virus.

H 1 virus A species in the genus PARVOVIRUS. Belongs serologically to RODENT PARVOVIRUS group 2. Isolated from transplantable human tumour, HEp1, hence the designation. Very similar in biological properties to LATENT RAT VIRUS but serologically distinct. Agglutinates preferentially guinea pig, hamster, human, and rat erythrocytes, in that order. Antibodies not often present in human serum but virus can replicate on injection into humans. The strain deposited in the American Type Culture Collection was isolated from the embryo of a pregnant woman with metastatic carcinoma of the breast. The natural host is probably the rat.

H 2 virus Does not exist.

H 3 virus A RODENT PARVOVIRUS of serological group 1. Isolated from a human tumour HEp3 which had been transplanted for several years in conditioned rats. Serologically different from H 1 VIRUS and LATENT RAT VIRUS. Agglutinates guinea pig and rat erythrocytes equally.
SYN: OLV virus.

hybridization The formation of DOUBLE-STRANDED NUCLEIC ACID molecules from SINGLE-STRANDED POLYNUCLEOTIDES with complementary base sequences. The process may be carried out in the laboratory with both the single strands in solution (liquid hybridization), or with one strand immobilized on a solid support (filter hybridization). The rate of hybridization increases with salt concentration, or with temperature up to just below the melting temperature (Tm).

Hydrocephalus of pike virus
Bootsma R. *et al.* (1975) *J. Fish Biology* **7**, 269
A species in the genus VESICULOVIRUS.

Hydrophobia virus Synonym for rabies virus.

β-[2-hydroxy-2-(3,5-dimethyl-2-oxocyclohexyl)ethyl]glutarimide *See* cycloheximide.

9-(2-hydroxyethoxymethyl)guanine *See* acycloguanosine.

hyperchromic effect Increase in absorbance of light of wave length 260 nm by DNA at the melting point or TRANSITION TEMPERATURE.

HYPR virus A species in the genus FLAVIVIRUS. Isolated from a boy with encephalitis in Brno, Moravia. Antigenically very similar or identical to HANZALOVA VIRUS. A strain of TICK-BORNE ENCEPHALITIS VIRUS (CENTRAL EUROPEAN SUBTYPE). Frequent human infections in Hungary, Poland, Yugoslavia, Austria, Bulgaria, Sweden and Finland.

IABS International Association of Biological Standardization.

IAMS International Association of Microbiological Societies.

Ibaraki virus
Ito Y. *et al.* (1973) *Arch. ges. Virusforsch.* **40**, 29
Inaba Y. (1975) *Aust. vet. J.* **51**, 178
A species in the genus ORBIVIRUS and a member of the BLUE TONGUE ANTIGENIC GROUP, isolated from cattle in Ibaraki Prefecture, Japan. Resembles BLUE TONGUE VIRUS, from which it is antigenically distinct, in causing a disease often severe in cattle in Japan, but has little pathogenicity for sheep. Probably transmitted by arthropods. Replicates in bovine cell cultures with CPE and in the yolk sac of embryonated eggs. Not pathogenic for guinea pigs or rabbits. Not to be confused with EPHEMERAL FEVER VIRUS which causes a somewhat similar disease. Found in Japan, Bali and Taiwan.
SYN: Keishi virus.

I.C.I. 73602 *See* 1-(*p*-chlorophenyl)-3-(*m*-3-isobutylguanidinophenyl)urea hydrochloride.

ICNV International Committee on Nomenclature of Viruses. Now the ICTV.

Icoaraci virus An unclassified ARBOVIRUS morphologically like BUNYAVIRUS but serologically not related to members of that genus. Belongs to the PHLEBOTOMUS FEVER ANTIGENIC GROUP. Isolated from the rodent *Proechimys guyannensis oris* in Para, Brazil, and sentinel mice in São Paulo, Brazil. Does not multiply in mosquitoes on salivary gland inoculation. Vector probably sand flies of *Phlebotomus* sp.

Icosahedral cytoplasmic deoxyribovirus Synonym for Iridoviridae.

Icosahedral cytoplasmic deoxyriboviruses of amphibians

Kelly D.C. & Robertson J.S. (1973) *J. gen. Virol.* **20**, suppl. p. 17

At least 9 species in the family IRIDOVIRIDAE, isolated from frogs, newts and toads. They have been designated FV 1, FV 2 etc., or Lt 1, Lt 2 etc. FV 3 is the species which has been most worked upon.

SYN: cytoplasmic amphibian viruses.

icosahedral symmetry

Crick F.H.C. & Watson J.D. (1956) *Nature, Lond.* **177**, 473

Caspar D.L.D. & Klug A. (1962) *Cold Spring Harbor Symp. Quant. Biol.* **27**, 1

One of the two types of symmetry found in viral CAPSIDS, the other being HELICAL SYMMETRY. Crystallographic considerations prescribe that the identical units forming the capsid of an ISOMETRIC PARTICLE must be arranged with cubic symmetry. Of the possible forms that this may take, icosahedral symmetry provides the facility to make a range of viral capsids with different numbers of structural units. The simplest has 60 identical units in regular relation to each other, 3 to a triangular face, and 5 at each vertex forming a PENTON. To make a large virus in this simple form with 60 units would require a large protein, which raises difficulties with GENOME coding capacity, and an alternative is to use a larger number of small units. This inevitably means that the units cannot all have identical relations to each other. Those not surrounding a vertex must be in groups of six called HEXONS. *See* icosadeltahedron.

icosadeltahedron An icosahedron in which the faces have been subdivided into triangles. If they have been divided into more than four triangles the 12 faces will be no longer flat. The 12 pentomeric vertices of the icosahedron remain but additional hexomeric vertices are formed on the non flat faces. *See* triangulation number.

icosahedron A solid with 20 triangular faces and 12 vertices. In a regular icosahedron the faces are equilateral triangles and there are axes of twofold, threefold and fivefold rotational symmetry.

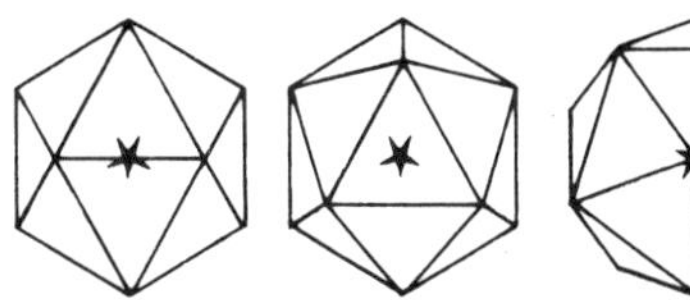

ICRO International Cell Research Organization.

ICSU International Council of Scientific Unions.

ICTV International Committee on the Taxonomy of Viruses. Formerly the ICNV.

ID_{50} The 50% infective dose. The dose which on average will infect 50% of the individuals to which it is administered. They may be human volunteers, experimental animals, tissue cultures or eggs. When eggs are used the term EID_{50} is often used.

idoxuridine 5-iodo-2′-deoxyuridine. An antiviral agent and an analogue of thymidine. Its action is due to its incorporation into DNA, and it is hence active against DNA viruses such as HUMAN HERPESVIRUS TYPES 1, 2 and 3, VACCINIA, and SUID HERPESVIRUS 1. RNA viruses which form a DNA intermediate (e.g. ROUS SARCOMA VIRUS) are also susceptible during the establishment of infection. The drug is probably inactive until enzymatic conversion into the NUCLEOTIDE which is a competitive inhibitor for the incorporation of thymidine nucleotides into DNA. This occurs during both cellular and viral DNA synthesis. Because of its toxicity it is used mainly as a topical application. Has been used with success in the treatment of herpes simplex keratitis, particularly dendritic ulcers of the cornea, but the emergence of idoxuridine-resistant herpesvirus has been reported. It has also been used systemically for the treatment of varicella pneumonia and herpesvirus encephalitis with little or no success. Side effects of systemic administration of the drug include hepatotoxicity, leukopenia, thrombocytopenia, haemorrhage, stomatitis, alopoecia and diarrhoea. Due to its low solubility in water, a solution in DIMETHYL SULPHOXIDE is usually preferred for topical purposes, except in the case of eye drops. Idoxuridine is rapidly inactivated by nucleotidases, which precludes its administration other than topically or by i/v injection. It is available as 1% eye drops or as 5% topical application.

SYN: Dendrid; Herpid; Kerecid; Stoxil.

IDU *See* idoxuridine.

Ieri virus Unclassified ARBOVIRUS. Isolated from mosquitoes in Trinidad and Brazil. Not known to cause disease in humans.

Iguana virus Synonym for iguanid herpesvirus 1.

Iguanid herpesvirus 1

Clark H.F. & Karzon D.T. (1972) *Infect. Immun.* **5**, 559

A species in the family HERPESVIRIDAE. Isolated from a spontaneously degenerating cell culture of tissue from a green iguana, *Iguana iguana.* On injection into iguanas it caused no consistent disease pattern observable on necropsy, but 7 of 12 animals injected died. Has narrow host range. Replicates in iguana cell cultures with CPE at certain temperatures.

SYN: iguana virus.

Ilesha virus A species in the genus BUNYAVIRUS, and a member of the BUNYAMWERA ANTIGENIC GROUP. Isolated in Nigeria, Uganda, Cameroon, Central African Republic and Senegal from the mosquito *Anopheles gambiae.*

Ilheus virus A species in the genus FLAVIVIRUS. Main natural host not known, but antibodies are found in man, horses, birds. The virus has been isolated from mosquitoes. Occurs in Brazil, Colombia, central America and the Caribbean. Usually causes an inapparent infection in man but a few cases of encephalitis are recorded. Mice injected i/c develop encephalitis. VIRAEMIA occurs in several species but not in chickens and pigeons. There is replication on the CAM but most virus is in the embryo. In chick embryo and hamster kidney cells virus replicates with CPE.

immobilized DNA (or RNA) Term used to describe NUCLEIC ACID attached to membrane filters for the purpose of DNA-RNA HYBRIDIZATION.

immortalization A change produced by virus infection of a cell culture, which results in continued growth of the cells beyond the time at which it would have been expected to stop. Similar or identical to TRANSFORMATION, but the term is used to emphasise the fact that there is no evidence of neoplastic transformation. Used especially to describe the continued growth of human cells after infection with EPSTEIN–BARR VIRUS.

immuno-electron microscopy

Almeida J.D. & Waterson A.P. (1969) *Adv. Virus Res.* **15**, 307

Techniques in which virus and specific antiserum are mixed before examination by EM. The antibody agglutinates the virus particles into small clumps which are easier to find.

The technique can also be used to test for the presence of antibodies to a known virus, or to identify a virus using a range of sera.

immunological drift Synonym for antigenic drift.

inactivation Loss of infectivity by a virus. Can result from exposure to certain chemicals, specific antibodies or adverse physical conditions such as heat or irradiation. *See also* neutralization.

inclusion body An area of abnormal staining in a virus-infected cell. Visible by light microscopy and may be single or multiple, large or small, round or irregular, intranuclear or intracytoplasmic, acidophilic or basophilic. Often composed of viral NUCLEIC ACID or proteins, but in some infections they are formed of cellular material. Of limited use in the diagnosis of certain infections, for example NEGRI BODIES in the brain cells of animals suspected of having rabies.

Inclusion-body disease virus Synonym for human (beta) herpesvirus 5.

Inclusion-body hepatitis of chickens virus

Fadley A.M. & Winterfield R.W. (1975) *Am. J. vet. Res.* **36**, 532

A species in the genus AVIADENOVIRUS. Causes a common and fatal disease of chickens. There are liver lesions, intramuscular haemorrhages and aplastic anaemia. Yolk sac inoculation of chick embryos causes death. Plaques are produced on the CAM. Birds with antibodies, and eggs from such birds are resistant to infection.

Inclusion-body rhinitis virus of pigs Synonym for suid herpesvirus 2.

Inclusion disease of pigeons virus Synonym for columbid herpesvirus.

incomplete virus Virus lacking some part necessary for its replication. Synonym for defective virus.

Indiana virus Several strains of VESICULAR STOMATITIS VIRUS: Indiana 1, 2 A, 2 C and 3.

indicator cells *See* co-cultivation.

Infantile gastroenteritis virus Synonym for human rotavirus.

Infantile paralysis virus Synonym for human poliovirus.

Infectious anaemia of horses virus

Henson J.B. & McGuire T.C. (1974) *Prog. med. Virol.* **18**, 143

Ishii S. & McGuire T.C. (1975) *Adv. Vet. Soc. Comp. Med.* **19**, 195

Cheevers W.P. *et al.* (1978) *J. Virol.* **28**, 997

A species in the subfamily LENTIVIRINAE causing acute or very chronic infections in horses. Incubation period 12–15 days or longer. There are acute episodes with fever, anaemia, nasal discharge and subcutaneous oedema. Remissions occur which may last for years but the infection is usually fatal. VIRAEMIA may be present for years, even during remissions. Transmission to other species is reported but not confirmed. Insect vectors, probably mechanical, are suspected but contact infection is possible as virus is present in milk, semen, saliva and urine. Control is by slaughter as there is no vaccine of proved efficacy. VIRION 80–120 nm in diameter, enveloped, possibly with small projections. Has a high mol. wt. RNA GENOME and virion-associated REVERSE TRANSCRIPTASE. Inactivated in 60 minutes at 60°, survives for at least 158 days in tap water at room temperature. Inactivated by lipid solvents and 1% formaldehyde in 1 month at 5° but not by 5% phenol under the same conditions. Inactivated by 4% sodium hydroxide in 15 minutes but not by sodium hypochlorite. Agglutination of fowl, frog and human erythrocytes by serum of infected horses is reported. Strains can be distinguished by virus NEUTRALIZATION but have a common CF antigen. Replicates in cell cultures of embryonic equine tissue without CPE. INTERFERENCE with VESICULAR STOMATITIS VIRUS multiplication has been used for assay. Replication in horse leucocyte cultures is accompanied by CPE.

SYN: equine infectious anaemia virus; swamp fever virus.

Infectious arteritis of horses virus Synonym for equine infectious arteritis virus.

Infectious bovine rhinotracheitis virus Synonym for bovid herpesvirus 1.

Infectious bronchitis virus *See* avian infectious bronchitis virus.

Infectious bulbar paralysis virus Synonym for suid (alpha) herpesvirus 1.

Infectious bursal disease virus

Wyeth P.J. *et al.* (1979) *Vet. Rec.* **104**, 188
Cursiefen D. *et al.* (1979) *Arch. Virol.* **59**, 39
Dubos P. *et al.* (1979) *J. Virol.* **32**, 593

Provisionally a species in the genus ORBIVIRUS, but is reported to have a single CAPSID structure and a GENOME of 2 segments of double-stranded RNA mol. wt. 2·5 and $2{\cdot}2 \times 10^6$. There is no ENVELOPE. Diameter 60 nm, density about 1·32 g/ml. Capsid composed of four major polypeptides. Replicates in chicken embryo fibroblasts rather than in epithelioid cells. Causes a lymphoproliferative condition of chickens, 2- to 15-week-old birds are most commonly affected. The bursa of Fabricius is involved, so that the immune system does not develop properly, resulting in an inability to resist other infections. There is nephrosis. Infectivity survives heating at 60° for 90 minutes, exposure to ether, chloroform, trypsin or low pH. Transmission is probably via food and water. Egg- or mouse-adapted attenuated virus has been used as a vaccine with success.

SYN: avian nephrosis virus; gumboro disease virus.

Infectious canine hepatitis virus Synonym for canine adenovirus.

infectious catarrh of rats *See* pneumonia of rats.

infectious centre assay A technique for determining the proportion of cells in a cell suspension which are able to release infectious virus. A suspension of cells infected with a virus is layered on a cell monolayer culture, and covered with a layer of solid medium to prevent the virus released spreading too widely. Cells which release virus form plaques in the monolayer.

Infectious dropsy of carp virus

Fijan N.N. (1972) *Symp. Zool. Soc. Lond.* **30**, 39

Synonym for RHABDOVIRUS CARPIO. But the chronic form of infectious dropsy, erythrodermatitis, is caused by a different, unidentified agent.

Infectious enteritis virus

Dees T.A. *et al.* (1972) *Am. J. vet. Res.* **33**, 765

A species in the genus REOVIRUS. Causes diarrhoea, hepatic necrosis and monocytosis in young turkeys and pullets. Replicates in 8 day-old chick embryos, causing death in 36–72 hours. A similar disease is caused by TURKEY BLUECOMB DISEASE VIRUS.

SYN: avian diarrhoea virus; avian monocytosis virus; pullet disease virus.

Infectious haematopoietic necrosis virus

McAllister P.E. *et al.* (1974) *Arch. ges. Virusforsch.* **44**, 270

A species in the genus VESICULOVIRUS. Causes necrosis of haematopoietic tissues of spleen and anterior kidney in young trout and salmon. Occurs as epidemic disease in fish hatcheries. Can be propagated in fathead minnow and other fish tissue cell lines with CPE. Probably related to OREGON SOCKEYE DISEASE VIRUS and SACRAMENTO RIVER SHINOOK SALMON DISEASE VIRUS.

Infectious hepatitis virus An old name for HEPATITIS A VIRUS. However, other viruses causing hepatitis are also infectious.

Infectious labial dermatitis virus Synonym for orf virus.

Infectious laryngotracheitis virus of fowls Synonym for avian infectious laryngotracheitis virus.

Infectious mononucleosis virus Synonym for human (gamma) herpesvirus 4.

Infectious myocarditis of gosling virus Provisionally a species in the genus REOVIRUS. The main lesion in infected birds is degeneration of smooth and striated muscle. Replicates in goose eggs and cell cultures with syncytium formation. Not inhibited by IDOXURIDINE and resistant to ether, chloroform, desoxycholate and pH 3.

SYN: goose influenza virus; septicaemia anserum exudativa virus.

infectious nucleic acid NUCLEIC ACID which is able to infect cells and initiate the production of complete virus particles. Nucleic acid removed from the virus particle is not protected from inactivation by tissue nucleases. It does not depend on cell receptors for ATTACHMENT to and ability to infect cells and so may be able to infect species which the intact virus cannot. For example HUMAN POLIOVIRUS nucleic acid injected i/c in a mouse can initiate one cycle of infection. Complete virus is produced but cannot infect further cells. Infectious nucleic acid is readily isolated from PAPOVAVIRIDAE, PICORNAVIRIDAE, TOGAVIRIDAE and HERPESVIRIDAE.

Infectious pancreatic necrosis virus

Dubos P. *et al.* (1979) *J. Virol.* **32**, 593

Moss L.H. III & Gravell M. (1969) *J. Virol.* **3**, 52

Macdonald R.D. (1978) *J. gen. Virol.* **41**, 623

Provisionally a species in the genus REOVIRUS. The cause of an acute, contagious and highly lethal disease of young trout in N. America, Europe and Japan. Adult trout and salmon are insusceptible. Infected fish swim erratically and eventually die. There is necrosis of the pancreatic acinar and islet tissue. Experimentally, the virus causes pancreatic lesions in mice. Replicates in various fish cell cultures with CPE but not in mammalian cells. Virus has a single CAPSID structure, is 55–65 nm in diameter, probably has 92 CAPSOMERES and two pieces of double-stranded RNA, mol. wt. 2·2 and $2{\cdot}4 \times 10^6$. Ether-resistant but acid-labile.

Infectious porcine encephalomyelitis virus Synonym for porcine enterovirus.

Infectious porcine poliomyelitis virus Synonym for porcine enterovirus.

Infectious pustular vulvo-vaginitis virus Synonym for bovid herpesvirus 1.

infectious units Single virus particles, or in some cases, small groups which plaque or titrate as units. The number of virus particles is always larger and often very much larger (up to 10^6 times) than the number of infectious units.

Influenzavirus A genus of the family ORTHOMYXOVIRIDAE consisting of two species: INFLUENZA VIRUS A and INFLUENZA VIRUS B. These are defined by the possession of ribonucleoprotein antigens A or B. Human strains in this genus are described according to a convention which sets out information in the following order: (1) antigen A or B; (2) geographic region; (3) isolation number; (4) year of isolation; (5) haemagglutinin antigen; (6) NEURAMINIDASE antigen.

Example: A/England/3/1975/H3/N2.

Influenza virus A

'Influenza', ed. Schild G.C., *Br. med. Bull.* **35** (1) (1979)

Burnet F.M. (1979) *Intervirology* **11**, 201

A species in the genus INFLUENZAVIRUS. Type species A/WS/33 (HON1). All species of the genus share a common ribonucleoprotein antigen, the NP protein. It is demonstrated by CF test or immunodiffusion and is found as part of the NUCLEOCAPSID or as soluble antigen. The viral ENVELOPE has two antigens – a haemagglutinin (HA protein) and a receptor-destroying enzyme (NEURAMINIDASE, NA protein). These envelope antigens are both species- and type-specific. HA is demonstrated by haemagglutination or NEUTRALIZATION and NA by enzyme-inhibition. There are 15 HA types: H 0–3 human, HSW 1 swine, HEq 1 and 2 equine, HAv 1–8 avian. There are 10 NA types: N1 and N2 human, NEg 1 and 2 equine, NAv 1–6 avian. Recombination is frequent between species within the genus but not outside it. Strains show ANTIGENIC DRIFT and more dramatic antigenic changes which may precipitate pandemic disease. Transmission is by air-borne virus or direct contact. They cause epidemic and sporadic respiratory disease. Natural hosts are man, pigs, horses, birds and occasionally non-human primates, dogs and cattle. Ferrets are experimentally susceptible to mammalian strains. Less susceptible are mice, hamsters and guinea pigs. Most strains replicate in eggs and primary cultures of monkey, human, and chick cells. Laboratory strains may be adapted to grow in cell lines.

Influenza virus A avian

Webster R.G. (1976) *J. gen. Virol.* **32**, 217

A subspecies of the species INFLUENZA VIRUS A whose natural hosts are birds: fowl, quail, ducks, turkey, pheasant, etc. Most isolates fall into one of six antigenic groups based on haemagglutination inhibition. Natural infection is widespread in birds, particularly water fowl in which infection is usually SILENT and intestinal. They may excrete the virus over prolonged periods. Many strains of virus are present and may provide a source of new mammalian strains. Infection of chickens and turkeys, usually called fowl plague, is a serious and commercially important disease which varies from a mild respiratory to a rapidly fatal pneumonic disease with CNS involvement. Stress may increase susceptibility. Transmission probably air-borne. A vaccine can protect birds but may not be economically practical. Mice, ferrets and other mammals have been infected experimentally usually by i/c inoculation. Can be propagated in eggs and in primary fowl or monkey kidney cells. Most strains produce plaques in chick embryo fibroblasts.

Influenza virus A equine A subspecies of the species INFLUENZA VIRUS A whose natural host is the horse. There are two distinct antigenic subtypes. Antibodies are found in human sera. Causes respiratory illness in horses and may be fatal in young animals. Causes inapparent infection in ferrets and can be adapted to produce pneumonia in mice. Replicates in eggs, primary cultures of bovine, human, monkey and chick cells. Agglutinates horse, pig, calf, rhesus, fowl, human and guinea pig erythrocytes.
SYN: equine influenza virus.

Influenza virus A hominis

Scholtissek C. (1978) *Curr. Top. Microbiol. Immunol.* **80**, 139
Schild G.C. (1979) *Br. med. Bull.* **35**, no. 1
Assaad F.A. *et al.* (1979) *Bull. WHO* **57**, 227

A subspecies of the species INFLUENZA VIRUS A whose natural host is man. Causes sporadic and epidemic respiratory disease. The HA and NA antigens of the virus change slowly, but every 8 years or so a radical change occurs and the human population has only slight immunity to the new strain, resulting in a pandemic. A vaccine can be prepared but the protection is strain specific. The virus is isolated in the amniotic cavity of embryonated eggs or in primary monkey kidney cell cultures. Virus multiplication is observed by HAEMADSORPTION or haemagglutination of human or guinea pig erythrocytes. Ferrets can be infected experimentally and after adaptation, pneumonia can be produced in mice and hamsters. In monkeys, horses, dogs, sheep, guinea pigs and rats infection is usually inapparent. Q strains are non-avid, reacting poorly with homologous antiserum in contrast to avid or P-phase strains. O-phase or recently isolated strains replicate better in the amniotic than in the allantoic cavity, and agglutinate human and guinea pig erythrocytes better than fowl cells. After adaptation to the allantoic cavity they agglutinate fowl cells equally well.

Influenza virus A porcine

Stewart-Harris C. (1976) *Health Trends* **8**, 84

A subspecies of the species INFLUENZA VIRUS A whose natural host is the pig. Antibodies reacting with swine virus haemagglutinin are present in many human sera especially from older people and it has been suggested that the pandemic of 1918–19 in humans was caused by a virus which spread from man to the pigs. Causes pneumonia in pigs especially when associated with *Haemophilus suis*. Ferrets and mice also susceptible to infection. Transmission is by air-borne droplets, also by ingestion of earthworms containing virus-infected swine lungworms. A vaccine gives some immunity.
SYN: swine influenza virus.

Influenza virus B A species in the genus INFLUENZAVIRUS. Typical strain B/Lee/40. All strains of the species share a common ribonucleoprotein antigen, the NP protein and a second internal antigen, the M protein. Haemagglutinin (HA protein) and NEURAMINIDASE (NA protein) distinguish antigenic variants within the species. There is no crossing of HA and NA antigens between the species of influenzavirus. Only natural host is man. Causes sporadic and epidemic respiratory disease. Ferrets can be infected experimentally causing mild disease or none at all. Strains have been adapted to produce pneumonia in mice. Easily propagated in eggs and monkey kidney cell cultures. Laboratory strains grow with CPE in human amnion, pig, calf and ferret cells.

Influenzavirus C

Chakraverty P. (1968) *Arch. Virol.* **58**, 341

A genus of the family ORTHOMYXOVIRIDAE. Type species C/Taylor/49. All strains of the genus share a common ribonucleoprotein antigen the NP protein. The haemagglutinin distinguishes antigenic variants of the genus. Differs from INFLUENZAVIRUS A in the VIRION having a lower density (1·17–1·19 g/ml). Receptors on cell surfaces do not contain sialic acid and the receptor-destroying enzyme is not NEURAMINIDASE. A natural infection of man causing mild sporadic respiratory disease. Isolated in the amniotic cavity of embryonated eggs. Replicates in canine kidney cell line (MDCK), best in presence of trypsin (20 mg/ml) *J. gen. Virol.* (1978) **39**, 179.

Influenza virus D Synonym for parainfluenza virus type 1 human.

Ingwavuma virus A species in the genus BUNYAVIRUS, and a member of the SIMBU ANTIGENIC GROUP. Isolated from pigs in Taiwan and Thailand, birds in S. Africa, Nigeria and the Central African Republic. Also found in India and Cyprus. Mosquito-borne. Not reported to cause disease in humans.

initiation The start of synthesis of a polypeptide or NUCLEIC ACID chain. The point at which TRANSLATION of mRNA begins is indicated by an initiation CODON.

initiation codon *See* codon.

Inkoo virus A species in the genus BUNYAVIRUS and a member of the CALIFORNIA ANTIGENIC GROUP. Isolated from mosquitoes in Finland up to 70° N. Antibodies found in man, cattle, hares, foxes and other wild animals. A few cases of febrile illness with rising antibodies are reported in humans.

inosine The RIBONUCLEOSIDE from hypoxanthine.

inosiplex

Ginsburg T. & Glasky A.J. (1977) *Ann. N.Y. Acad. Sci.* **284**, 128

The 3:1 molar complex of *N-N*-dimethylamino-2-propanol *p*-acetamidobenzoate and inosine. Shows some anti-viral activity *in vitro* and in animals, but attempts to use it as a prophylactic have been disappointing. However, a controlled double-blind study in human volunteers challenged with RHINOVIRUS suggests that the drug exerts significant

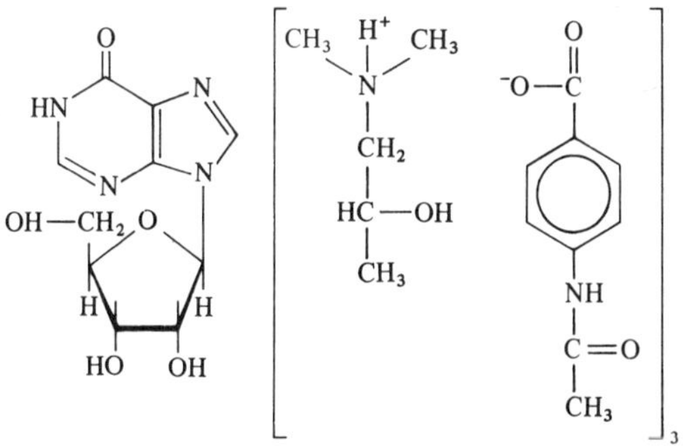

O HN N N N OH—CH_2 O H H HO OH
[CH_3 H^+ CH_3 N CH_2 HC—OH CH_3 O $^-$O—C NH C=O CH_3 $]_3$

effects when used therapeutically. Symptomatic improvement was also noted in a study involving natural infections of HUMAN HERPESVIRUS 1, and it is thought that the clinical effectiveness of the drug is due to its activity as an immunopotentiator.

SYN: Isoprinosine.

Inoue virus Synonym for subacute myelo-optico-neuropathy virus.

integrase Virus-induced enzyme which cuts and joins TEMPERATE BACTERIOPHAGE DNA molecules at specific sites. Involved in the insertion of viral DNA into chromosomal DNA.

integrated viral genome A viral GENOME which is incorporated into the cellular DNA and is replicated with it.

integument Structural component of some VIRIONS situated between the CAPSID and the ENVELOPE.

interference Prevention of the replication of one virus by another, and the result of a number of different mechanisms. Thus, virus ATTACHMENT to cell receptors can be prevented by prior exposure to any virus which alters or destroys them. An example of this is the interference of u.v.-irradiated NEWCASTLE DISEASE VIRUS with the replication of an infective preparation of the same virus added later. This is also an example of homologous interference, in which a virus interferes with its own replication. Interference which is strictly homologous cannot be due to INTERFERON which is active against a range of viruses. Autointerference is said to occur where a large dose of virus produces a smaller yield than a small dose, or fails to kill an animal whereas a small dose will. This may be due to interferon or some other inhibitor in the inoculum, but is generally due to the presence of non-infective (DEFECTIVE) particles which block the replication of infective ones. Heterologous interference is observed between different virus species and is most often due to interferon production. It can also be due to attachment interference, or to some blocking of virus replication which is poorly understood and probably varies from one case to another. Examples of heterologous interference are FROG VIRUS 3 or adenovirus with VACCINIA. The interference of RUBELLA VIRUS with Newcastle disease virus is another, though it has been described as 'intrinsic interference' by Marcus P.I. & Carver D.H. (1967) *J. Virol.* **1**, 334.

interferons

Baron S. (1979) *A.S.M. News* **45**, 358

Baron S. & Dianzani F. (Eds) *The Interferon System*, Texas Reports on Biology and Medicine (1977), vol. 35

A group of closely related non-viral proteins of differing mol. wt. 15,000–30,000 liberated by cells following exposure to a variety of inducing agents. Viruses are most potent in this respect, but interferons can also be induced by the exposure of cells to other micro-organisms including protozoa, bacteria, mycoplasma and rickettsias; to bacterial endotoxins, HELENINE, STATOLON, phytohaemagglutinin, and NUCLEIC ACIDS. They are a new class of proteins which are not ordinarily present in the un-induced cell. Once released, interferons act upon other cells to reduce their susceptibility to a wide range of virus infections. With few exceptions this protection is limited to cells of the animal species in which the interferons were produced, or to those of species closely related to the producer. Interferons do not prevent virus PENETRATION of the cell, and have no effect on extracellular virus. They are stable over a pH range 2–10, but activity is inhibited by trypsin and other proteolytic enzymes, hydrocortisone, and oxygen at high concentrations. The protective action of interferons is due to their INDUCTION within the cells of a complex of protein synthesis inhibitors which block TRANSLATION of viral mRNA at the RIBOSOMES. The induced inhibitors include a protein kinase, and an enzyme which catalyses the synthesis of a trinucleotide, pppA2′p5′A2′p5′A (two-five A). The trinucleotide in turn activates a latent cellular endonuclease which degrades the viral mRNA. Interferons are poorly antigenic but it is not known if more than one antigenic type can be produced by a single cell. Interferon inducers have been administered intranasally to human volunteers experimentally infected with RHINOVIRUS or INFLUENZA VIRUS but only minimal amounts of nasal interferon were induced and the overall results were unimpressive. However, rhinovirus infection can be prevented by intranasal instillation of human leucocyte interferon. The interferon system has not yet been developed to the point where it can be used to control viral infections of man, but the short term prospects seem good.

intergenic complementation *See* complementation.

interjacent RNA 26 S single-stranded RNA found in cells infected with certain TOGAVIRIDAE such as SEMLIKI FOREST VIRUS. It has the same polarity as the viral RNA but shares only $\frac{1}{3}$ of its base sequences from the 3′ end; it is thus termed SUBGENOMIC RNA. Interjacent RNA codes for all the viral COAT proteins.

intramolecular recombination *See* recombinants.

intrinsic interference *See* interference.

intron

Gilbert W. (1978) *Nature, Lond.* **271**, 501

A region of the GENOME NUCLEIC ACID of a virus or a cell which is lost from mature mRNA during processing – an intragenic region. *See also* exon, splicing.

5-iodo-2′-deoxyuridine *See* idoxuridine.

Ippy virus An unclassified ARBOVIRUS. Isolated in suckling mice from the pooled liver, spleen and brain of an adult rat of *Arvicanthis* sp. trapped in Ippy, Central African Republic. Not known to cause disease in man.

Iridoviridae

McAuslan B.R. & Armentrout R.W. (1974) *Current Top. in Microbiol. Immunol.* **68**, 77

A family of large DNA-containing viruses 130–300 nm in diameter, having ICOSAHEDRAL SYMMETRY with about 1,500 CAPSOMERES. Contains many proteins, several enzymes, lipid and a single structural unit membrane associated with the viral CORE. The GENOME is a single molecule of double-stranded DNA of mol. wt. $100–130 \times 10^6$. G+C CONTENT 30–58%. Replication occurs in the cytoplasm. There is one genus, IRIDOVIRUS, containing viruses of arthropods, but a second genus containing viruses of vertebrates may be set up. It would contain AFRICAN SWINE FEVER VIRUS, ICOSAHEDRAL CYTOPLASMIC DEOXYVIRUSES OF AMPHIBIANS, GECKO VIRUS and LYMPHOCYSTIS VIRUSES.

SYN: icosahedral cytoplasmic deoxyribovirus, polyhedral cytoplasmic deoxyribovirus.

Iridovirus A genus of the family IRIDOVIRIDAE. Non-enveloped, ether-resistant viruses of arthropods. GENOME mol. wt. about 130×10^6. G+C CONTENT about 30%.

Irituia virus A species in the genus ORBIVIRUS, which with CHANGUINOLA VIRUS forms the Changuinola antigenic group. Isolated from rodents of *Oryzomys* sp. in Para, Brazil. Not reported to cause disease in humans.

Isfahan virus

Tesh R. *et al.* (1977) *Am. J. trop. Med. Hyg.* **26**, 299

A species in the genus VESICULOVIRUS. Antigenically related to VESICULAR STOMATITIS VIRUS. Isolated from the sand fly *Phlebotomus papatasi* in Iran. Animal pathogenicity, growth rate, morphology, CPE and plaque morphology are similar to those of other serotypes. Neutralizing antibodies are common in humans in several regions of Iran. They are also found in gerbils but not in domestic animals. The ecology of the virus may thus be different from that of other serotypes and involve chiefly humans, gerbils and sandflies. Not known to cause disease in humans.

Isiolo virus Strain of SHEEP POX VIRUS.

isolate A virus propagated in pure culture as far as is known. May later prove to be a mixture. Often used incorrectly to describe what would be better known as a RECOGNIZATE.

isometric particle Particles with identical linear dimensions, distinct from the rod-shaped and bullet-shaped virus particles and viruses enclosed by irregular capsules. They appear spherical; however, their CAPSIDS are constructed with ICOSAHEDRAL SYMMETRY.

Isoprinosine Trade name for inosiplex.

isopycnic gradient centrifugation A form of DENSITY GRADIENT CENTRIFUGATION in which the supporting gradient column includes the entire range of densities of the particles to be tested. In this case, sedimentation of an individual particle will cease when it reaches that point in the gradient matching its own density, i.e. the point of buoyant density. Separation of particles into zones by this technique depends only upon their density differences and is independent of time. *See also* rate zonal centrifugation.

Israel turkey meningoencephalitis virus A species in the genus FLAVIVIRUS. Isolated from domestic turkeys in Israel. Not associated with human disease.

Issyk-Kul virus An unclassified ARBOVIRUS. Isolated from bats and ticks in Kirghiz, U.S.S.R. Antibodies are found in man but the virus is not reported to cause disease.

Itakura virus Antigenically identical to SAGIYAMA VIRUS. Isolated in Japan.

Itaporanga virus An unclassified ARBOVIRUS, morphologically similar to BUNYAVIRUS but serologically unrelated to members of that group. A member of the PHLEBOTOMUS FEVER ANTIGENIC GROUP. Isolated from mosquitoes of *Culex* sp. Natural hosts inhabit the forest canopy, e.g. bats and birds. Forest floor animals are not infected. Found in São Paulo, Amapa and Para, Brazil; and in Trinidad and French Guiana. Not reported to cause disease in humans.

Itaqui virus A species in the genus BUNYAVIRUS, and a member of the C GROUP VIRUSES. Isolated from SENTINEL *Cebus* monkeys and mice, forest rodents and marsupials in Para, Brazil. Mosquito-borne. Causes CPE in HELA CELL cultures. Not reported to cause disease in humans.

IUBS International Union of Biological Sciences.

IUdR *See* idoxuridine.

Jaagsiekte virus (driving sickness)

Martin W.B. *et al.* (1976) *Nature, Lond.* **264**, 183

A term which has been used for two diseases: chronic progressive pneumonia and pulmonary adenomatosis. BOVID HERPESVIRUS 4 has been isolated from pulmonary adenomatosis but is probably not the cause of the disease.

SYN: Lungers virus.

Jamestown Canyon virus

Watts D.M. et al. (1979) *Am. J. trop. Med. Hyg.* **28**, 344

A species in the genus BUNYAVIRUS and a member of the CALIFORNIA ANTIGENIC GROUP. Isolated from mosquitoes, horse and deer-flies in Wisconsin and Colorado, U.S.A. and in Canada. Serological studies suggest the white-tailed deer, *Odocoileus virginianus* is an important host in Maryland. Not known to cause disease in humans.

Japanaut virus A species in the genus ORBIVIRUS. Isolated from culicine mosquitoes and a bat in the Sepik district of New Guinea. Not reported to cause disease in humans.

Japanese B virus

Takahashi M. & Suzuki K. (1979) *Am. J. trop. Med. Hyg.* **28**, 122

A species in the genus FLAVIVIRUS. Mainly an infection of birds spread by culicine mosquitoes, but infection of bats may be a factor in winter survival. In man it causes mild febrile illness but 0·1–0·2% show signs of encephalitis. There may be pareses and sequelae are common. Encephalitis occurs in horses. Domestic pigs are often infected and have a VIRAEMIA. Virus found in S.E. Asia from Siberia to Malaya and S. India. Replicates in eggs, the best method of infection being into the yolk-sac. Replication also occurs in cell cultures of chick and various mammalian tissues, as well as mosquito cells. Causes encephalitis on i/c injection of mice, hamsters and monkeys. An inactivated vaccine has been used but is of doubtful value. An attenuated strain may be more useful.

SYN: Japanese encephalitis virus; Russian autumn encephalitis virus

Japanese encephalitis virus Synonym for Japanese B virus.

J 111 cells (CCL 24) A heteroploid cell line derived from peripheral blood of a 25-year-old human female with monocytic leukaemia.

JC virus

ZuRhein G.M. (1969) *Prog. med. Virol.* **11**, 185

Weiner L.P. & Narayan, O. (1974) *Prog. med. Virol.* **18**, 229

Gardner S.D. (1977) *Recent Adv. Clin. Virol.* **1**, 93

A species in the genus POLYOMAVIRUS. Antigenically distinct from BK VIRUS and SV 40 VIRUS. Agglutinate human group O erthrocytes. Originally isolated from the brain of a patient with progressive multifocal leukoencephalopathy by inoculation of homogenized brain tissue into primary human foetal glial cell cultures. Has been associated with at least 20 cases of this disease. Can be propagated in primary human foetal glial cell cultures which show a CPE in 3–4 days. Presence of antibodies suggests it is a common human infection. Highly oncogenic in new-born hamsters, especially on i/c injection.

Jerry slough virus A species in the genus BUNYAVIRUS, belonging to the CALIFORNIA ANTIGENIC GROUP. Isolated from the mosquito *Culiseta inornata* in Kern County, California. Antigenically very closely related to JAMESTOWN CANYON VIRUS. Not known to cause disease in humans.

JHM strain of mouse hepatitis virus

Nagashima K. *et al.* (1978) *Adv. Exp. Med. Biol.* **100**, 395

Wege H. *et al.* (1979) *J. gen. Virol.* **42**, 37

Robb J.A. & Bond C.W. (1979) *Virology* **94**, 352

Synonym for Mouse Hepatitis Virus Type 4. A neurotropic variant. JHM indicates association with Professor J. Howard Mueller of Harvard.

JH virus Originally classified as ECHO 28 VIRUS. Now designated HUMAN RHINOVIRUS strain 1A.

Jijoye cells (CCL 87) A cell line derived from ascitic fluid of an African negro boy with Burkitt's lymphoma of the liver.

Joest's Bodies Intranuclear INCLUSION BODIES found in the brain cells of animals infected with BORNA DISEASE VIRUS.

Johnston atoll virus

Austin F.J. (1978) *Am. J. trop. Med. Hyg.* **27**, 1045

An unclassified ARBOVIRUS. With QUARANFIL VIRUS forms the Quaranfil antigenic group. Isolated from a tick *Ornithodoros capensis* from the nest of a common noddy tern on Sand Island, Johnston Atoll in the central Pacific. Also isolated in South Island, New Zealand and Queensland, Australia. Not known to cause disease in humans.

Joinjakaka virus A species in the genus VESICULOVIRUS. Isolated from a pool of mixed culicines in the Sepik district of New Guinea. Not reported to cause disease in humans.

Juan Diaz virus A species in the genus BUNYAVIRUS, belonging to the CAPIM ANTIGENIC GROUP. Isolated from a SENTINEL mouse in Panama. Not reported to cause disease in humans.

Jugra virus A species in the genus FLAVIVIRUS. Isolated from mosquitoes and a bat in peninsular Malaysia. Not reported to cause disease in humans.

Junco pox virus *See* avipoxvirus.

Junin virus

Coto C.E. (1974) *Prog. med. Virol.* **18**, 127

Weissenbacker M.C. *et al.* (1979) *Intervirology* **11**, 363

A species in the genus ARENAVIRUS belonging to the TACARIBE ANTIGENIC GROUP. One of the AMERICAN HAEMORRHAGIC FEVER VIRUSES. Associated with Argentina haemorrhagic fever, a disease of corn-harvesters in Buenos Aires, Cordoba and Santa Fe provinces. Characterized by fever, leucopenia, exanthema and renal involvement. Mortality rate probably 3–15% but most cases recover without sequelae. Transmission from man to man rarely, if ever, occurs. Isolated from wild rodents and mites, and transmission to man is probably via contamination with rodents urine and faeces. Experimental infection of guinea pigs causes haemorrhagic disease with depression of the immune response. A disease very like that in man is produced in the New World primate *Callithrix jacchus*. Thymectomy protects mice against the lethal effects of infection. Causes chronic carrier state in wild rodents and persistent infection in cell cultures. Replication in wide range of cell cultures usually without CPE, but VERO CELLS are best for isolation, usually with CPE, though some cells survive to form a chronically infected culture.

SYN: Argentine haemorrhagic fever virus; endo-epidemic haemorrhagic fever virus; O'Higgins disease virus.

Jurona virus A species in the genus BUNYAVIRUS. Not assigned to an antigenic group. Isolated from mosquitoes in Para, Brazil. Not reported to cause disease in humans.

Jutiapa virus A species in the genus FLAVIVIRUS. Isolated from the cotton-rat *Sigmodon hispidus* in Guatemala. Not reported to cause disease in humans.

J virus

Jun M.H. *et al.* (1977) *Aust. J. exp. Biol. Med. Sci.* **55**, 645

A species in the genus PARAMYXOVIRUS. Isolated by kidney cell culture from moribund wild mice (*Mus musculus*) with haemorrhagic lung lesions. Replicates with CPE in a variety of cell cultures including MRC5, HEP2, BHK 21 and VERO but not HELA. Does not haemagglutinate. Antibodies present in wild mice, rats, pigs, bovines and humans. On infection via the nose or s/c injection, rats and mice became VIRAEMIC and lethargic, produced antibodies and developed haemorrhagic interstitial pneumonia. No antigenic relationship to PARAINFLUENZA I–IV, INFLUENZA A, B or C, NEWCASTLE DISEASE VIRUS, NARIVA, PEROMYSCUS, MOSSMAN, RAT CORONA, or LYMPHOCYTIC CHORIOMENINGITIS VIRUS. Appears to be a natural respiratory pathogen of wild mice in N. Queensland, Australia.

JVI virus Synonym for echo 20 virus.

Kadam virus A species in the genus FLAVIVIRUS. Isolated from a tick *Rhipicephalus pravus* in Uganda. Not reported to cause disease in humans.

Kaeng Khoi virus A species in the genus BUNYAVIRUS. Not assigned to an antigenic group. Isolated from bats and rats caught in caves in Thailand. Not reported to cause disease in humans.

Kaffir-pox virus Synonym for variola minor virus. *See* variola virus.

Kaikalur virus

Rodrigues F.M. *et al.* (1977) *Indian J. med. Res.* **66**, 719

A species in the genus BUNYAVIRUS, and belonging to the SIMBU ANTIGENIC GROUP. Isolated in suckling mice from a pool of mosquitoes *Culex tritaeniorhynchus* collected at Kaikalur, Andra Pradesh, India. Not known to infect man.

Kairi virus A species in the genus BUNYAVIRUS, belonging to the BUNYAMWERA ANTIGENIC GROUP. Isolated in Trinidad, Brazil and Colombia. Mosquito-borne. Not reported to cause disease in humans.

Kaisodi antigenic group viruses Three tick-borne viruses, morphologically like BUNYAVIRUS but not serologically related to members of that genus.

Kaisodi Silverwater
Lanjan

Kaisodi virus An unclassified ARBOVIRUS morphologically like BUNYAVIRUS but serologically unrelated to members of that genus. A member of the KAISODI ANTIGENIC GROUP. Isolated from ticks and a ground thrush in Shimoga district of Mysore, India. Not reported to cause disease in humans.

Kakalur virus

Rodrigues F.M. *et al.* (1977) *Indian J. med. Res.* **66**, 719

A species in the genus BUNYAVIRUS, belonging to the SIMBU ANTIGENIC GROUP. Isolated from a pool of 100 *Culex tritaeniorhynchus* mosquitoes, collected in Maikolur, Andhra Pradesh. Kills mice on i/c injection.

Kamese virus A species of the family RHABDOVIRIDAE. With MOSSURIL VIRUS forms the Mossuril antigenic group. Isolated from *Culex annulirostris* in Uganda and Central African Republic. Not reported to cause disease in humans.

Kammavanpettai virus An unclassified ARBOVIRUS. Isolated from a Brahminy myna bird *Sturnus pagoderum* in Vellore, Tamil Nadu, India.

Kannamangalam virus An unclassified ARBOVIRUS. Isolated from a house crow *Corvus splendeus* in Vellore, Tamil Nadu, India. Not reported to cause disease in humans.

Kao Shuan virus An unclassified ARBOVIRUS, belonging to the DERA GHAZI KHAN ANTIGENIC GROUP. Isolated from a tick *Argas robertsi* in Taiwan. Not reported to cause disease in humans.

Kaplan leukaemia virus A strain of mouse leukaemia virus isolated from tissues of a mouse in which leukaemia had been induced by exposure to X-irradiation.

Karimabad virus

Robeson G. *et al.* (1979) *J. Virol.* **30**, 339

An unclassified ARBOVIRUS, morphologically like BUNYAVIRUS but serologically unrelated to members of that genus. Belongs to the PHLEBOTOMUS FEVER ANTIGENIC GROUP. Isolated from females of *Phlebotomus* sp. in Iran and Pakistan. Not reported to cause disease in humans.

Karshi virus A species in the genus FLAVIVIRUS. Isolated from *Ornithodoros papillipes* ticks in the Karshi desert, Uzbekistan S.S.R. Related to WEST NILE VIRUS. Agglutinates goose erythrocytes and causes paralysis in 2- to 3-week-old mice. Not reported to cause disease in humans.

Kasba virus A species in the genus ORBIVIRUS belonging to the PALYAM ANTIGENIC GROUP. Isolated from *Culex vishnui* in North Arcot District, Tamil Nadu, India. Not reported to cause disease in humans.

Kata virus

Paul, E. *et al.* (1979) *Intervirology* **11**, 268.

A species in the genus MORBILLIVIRUS. Causes an important disease of sheep and goats in W. Africa, similar to rinderpest but cattle are not affected. There is pyrexia with nasal and ocular discharge, necrotic stomatitis, and later severe enteritis and pneumonia. Mortality may be over 90%. Antigenically related to DISTEMPER, MEASLES, and RINDERPEST VIRUSES but distinct from them. Rinderpest vaccine can be used to prevent this disease. Non-pathogenic for cattle though infection gives immunity to rinderpest virus. Replicates with CPE in a variety of cell cultures but sheep and goat cells are more sensitive. CPE develops 6–15 days after infection. Syncytia are formed. There are cytoplasmic and intranuclear inclusions.

SYN: peste des petits ruminants virus; pseudorinderpest virus; stomatitis/pneumo-enteritis complex virus.

Kawakami–Theilen strain of cat leukaemia virus

Salerno R.A. *et al.* (1979) *Proc. Soc. exp. Biol. Med.* **160**, 18

Isolated from a case of spontaneous lymphosarcoma in a Persian cat. Produces leukaemia in kittens if injected when they are 1–2 days old but is not pathogenic in cats more than 5 months old. The development of antibodies prevents VIRAEMIA and the induction of leukaemia.

KB cells (CCL 17) A heteroploid cell line derived from an epidermoid carcinoma in the mouth of an adult human male.

KBSH virus

Hallauer C. *et al.* (1971) *Arch. Virol.* **35**, 80

Very similar or identical to PORCINE PARVOVIRUS. The type strain of group 1 of the parvoviruses isolated from permanent cell lines. Group 1 viruses are the most frequently isolated parvoviruses from cell lines, and this may be the result of using infected pig trypsin. KBSH virus was isolated from a KB cell subline originating from a Hamburg laboratory.

Kedong virus Strain of SHEEP POX VIRUS.

Kedougou virus

Robin Y. *et al.* (1978) *Ann. Microbiol., Paris* **129** A, 239

A species in the genus FLAVIVIRUS. Isolated from a pool of *Aedes minutus* mosquitoes collected on human bait. Antibodies present in human sera but no evidence of pathogenicity for man.

Keishi virus

Omori T. (1970) *Natn. Inst. Anim. Hlth Quart.* **10** (suppl.), 45

A strain of IBARAKI VIRUS.

Kemerovo antigenic group viruses At least 15 serologically related viruses in the genus ORBIVIRUS. Double-stranded RNA GENOME, relatively resistant to lipid solvents and labile at acid pH. All have been isolated from ticks but not from other arthropods. Members occur in all continents except Australasia. Seldom isolated from vertebrate hosts. Replicate in chick embryo, human diploid and tick cells with CPE. Isolated from ticks in eastern Europe, Egypt and Sudan. May infect horses, cattle, birds and small mammals. KEMEROVO VIRUS has been associated with benign encephalitis in man.

Baku (Ar)
Bauline (I)
Cape Wrath (I)
Chenuda (Ar)
Great Island (I)
Huacho (Ar)
Kemerovo (I,H,B)
Lipovnik (I)
Mono Lake (Ar)
Okhotskiy (I)
Seletar (I)
Sixgun City (I)
Tribec (I,R)
Wad medani (I)
Yaquina Head (I)

Isolated from:
(I) Ixodid ticks
(Ar) Argasid ticks
(H) Humans
(R) Rodents
(B) Birds

Kemerovo virus A species in genus ORBIVIRUS belonging to the KEMEROVO ANTIGENIC GROUP. Isolated from female ticks *Ixodes persulcatus* and two humans with a febrile illness in western Siberia. Also from a bird *Phoenicurus phoenicurus* in Egypt. Antibodies are found in humans, cattle, horses, small mammals and birds in Siberia.

kennel cough *See* canine adenovirus, *also* canid herpesvirus 1.

Kerecid Trade name for IDOXURIDINE eye drops.

Kern Canyon virus A species in the genus VESICULOVIRUS, isolated from a bat in California. Not reported to cause disease in humans.

Ketapang virus An unclassified ARBOVIRUS, morphologically like BUNYAVIRUS but serologically unrelated to members of that genus. With BAKAU VIRUS forms the Bakau antigenic group. Isolated from mosquitoes in Malaya. Antibodies are found in humans but the virus is not associated with disease.

Ketarax Trade name for levamisole hydrochloride. *See* levamisole.

Keterah virus An unclassified ARBOVIRUS. Isolated from *Argas pusillus* ticks and a bat *Scotophilus temmenckii* in western Malaysia. Not reported to cause disease in humans.

Keuraliba virus An unclassified ARBOVIRUS. Isolated from gerbils and a rodent in Senegal. Not reported to cause disease in humans.

Keystone virus

Fine P.E.M. & Le Duc J.W. (1978) *Am. J. trop. Med. Hyg.* **27**, 322

Watts D.M. *et al.* (1979) *Am. J. trop. Med. Hyg.* **28**, 344

A species in the genus BUNYAVIRUS, belonging to the CALIFORNIA ANTIGENIC GROUP. Isolated from mosquitoes of *Aedes* sp. in the Tampa Bay area of Florida; also in Texas, Louisiana, Mississippi, Georgia, N. Carolina and Virginia, U.S.A. The natural mammalian host has not been identified, but studies in Florida, Texas and Virginia suggest that cotton-tail rabbits, grey squirrels and cotton-rats contribute to the maintenance of the virus. Not reported to cause disease in humans.

Khasan virus

Lvov D.K. *et al.* (1978) *Acta Virol.* **22**, 249

A species in the genus BUNYAVIRUS. Isolated from *Haemaphysalis longicornis* ticks in the Primorie region of U.S.S.R. Contains RNA. Relatively sensitive to inactivation by ether or sodium deoxycholate. Pathogenic when injected i/c into suckling and 2-week-old mice. Replicates in primary cultures of chick, duck, and green monkey cells without CPE. No haemagglutinin. Size 90–110 nm and morphology typical of family BUNYAVIRIDAE.

Kilham rat virus Synonym for latent rat virus.

kilobase A measure of the size of a NUCLEIC ACID molecule. One kilobase = 1,000 NUCLEOTIDES. Animal virus DNAs range in size from a few kilobases (PARVOVIRUSES) up to several hundred (poxviruses).

Kinkajou herpesvirus Synonym for procyonid herpesvirus 1.

Kinkajou kidney virus Synonym for procyonid herpesvirus 1.

Kirk virus A species in the genus PARVOVIRUS. Serologically belongs to RODENT PARVOVIRUS group 1. Isolated from a line of DETROIT 6 CELLS which had been inoculated with plasma from an individual who had ingested MS-1 infectious hepatitis serum.

Kirsten leukaemia virus

Kirsten W.H. *et al.* (1967). *J. natn. Cancer Inst.* **38**, 117

A strain of MOUSE TYPE C ONCOVIRUS recovered from C3Hf/Gs mice which had been injected with a cell-free extract of thymic lymphoma tissue. New-born mice injected with the virus develop splenomegaly, excessive proliferation of red cell precursors and a severe, rapidly fatal anaemia.

Kirsten mouse sarcoma virus

Kirsten W.H. & Mayer L.A. (1967) *J. natn. Cancer Inst.* **39**, 311

A strain of MOUSE SARCOMA VIRUS, isolated from a W/Fu rat injected when new-born with KIRSTEN LEUKAEMIA VIRUS. It appears to be a recombinant between the leukaemia virus and an ENDOGENOUS RAT TYPE C ONCOVIRUS genetic sequence.

Klamath virus

Murphy F.A. *et al.* (1972) *Arch. ges. Virusforsch.* **37**, 323

A species in the genus LYSSAVIRUS. Isolated from a meadow mouse *Microtus montanus* in Klamath County, Oregon, U.S.A. Replicates in BHK-21 CELLS with CPE. Day-old mice die 7 days after i/c injection. Resembles rabies in cytopathology but is not antigenically related to that or any other virus. Not reported to cause disease in humans.

Koch's postulates Criteria for determining whether a particular micro-organism is the aetiological agent of a disease. They are:

(1) the microbe is regularly found in lesions of the disease;

(2) it can be grown in pure culture *in vitro*;

(3) when such a pure culture is inoculated into experimental animals, a similar typical disease results;

(4) the microbe can be reisolated from the experimentally induced disease in animals.

These postulates were modified for application to virus diseases by Rivers T.M. (1937) *J. Bact.* **33**, 1 to read: (1) isolation of virus from diseased hosts; (2) cultivation in experimental hosts or host cells; (3) proof of filterability (to exclude larger pathogens); (4) production of a comparable disease in the original hosts species or in related ones; (5) re-isolation of the virus; (6) detection of a specific immune response to the virus.

Kokobera virus A species in the genus FLAVIVIRUS. Isolated from mosquitoes in Queensland, Australia, and in New Guinea. No known association with disease in man or other animals.

Kolongo virus An unclassified ARBOVIRUS. Isolated from birds in Central African Republic. Not reported to cause disease in humans.

Koongol virus A species in the genus BUNYAVIRUS. With WONGAL VIRUS forms the Koongol antigenic group. Isolated from mosquitoes in Queensland, Australia and New Guinea. Not reported to cause disease in humans. Antibodies are common in cattle in Queensland.

Korean haemorrhagic fever virus

Lee H.W. *et al.* (1978) *J. inf. Dis.* **137**, 298

The disease was first described in soldiers in Korea in 1951 and has remained endemic in the area of the demilitarized zone. A similar haemorrhagic fever is seen in Manchuria, U.S.S.R., Scandinavia and eastern Europe. It is a severe disease with damage to the kidneys, shock and oliguria. Infectivity can pass through bacteria-proof filters, and epidemiology suggests the cause is probably a rodent ARBOVIRUS carried by *Apodemus agrarius coreae*. Sections of lung tissue from certain animals of this species fluoresce with labelled serum from convalescent patients. Viral antigen in the lung tissue can be serially passaged in *A. agrarius coreae* but in no other laboratory animal or cell culture. MARBURG or EBOLA VIRUS antiserum did not react with *A. agrarius coreae* infected tissue.

SYN: epidemic haemorrhagic fever virus; haemorrhagic fever with renal syndrome virus; haemorrhagic nephroso-nephritis virus; nephropathia epidemica virus; Scandinavian epidemic nephropathy virus.

Kotonkan virus

Kemp G.E. *et al.* (1973) *Am. J. Epidemiol.* **98**, 43

Bauer S.P. & Murphy F.A. (1975) *Infect. Immun.* **12**, 1157

A species in the genus LYSSAVIRUS isolated from *Culicoides* sp. in Nigeria. There is serological evidence of infection in man and domestic animals. Probably the cause of an acute febrile illness similar to ephemeral fever in Nigeria. Antigenically related to OBODHIANG VIRUS and MOKOLA VIRUS, but not to EPHEMERAL FEVER VIRUS.

Koutango virus A species in the genus FLAVIVIRUS. Isolated from Kemp's Gerbil *Tatera kempi*, and rodents of *Mastomys* and *Lemnyscomys* sp. in Senegal and Central African Republic. Not reported to cause disease in humans.

Kowanyama virus

Doherty R.L. *et al.* (1968) *Trans. R. Soc. trop. Med. Hyg.* **62**, 430

An ARBOVIRUS, possibly in the genus BUNYAVIRUS. Isolated from *Anopheles* sp. in the Mitchell River area, N. Queensland, Australia. Antibodies found in domestic fowls, horses and kangaroos. Not reported to cause disease in humans, though antibodies are found in aborigines.

Kumba virus A strain of SEMLIKI FOREST VIRUS isolated in Cameroon.

Kumlinge virus A species in the genus FLAVIVIRUS. A strain of TICK-BORNE ENCEPHALITIS VIRUS (CENTRAL EUROPEAN SUBTYPE). Isolated from the tick *Ixodes ricinus*, squirrel *Sciurus vulgaris*, field vole *Microtus agrestis*, hare *Lepus timidus*, thrushes *Turdus* sp. and a bunting *Emberiza citrinella* in Finland. Causes a febrile illness with encephalitis in man. 5–20 cases annually.

Kunitachi virus

Nerome K. *et al.* (1978) *J. gen. Virol.* **38**, 293

A species in the genus PARAMYXOVIRUS. Isolated from the lung of a budgerigar which died during an epizootic in Kunitachi, Tokyo, Japan. Replicates in amniotic cavity of embryonated hens eggs and in chick-embryo cell cultures. Agglutinates chicken, goose, duck, guinea pig and human O erythrocytes at 4° and 25°, but activity not stable in amniotic fluid. Causes a fatal disease on injection into budgerigars. Not antigenically related to any of the other avian paramyxoviruses.

Kunjin virus A species in the genus FLAVIVIRUS. Isolated from mosquitoes in Queensland, Australia, and in Borneo and Sarawak. Can cause fever with a rash in humans, and has been isolated from one case of infection in a laboratory worker.

Kununurra virus

Liehne C.G. *et al.* (1976) *Aust. J. exp. Biol. Med. Sci.* **54**, 499

A species in the family RHABDOVIRIDAE. Isolated in suckling mice from a pool of female mosquitoes *Aedeomyia catasticta* collected with chicken-baited traps at Kununurra in Western Australia. Not reported to infect man.

Kuru virus One of the SPONGIFORM ENCEPHALOPATHY VIRUSES. Causes a subacute progressive degeneration of the brain in man. The natural disease is restricted to a small area in the highlands of Papua New Guinea, centred round the Fore people. It appears to have been caused by ritual cannibalism of the dead. With the discontinuance of this practice the disease is disappearing. VERTICAL TRANSMISSION does not occur nor is the virus transmitted by suckling from a diseased mother. The virus has been transmitted by human brain extracts to chimpanzees, rhesus monkeys and 5 species of New World monkeys in which it caused progressive degeneration of the brain. Infectivity survives 80° with little fall in titre and some will survive 100°. Virus replicates in brain cell cultures without CPE. It has not been visualized probably because of its small size, indicated by extreme resistance to radiation.

K virus

Kilham L. & Murphy H.W. (1953). *Proc. Soc. exp. Biol. Med.* **82**, 133

Law M-F. *et al.* (1979) *J. Virol.* **30**, 90

A species in the genus POLYOMAVIRUS. A natural and probably silent infection of wild mice. Causes fatal pneumonia and sometimes liver lesions on injection into mice less than 10 days old. In mouse lung cell cultures, foci of transformed cells appear which produce tumours on injection into new-born or X-irradiated mice. Agglutinates sheep erythrocytes at room temperature or 37°.

K9 virus

Glaser R. *et al.* (1977) *J. natn. Cancer Inst.* **59**, 55

A strain of human cytomegalovirus isolated from a cell line derived from a tumour biopsy specimen from a patient with Kaposis sarcoma. Similar to Mj strain in producing a slow and incomplete CPE in human embryo lung cells.

Kwatta virus

A species of the family RHABDOVIRIDAE. The only member of the Kwatta antigenic group. Isolated from *Culex* sp. in Surinam. Not reported to cause disease in humans.

Kyasanur Forest disease virus

Bhat H.R. *et al.* (1979). *Indian J. med. Res.* **69**, 697 and following papers

Rajagopalan P.K. *et al.* (1968) *Indian J. med. Res.* (suppl.) **56**, 497

A tick-borne species in the genus FLAVIVIRUS. The vector is a *Haemaphysalis spingera.* In an epidemic among forest workers in Mysore state, India, in 1957, symptoms included headache, fever, back and limb pains, prostration, conjunctivitis, diarrhoea, vomiting and haemorrhages into the intestine and at other sites. No CNS involvement. A number of dead langurs and bonnet macaques were found during the epidemic and the disease may be disseminated by movement of monkeys and birds. Antibodies are present in small forest mammals. The virus is widely distributed in India, but human infections occur only in Mysore. Mice develop encephalitis on injection by various routes. They may fail to develop antibodies and remain chronically sick for long periods. Suckling hamsters are also susceptible but other rodents are resistant. Rhesus and bonnet monkeys develop VIRAEMIA on i/c or i/p injection but show no disease. No vaccine yet available.

laboratory strains Viruses which have been propagated in the laboratory *in vivo* or *in vitro*. They may be different in many properties from WILD STRAINS. *See* vaccine virus markers.

La Crosse virus

Hamdy El Said, L. *et al.* (1979) *Am. J. trop. Med. Hyg.* **28**, 364

A species in the genus BUNYAVIRUS, belonging to the CALIFORNIA ANTIGENIC GROUP. Isolated from the brain tissue of a woman with fatal meningoencephalitis, in Wisconsin,

U.S.A. during 1960. Between 1960 and 1970, 509 cases of human infection were reported, mainly in Wisconsin and Minnesota. Antibodies are found in small forest mammals, and virus can be isolated from mosquitoes of *Aedes* sp.

Lactate dehydrogenase virus A name suggested for lactic dehydrogenase virus because the enzyme lactic dehydrogenase is now named lact*ate* dehydrogenase.

Lactic dehydrogenase virus

Rowson K.E.K. & Mahy B.W.J. (1975) *Virology monographs* **13**

An RNA virus of mice, probably a species in the family TOGAVIRIDAE, infecting only species of *Mus*. Has been isolated from wild and laboratory mice *Mus musculus* in Europe, U.S.A. and Australia. *Mus caroli* can be infected experimentally. Causes a life-long infection with permanant VIRAEMIA but no disease. Infection recognized by abnormally high level of plasma lactic dehydrogenase. Certain other plasma enzyme levels are also raised in infected mice due to a failure to clear them from the circulation, probably as a result of impaired function of the reticulo-endothelial system. Antibodies are produced but infectious virus–antibody complexes continue to circulate. There is a minor degree of splenomegaly and certain immuno-pathological changes. Virus is found in all the body tissues, excreted in urine, saliva and faeces. Transmission between mice does not occur readily and probably results mainly from fighting, and possibly by blood-sucking parasites. Foetuses and young can be infected by a mother who becomes infected during pregnancy or lactation. Viral diameter 45 nm by filtration. VIRION spherical or oval, or possibly bottle-shaped, hence the proposed name LAGENAVIRUS. Detailed structure has not been determined. Infectivity destroyed on exposure to lipid solvents. Infective RNA can be extracted but its mol. wt. and strandedness is in doubt. Replication occurs in mouse cell cultures, probably best in macrophage cultures, but there is no CPE. Virus titration is possible only in mice.

SYN: enzyme elevating virus; lactate dehydrogenase virus; Riley virus.

Lagenavirus

Almeida J.D. & Mims C.A. (1974) *Microbios* **10**, 175

A name proposed for viruses which appear bottle-shaped on electron microscopy. The only one so far reported is LACTIC DEHYDROGENASE VIRUS.

Lagomorph herpesvirus Synonym for leporid herpesvirus 1.

Lagos bat virus

Shope R.E. (1970) *J. Virol.* **6**, 690

Tignor G.H. *et al.* (1973) *J. infect. Dis.* **128**, 471

A species in the genus LYSSAVIRUS. Antigenically related to, but distinguishable from, RABIES VIRUS. Isolated from a Nigerian fruit bat *Eidolon helvum* in 1956 at Lagos Island, Nigeria. Not known to cause disease in man. Pathogenic for adult mice, dogs and rhesus monkeys on i/c injection, but adult mice are not affected by i/p injection. Guinea pigs, rabbits and *Cercocebus torquatus* monkeys are not killed by peripheral inoculation.

La Joya virus An unclassified ARBOVIRUS. Isolated from *Culex dunni* in Panama. Not reported to cause human disease.

Landjia virus An unclassified ARBOVIRUS. Isolated from a bird *Riparia paludicola* in the Central African Republic. Not reported to cause disease in humans.

Langat virus A tick-borne species in the genus FLAVIVIRUS. Isolated from a pool of *Ixodes granulatus* ticks in Malaya. Antibodies found in forest ground-rats. Has low pathogenicity for mice and monkeys. Baby mouse brain cell cultures show loss of CONTACT INHIBITION, and the cells pile up. Cultivation in chick embryo fibroblasts causes attenuation and this virus protects mice against homologous and heterologous tick-borne flavivirus. In humans it has caused an antibody response but no disease, except in two leukaemia patients infected experimentally who developed encephalitis.

Langur retrovirus

Colcher D. *et al.* (1978) *Virology* **88**, 384

A species in the genus TYPE D ONCOVIRUS GROUP. An ENDOGENOUS VIRUS isolated from a langur *Presbytis obscuris* by CO-CULTIVATION of lung cells with bat or human cells. Antigenic properties and RNA GENOME suggest it is related to MASON-PFIZER MONKEY VIRUS but distinguishable from it.

Lanjan virus An unclassified ARBOVIRUS morphologically like BUNYAVIRUS but serologically unrelated to members of that genus. Belongs to the KAISODI ANTIGENIC GROUP. Isolated from the tick *Dermcentor auratus* in Malaya. Not reported to cause disease in humans.

Lapine parvovirus Synonym for rabbit parvovirus.

lapinized virus Virus adapted to rabbits. When RINDERPEST VIRUS is so adapted it ceases to be virulent for cattle.

Lassa virus of S.E. Africa

Wulff H. *et al.* (1977) *Bull. W.H.O.* **55**, 441

Similar to, but distinguishable from, LASSA VIRUS OF W. AFRICA. May be a strain of that virus or a separate species. Isolated from the field rat *Mastomys natalensis* in Mozambique, by injection of tissue homogenate i/c into suckling mice. Causes paralysis and death, unlike lassa virus of W. Africa. Not known to cause disease in humans. *M. natalensis* appears to be the natural host and may not be identical to the *M. natalensis* of W. Africa. SYN: Mozambique virus.

Lassa virus of W. Africa

Casals J. & Buckley S.M. (1974) *Prog. med. Virol.* **18**, 111

Porterfield J.S. (1977) *Recent Adv. clin. Virol.* **1**, 135

A species in the genus ARENAVIRUS. Causes a severe human disease in W. Africa (Nigeria, Liberia and Sierra Leone). Onset insidious: 4 days malaise, headache, fever, followed by severe limb and back pains, diarrhoea, vomiting and severe prostration greater than expected from degree of fever. Sore throat with white patches overlaid by red membrane. Low blood pressure. Temperature settles in 2 weeks. Infectivity survives 1 hour at 56°. Has been isolated from the field rat *Mastomys natalensis*, probably the only natural host, which comes into villages in the winter. Mild cases probably also occur in W. Africa, and close contact is probably required for case-to-case transmission. Human convalescent serum may be useful in treatment. Mice can be infected and produce antibodies, but develop no signs except that some adults on stimulation may have tonic convulsions. May be isolated in guinea pigs. Liver infection diagnosed by fluorescent antibody. Liver biopsy may show virus on EM. Replication in VERO CELLS can be detected by fluorescent antibody.

late genes Those segments of the viral NUCLEIC ACID whose TRANSCRIPTION rate becomes significant after replication of the GENOME has commenced.

Latent hamster virus

Hannoun C. *et al.* (1974) *Ann. Microbiol.* **125** A, 215

A species in the genus POLYOMAVIRUS. Has been isolated from the spleen and kidneys of normal European hamsters *Cricetus cricetus*. Causes fatal meningitis on i/c injection into new-born mice or golden hamsters *Mesocricetus auratus*. *See* hamster papilloma virus. SYN: hamster polyoma virus.

latent infection An infection in which infectious virus is not demonstrable until activated, as for example, HUMAN (ALPHA) HERPESVIRUS 1 infection of the dorsal root ganglia between episodes of 'cold sores'. It may be possible to demonstrate the presence of viral NUCLEIC ACID or other components in latently infected tissues, but the true molecular basis of latency is unknown.

Latent period The time between the disappearance of the infecting virus and the appearance of new virus in the *surrounding medium*. *See also* eclipse period.

Latent rat virus

Kilham L. & Oliver L.J. (1959) *Virology* **7**, 428

Siegl G. (1976) *Virology monographs* **15**

Salzman L.A. & Fabisch, P. (1978) *J. gen. Virol.* **39**, 571

Type species of the genus PARVOVIRUS. Belongs seriologically to RODENT PARVOVIRUS group 1. A natural and latent infection of rats. Causes an acute fatal enteritis on i/p injection into new-born hamsters or *Mastomys* sp. A smaller dose or given to slightly older hamsters results in stunted growth with abnormal development of teeth and skull bones. On i/c injection in new-born hamsters there may be cerebellar hypoplasia and ataxia. Infection in pregnant hamsters and rats may cause congenital abnormalities. Replicates in rat but not mouse cell cultures with CPE. Agglutinates guinea pig, hamster, human and rat erythrocytes at 23–24°. Does not spontaneously elute. Infected cells haemadsorb. SYN: Kilham rat virus; rat virus.

late proteins Proteins produced after the replication of the viral GENOME has commenced. They are mainly structural proteins of the virus particle.

Latino virus A species in the genus ARENAVIRUS. One of the AMERICAN HAEMORRHAGIC FEVER VIRUSES. Belongs to the TACARIBE ANTIGENIC GROUP. Isolated from a rodent *Calomys callosus* in Bolivia and Brazil. Not reported to cause disease in humans.

laurusin *See* formycin B.

L-132 cells (CCL 5) A heteroploid cell line derived from normal human embryonic lung. Reported to be a sensitive line for the primary isolation of ENTEROVIRUSES.

L cell virus

Botis S. *et al.* (1976) *J. Virol.* **20**, 690

Cultures of L cells (a line of mouse cells) release virus particles. These particles resemble C TYPE VIRUSES. On injection into new-born mice and hamsters no tumours were induced. Infection could not be transmitted to mouse or rat embryo cultures. A subline of L cells, A9, which is 8-azaguanine-resistant, also releases virus particles, but they induce morphological changes (foci) in mouse embryo fibroblast cultures. Focus formation was more efficient on N type than B type mouse cells.

leaky mutants Mutants which do not conform completely to the mutant characteristic: they have residual activity under the non-permissive condition. For example, a TEMPERATURE-SENSITIVE MUTANT which has some activity at the restrictive temperature.

Lebombo virus A species in the genus ORBIVIRUS, isolated from mosquitoes in S. Africa and Nigeria. Not reported to cause disease in humans.

Le Dantec virus An unclassified ARBOVIRUS. Isolated in Senegal from a girl with liver and spleen enlargement. Confined to W. Africa save for rare exceptions: a dock worker in Wales suffered a severe febrile illness after infection following an insect bite while unloading a cargo from W. Africa.

Lednice 110 virus Synonym for Yaba 1 virus.

Lenny virus

Burke A.T.C. & Dumbell K.R. (1972) *Bull. W.H.O.* **46**, 621

A species in the genus ORTHOPOXVIRUS. Isolated from a case of smallpox in a severely undernourished patient in Nigeria. Similar to VACCINIA VIRUS, producing mixed pocks on the CAM in 48 hours, and replicating in rabbit skin; though it does not produce pocks on the CAM above 38·5°. It is similar to BUFFALO POX VIRUS, but produces somewhat larger plaques in VERO CELL cultures.

Lentivirinae (Latin: *lentus* = slow)

Stowring L. *et al.* (1979) *J. Virol.* **29**, 523

A subfamily of the family RETROVIRIDAE. Cause slowly progressive disease of the CNS and/or lungs. Do not cause neoplasms but will transform cells in culture from which the virus can be rescued by CO-CULTIVATION. VISNA VIRUS, MAEDI VIRUS and PROGRESSIVE PNEUMONIA VIRUS belong in this subfamily.

lentogenic strains A term used to describe mild or avirulent virus strains.

Leporid herpesvirus 1 A species in the family HERPESVIRIDAE. A widespread silent infection of domestic rabbits. 'BLIND' PASSAGE of the virus in rabbits leads to increased virulence and the ability to produce pericarditis and encephalitis. Other species are not susceptible. There is replication in rabbit cell cultures, but the virus has not yet been grown in eggs.

SYN: herpesvirus cuniculi; virus III of rabbits; lagomorph herpesvirus 1; rabbit herpesvirus.

Leporid herpesvirus 2

Hinze H.C. & Chipman P.J. (1972) *Fedn Proc. Fedn Amer. Socs. exp. Biol.* **31**, 1639

A species in the family HERPESVIRIDAE. An indigenous virus of the cotton-tail rabbit *Sylvilagus floridanus* in which it causes a lymphoproliferative disease in the young in 6–8 weeks.

SYN: cotton-tail herpesvirus; Hinze virus.

Leporipoxvirus A genus in the subfamily CHORDOPOXVIRINAE containing viruses of leporids and squirrels. Infectivity is ether-sensitive. Species show serological cross-reactivity. Haemagglutinin not produced. Mechanical transmission by arthropods is common. Type species is MYXOMA VIRUS; other species are HARE FIBROMA VIRUS, RABBIT FIBROMA VIRUS and SQUIRREL FIBROMA VIRUS.

SYN: myxoma subgroup viruses.

Lethal intestinal disease of infant mice virus

Kraft L.M. (1962) *Science* **137**, 282

Hierholzer J.C. *et al.* (1979) *Infect. Immun.* **24**, 508

A CORONAVIRUS which causes a severe disease in infant mice. They do not suckle, lose weight, become lethargic and die after a short period of cyanosis. Older animals may have diarrhoea. The disease can be produced in day-old mice by feeding virus. Antigenically distinct from EPIDEMIC DIARRHOEA OF INFANT MICE VIRUS.

Leukaemia viruses

Beeman K.L. (1978) *Current Topics Microbiol. Immunol.* **79**, 73

Species of the genus TYPE C ONCOVIRUS GROUP. Isolated from many species of birds and mammals, the most extensively investigated being those from fowls, mice and cats. Do not transform cells in culture but will replicate in them. They cause leukaemia of various types, depending on the strain of virus and the strain of host animal, but usually have to be injected into new-born animals to induce the disease. The latent period before leukaemia develops may be several months. They act as HELPERS for sarcoma viruses, coding for the ENVELOPE of the sarcoma virus, i.e. PHENOTYPIC MIXING. Usually vertically transmitted, but can be passed between animals in close contact, especially in cats. There are intraspecies group-specific antigens (gs 1) and inter-species antigens (gs 3). There is no cross-reaction between the avian and mammalian gs antigens. They can be grouped by their virus envelope antigens and by their tropism for cells of a particular genotype: for example NIH Swiss (N tropic) and BALB/c (B tropic). Some passaged viruses are NB tropic. Avian virus differs from mouse and cat viruses in having prominent surface spikes. Strains vary in leukaemogenic potential, and infection with viruses of low virulence may protect against strains of high virulence.

Leukocyte-associated herpesvirus

Frank A.L. *et al.* (1973) *J. infect. Dis.* **128**, 618 and 630

Synonym for cercopithecid herpesvirus 6.

Leukosis-sarcoma virus group A group of viruses in the subfamily ONCOVIRINAE. In this group are the viruses inducing leukaemias and sarcomas in birds and mammals. No antigenic cross reaction between the avian and mammalian viruses but the latter share a group specific (gs 3) antigen. Morphologically C TYPE VIRUS PARTICLES. The sarcoma viruses can transform cells in culture whereas the leukaemia viruses do not, although they replicate in them. The sarcoma viruses are in general DEFECTIVE and require a leukaemia virus to provide information for an outer ENVELOPE. It thus has an envelope with surface specificities of the HELPER VIRUS, i.e. PHENOTYPIC MIXING.

Leukovirus An old name for a group of RNA tumour viruses now included in the family RETROVIRIDAE as the genus TYPE C ONCOVIRUS.

levamisole L-2,3,5,6,-tetrahydro-6-phenylimidazo (2,1-*b*)-thiazole. An anthelmintic drug which boosts cell-mediated immunity. Thus, while not a directly antiviral agent, it may alter the course of virus infection. Has been used in recurrent herpetic lesions of the skin, and in children with frequent respiratory disease. Common side effects are anorexia, diarrhoea, irritability, fatigue, nausea and skin rashes.
SYN: Ketarax

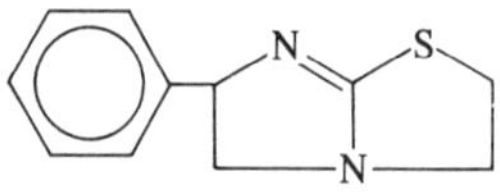

ligase *See* DNA ligase.

Lipovirus
Dunnebacke T.H. & William R.C. (1967) *Proc. natn. Acad. Sci. U.S.A.* **57**, 1363
Obtained during attempts to isolate and propagate the causal agent of human infectious hepatitis. Could be propagated, and caused changes in cells with which it was grown, but proved to be an amoeboid cell and not a virus. Similar to a Hartmannellid amoeba.

Lipovnik virus A species in the genus ORBIVIRUS and a member of the KEMEROVO ANTIGENIC GROUP. Isolated from the tick *Ixodes ricinus* in Czechoslovakia. Not known to cause disease in humans, but antibodies have been found in 18% of the inhabitants of Lipovnik.

Lipschütz bodies Intranuclear INCLUSION BODIES found in cells infected with HUMAN HERPESVIRUS 1, 2 OR 3.

Liverpool vervet monkey virus
Clarkson M.J. *et al.* (1976) *Arch. ges. Virusforsch.* **22**, 219
Synonym for cercopithecid herpesvirus 5.

LLC-MK$_2$ cells (CCL 7) A heteroploid cell line derived from a pooled suspension of cells from kidneys of six adult rhesus monkeys *Macaca mulatta*. Reported to be susceptible to a broad range of viruses, including species in the genera ENTEROVIRUS and RHINOVIRUS, and in the families ORTHOMYXOVIRIDAE and POXVIRIDAE.

LLC-RK$_1$ cells (CCL 106) An aneuploid epithelial-like cell line derived from pooled kidneys of several New Zealand white rabbits *Oryctolagus cuniculus* of undetermined sex. Susceptible to a number of viruses including RUBELLA, VACCINIA and HUMAN (ALPHA) HERPESVIRUS 1 and 2. Rubella virus grows to substantial titres.

LLC WRC 256 cells (CCL 38) A heteroploid cell line derived from a Walker rat *Rattus norvegicus* carcinoma maintained in adult Harlan-Wistar rats. Supports the propagation HUMAN (ALPHA) HERPESVIRUS 1 and 2, PSEUDORABIES VIRUS and VACCINIA VIRUS with CPE.

Lokern virus A species in the genus BUNYAVIRUS and a member of the BUNYAMWERA ANTIGENIC GROUP. Isolated from the hare *Lepus californicus*, rabbit *Sylvilagus auduboni*, mosquitoes *Culex tarsalis* and *Culicoides variipennis*, in Kern County, California, U.S.A. Not reported to cause disease in humans.

lollipops
Uhlenhopp E.L. *et al.* (1974) *J. molec. Biol.* **89**, 689
Abnormal particles of T-even bacteriophage produced in bacteria in the presence of the amino acid analogue canavanine.

Lone Star virus An unclassified ARBOVIRUS morphologically like BUNYAVIRUS but serologically unrelated to members of that genus. Isolated from the Lone Star tick *Amblyomma americanum*. Antibodies have been found in raccons. Found in Kentucky, U.S.A.

Louping-ill virus A tick-borne species in the genus FLAVIVIRUS. Causes disease in sheep, and less often, in cattle. The disease has two phases: in the first there is fever and VIRAEMIA,

and in the second several days later, incoordination of movement followed by paralysis and often death. The second phase may be absent and probably many infections are subclinical. Laboratory workers and men in contact with sheep may be infected, showing signs of severe meningitis and some encephalitis. Rodents, deer, shrews and red grouse may be naturally infected but without clinical disease. Injection i/c in mice causes encephalitis. Pigs can be infected but not guinea pigs or rabbits. Virus is present in Scotland, Ireland, N. and S.W. England. *Ixodes ricinus* is the vector and may also be the reservoir of infection. A formalinized vaccine is available for sheep and man.
SYN: ovine encephalomyelitis virus

L-R cells
Hanafusa H. & Hanafusa T. (1968) *Virology* **34**, 630
Leukosis virus-negative Rous cells. A name suggested for cells transformed by ROUS SARCOMA VIRUS which are not producing infective virus particles. They were formerly known as NON-PRODUCER CELLS but by electron microscopy can be seen to be producing virus particles indistinguishable from the infective ones. The term is not in common use.

LS virus A species in the genus PARVOVIRUS. A RODENT PARVOVIRUS of serological group 1. Isolated from a Wistar rat chloroleukaemic tumour. Serologically similar to LATENT RAT VIRUS but not pathogenic for new-born hamsters except when given i/c, when it may cause cerebellar hypoplasia and ataxia.

Lucké virus Synonym for ranid herpesvirus 1.

Lunkuni virus An unclassified ARBOVIRUS morphologically like BUNYAVIRUS but serologically unrelated to members of the genus. A member of the ANOPHELES A ANTIGENIC GROUP. Isolated from mosquitoes in Trinidad and in Belem, Brazil. Not associated with disease in humans.

Lumbo virus
Ozden S. & Hannoun C. (1978) *Virology* **84**, 210
A species in the genus BUNYAVIRUS belonging to the CALIFORNIA ANTIGENIC GROUP. Originally isolated from the mosquito, *Aedes pembaensis* in Mozambique. Antigenically indistinguishable from TAHYNA VIRUS but distinct from other members of the California antigenic group.

Lumpy skin disease virus A species in the genus CAPRIPOXVIRUS. Replicates in eggs and cell cultures of embryo calf and lamb, with CPE. Causes fever with multiple skin nodules and lesions in viscera of cattle in Africa. Virus attenuated by egg passage is used as vaccine.
SYN: neethling virus

Lungers virus Synonym for Jaagsiekte virus

Lu III virus
Soike K.F. *et al.* (1976). *Arch. Virol.* **51**, 235
A species in the genus PARVOVIRUS. Isolated from a line of human lung cells Lu 106, originating from Stockholm. Antigenically different from KBSH, RT and TVX VIRUSES. Can be maintained in HELA CELLS. Douglas chimpanzee cell line is highly susceptible. Agglutinates erythrocytes of the same species as H-1, H-2 and LATENT RAT VIRUS, but differs from these viruses in replicating in human cells and not in rodent cells. On passage in new-born hamsters becomes adapted and causes massive intestinal haemorrhage. In pregnant hamsters it cross the placenta, infects the foetuses and causes abortion.

Lymphocystis viruses
Weissenberg R. (1965) *Ann. N.Y. Acad. Sci.* **126**, 362
Several species in the family IRIDOVIRIDAE, varying in size from 300 to 130 nm. Lymphocystis is a common, chronic, but rarely fatal disease affecting fish of several of the higher orders. Tumour-like masses appear on the skin and fins, persist for long periods but ultimately regress. Outbreaks in the wild occur mainly in the summer. Parasites may help to spread the disease but the large lymphocystis cells with large inclusions burst in

water and may release infective virus. Transmission by implantation is possible, but may be difficult between species. The bluegill *Lepomia macrochirus* is a useful experimental subject. The viruses are ether-sensitive.

Lymphocytic choriomeningitis virus

Bro-Jorgenson K. (1978) *Adv. Virus Res.* **22**, 327

Lehmann-Grube F. (1971) *Virology Monographs* **10**

Cole G.A. & Nathanson N. (1974) *Prog. med. Virol.* **18**, 94

A species in the genus ARENAVIRUS. In sections VIRIONS are pleomorphic, 50–200 nm in diameter, consisting of a 2 layered ENVELOPE with thin projections and an interior containing electron-dense granules appearing at the time of budding from the cell surface. NUCLEIC ACID single-stranded RNA separable into 3 components of total mol. wt. $3{\cdot}5 \times 10^6$. Replicates on the CAM but no lesions are produced. Also replicates in chick, mouse, cattle and monkey cell cultures but CPE may only be seen on adaptation. In mouse cell cultures a persistent, non-cytolytic infection is established. Inhibited by ACTINOMYCIN D. Probably an inapparent infection in naturally infected house mice, but has been isolated from man, monkeys, dogs, field mice of *Apodemus* sp. hamsters and guinea pigs. When a colony of laboratory mice becomes infected, disease appears in young mice infected *in utero* but the infection soon becomes latent. In guinea pigs there is a generalized disease, often fatal, with patchy pneumonia. In man infection may be inapparent or an influenza-like fever; sometimes meningitis or meningo-encephalomyelitis may occur. Mice infected i/c develop tremors and have tonic convulsions in which they may die.

Lymphoid leukaemia viruses A name used for mouse leukaemia viruses, usually of low leukaemogenic potency, which may be separated from FRIEND or RAUSCHER LEUKAEMIA VIRUSES. They cause immunodepression and may also act as HELPER VIRUS for the other component of Friend virus.

Lymphoproliferative disease of turkeys virus

Yaniv A. *et al.* (1979) *J. Virol.* **30**, 351

A species in the subgenus AVIAN TYPE C ONCOVIRUS GROUP. Present in the blood of birds with lymphoproliferative disease, a leukotic condition occurring spontaneously in turkeys. There is splenomegaly, hepatomegaly, and infiltration of other organs and nerves with pleomorphic mononuclear cells. The disease is of economic importance as in 10–12 week old birds the mortality may exceed 20%. Can be transmitted by injecting the cell-free serum of diseased birds into young birds. Cross NUCLEIC ACID hybridization tests showed no sequence homology between the viral GENOME and that of MYELOBLASTOSIS VIRUS or AVIAN RETICULOENDOTHELIOSIS VIRUS.

Lymphoproliferative herpesvirus group Synonym for Gammaherpesvirinae.

Lyovac Cosmegen Trade name for a preparation of ACTINOMYCIN D, 0·5 mg with 20 mg of mannitol, in vials.

lysis from without Lysis due to absorption of a large number of bacteriophage particles to the surface of a bacterium. The cell is destroyed by leakage of cell contents.

lysogenic Having a PROPHAGE integrated into the bacterial GENOME. The prophage may become activated spontaneously or under the influence of certain stimuli, when it will replicate phage particles and destroy the cell, releasing infective BACTERIOPHAGE. Lysogenic bacteria may have certain properties determined by the prophage, such as diphtheria toxin production or antigens.

Lyssavirus

Brown F. *et al.* (1979) *Intervirology* **12**, 1

A genus of the family RHABDOVIRIDAE. Morphologically similar to species in the genus VESICULOVIRUS but antigenically distinct. Replicate in vertebrates and insects. The viral ENVELOPE may be formed within the cytoplasm or by budding from the plasma membrane.

VIRIONS agglutinate goose erythrocytes. There is serological cross-reaction between species. Type species RABIES VIRUS. Other species are DUVENHAGE VIRUS, KOTONKAN VIRUS, LAGOS BAT VIRUS, MOKOLA VIRUS and OBODHIANG VIRUS.

Lyssa virus Synonym for rabies virus.

Macaque monkey virus

Blakely G.A. *et al.* (1973) *J. infect. Dis.* **127**, 617

Synonym for cercopithecid herpesvirus 5.

Machupo virus A species in the genus ARENAVIRUS belonging to the TACARIBE ANTIGENIC GROUP. One of the AMERICAN HAEMORRHAGIC FEVER VIRUSES. Associated with human disease in Bolivia and the cause of Bolivian haemorrhagic fever which is often severe or even fatal. Haemorrhages occur, with rash, myalgia, CNS involvement and conjunctival inflammation. Sporadic outbreaks occur in the Beni region. The most notable of these affected 700 people in one town and there was 18% mortality. Transmission from man to man is unusual but does occur. The natural host is a rodent *Calomys callosus*. Experimental infection of guinea pigs causes subclinical infection, but in marmosets *Sanguinus geoffroyi* the infection is fatal.

SYN: Bolivian haemorrhagic fever virus.

Macropodid herpesvirus 1

Finnie E.P. *et al.* (1976) *Aust. vet. J.* **52**, 294

Webber C.E. & Whalley J.M. (1978) *Aust. J. exp. Biol. med. Sci.* **56**, 351

A species in the family HERPESVIRIDAE. Isolated from a culture of kidney cells of a Parma wallaby *Macropus parma*. The animal was one of a number with a fatal generalized disease taken from Kawan Island in Auckland Bay, New Zealand. The culture developed foci of CPE which extended rapidly. Experimental infection of Parma wallabies causes a severe generalized disease with lesions in lungs and liver. Antibodies are found in a wide range of marsupials from different parts of Australia. No CPE in bovine, mouse or hamster cells.

SYN: Parma wallaby herpesvirus.

Mad itch virus Synonym for suid (alpha) herpesvirus 1.

Madrid virus A species in the genus BUNYAVIRUS, belonging to the C GROUP VIRUSES. Isolated from a man with a febrile illness in Panama. Also isolated from SENTINEL mice in the same area, the mosquito *Culex vomerifer* and the spiny rat *Proechimys semispinosus*. Antibodies found in 3 of 96 humans but no further cases of disease reported.

Maedi virus (Icelandic: *maedi* = dyspnoea)

Cutlip R.C. & Laird G.A. (1976) *Am. J. vet. Res.* **37**, 1377

de Boer G.F. *et al.* (1979) *Res. vet. Sci.* **26**, 202

A species in the subfamily LENTIVIRINAE. Causes chronic pulmonary disease of sheep very similar to or the same as progressive pneumonia of sheep. Virus very similar to VISNA VIRUS. NUCLEIC ACIDS from the two viruses are indistinguishable. Occurs in Europe and America. Maedi and visna viruses probably represent the two ends of a spectrum: laboratory strains will cause maedi or visna in experimental animals, but in the wild maedi is much commoner. In flocks where maedi is occurring a few cases of visna will be found, and on postmortem of maedi cases changes in the brain of some animals will be seen to be typical of visna. *See also* progressive pneumonia virus.

SYN: chronic progressive pneumonia of sheep virus; Zwoegerziekte virus.

Maguari virus A species in the genus BUNYAVIRUS and a member of the BUNYAMWERA ANTIGENIC GROUP. Isolated from SENTINEL mice and mosquitoes in Brazil and from a horse in Guyana. Present also in Trinidad, Colombia and Argentina. Antibodies found in cattle, sheep and birds. Not reported to cause disease in humans.

Mahogany hammock virus A species in the genus BUNYAVIRUS belonging to the GUAMA

ANTIGENIC GROUP. Isolated from mosquitoes and a cotton-rat in Florida. Not known to cause disease in humans.

Main drain virus A species in the genus BUNYAVIRUS, belonging to the BUNYAMWERA ANTIGENIC GROUP. Isolated from the hare *Lepus californicus* and from *Culicoides variipennis*. Antibodies found in cattle, sheep and wild animals. The virus is found in Kern and Mendocino counties, California, U.S.A.

Makonde virus Synonym for Uganda S virus.

maladie de jeune age Synonym for distemper.

Malakal virus An unclassified ARBOVIRUS. With PUCHONG VIRUS forms the Malakal antigenic group. Isolated from the mosquito *Mansonia uniformis* in the Sudan. Not reported to cause disease in humans.

mal de los rastrojos (corn pickers' disease) A local name for JUNIN VIRUS infection.

Malignant aphtha virus A severe form of ORF VIRUS infection.

Malignant catarrhal fever virus Synonym for bovid herpesvirus 3.

Mammalian type C oncovirus group A subgenus of the genus TYPE C ONCOVIRUS GROUP. They have a common interspecies (gs-3) antigen on p30 and are divided into species of SARCOMA LEUKAEMIA VIRUS by their natural host, e.g. mouse, cat, monkey, etc. There are two types of cross-reacting antigens: those shared by strains of virus from one host species (gs-1 species-specific antigens) and those shared by different virus species from different mammalian hosts. There are two interspecies antigens a and b, both present in the mouse virus, but in the cat, pig, woolly monkey and RD114 VIRUSES there is only b. The sarcoma viruses have genetic information which, when integrated into a host cell causes TRANSFORMATION to a neoplastic cell, but they lack the information to make their COAT proteins and are thus DEFECTIVE, being unable to produce infective virus particles without the help of the leukaemogenic viruses. The HELPER VIRUS provides the coat proteins and thus determines the host range of the progeny sarcoma virus. Not all type C oncoviruses are oncogenic since they may lack the oncogene. The genetic information of C type oncoviruses, the VIROGENE, which may or may not contain the oncogene, is present in all the cells of many species of animal. These virogenes are transmitted with the cell genetic material. The virogene on activation can produce a virus which may or may not be oncogenic. The role of these viruses in the development of spontaneous tumours is not clear. Laboratory strains of C type oncoviruses replicate and produce much free virus: they are EXOGENOUS. In contrast, the integrated C type oncoviruses which only appear as virus particles on activation are ENDOGENOUS. When produced they may be detected by EM, by the presence of their DNA polymerase or other viral proteins, and by NUCLEIC ACID hybridization. They may be ecotropic (replicating only in the species of origin), xenotropic (unable to replicate in species of origin) or amphitrophic (can replicate in the species of origin and in other species). The mammalian type C oncoviruses of different species appear to differ in their mode of transmission, and in disease production.

Mammary tumour viruses A group of viruses in the genus TYPE B ONCOVIRUS GROUP. Mammary tumour-inducing viruses have been obtained from a number of species, but the best studied is the group of MOUSE MAMMARY TUMOUR VIRUSES. The VIRION is a B TYPE PARTICLE.

Manawa virus An unclassified ARBOVIRUS morphologically like BUNYAVIRUS but serologically unrelated to members of that genus. A member of the UUKUNIEMI ANTIGENIC GROUP. Isolated from the ticks *Argas abdussalami* and *Rhipicephalus* sp. in W. Pakistan. Not reported to cause disease in humans.

Manzanilla virus A species in the genus BUNYAVIRUS and a member of the SIMBU ANTIGENIC GROUP. Isolated from the howler monkey *Alouatta siniculus insularis* in Trinidad. Not associated with disease in humans.

Mapputta antigenic group viruses Morphologically similar to BUNYAVIRUS but unrelated antigenically to members of that genus. Isolated only from mosquitoes and only in Australia.

Mapputta

Maprik

Trubanaman

Mapputta virus An unclassified ARBOVIRUS morphologically like BUNYAVIRUS but serologically unrelated to members of that genus. Belongs to the MAPPUTTA ANTIGENIC GROUP. Isolated from *Anopheles meraukensis* in Queensland, Australia. Antibodies present in man, cattle, horses, pigs, kangaroos and rats. Not reported to cause disease.

Maprik virus An unclassified ARBOVIRUS morphologically like BUNYAVIRUS but serologically unrelated to members of that genus. Belongs to the MAPPUTTA ANTIGENIC GROUP. Isolated from mosquitoes in Sepik District of New Guinea. Not reported to cause disease in humans.

Marble bone disease virus Synonym for osteopetrosis virus.

marble spleen disease of pheasants A disease of pen-raised ring-necked pheasants. Young adult birds die after an inapparent or short illness due to pulmonary oedema. The spleen is enlarged with extensive necrosis and amyloidosis. A virus with the morphology of an adenovirus can be seen in the diseased tissue and extracted, but has not been replicated in cell culture. Related antigenically to TURKEY ADENOVIRUS strains TA-1 and TA-2.

Marboran Trade name for methisazone.

Marburger Affenkrankheit virus Synonym for Marburg fever virus.

Marburg fever virus An as yet unclassified RNA virus which may belong to the family RHABDOVIRIDAE but is morphologically not typical and serologically unrelated to other species in the family. Causes a severe and often fatal disease in man. Onset sudden with fever, head and limb pains, bradycardia, diarrhoea, vomiting and confused aggressive mental state. Cardiac and renal failure with haemorrhages develop. First reported in 1967 when 31 cases, 7 fatal, occurred in Germany and Yugoslavia, all traced to contact with tissue from a batch of African green monkeys *Cercopithicus aethiops*, trapped in Uganda. Five secondary cases occurred in hospital workers due to contact with blood from patients, and one case in which the virus was sexually transmitted 83 days after the initial illness. The virus appears to persist in the body for 2–9 months. A second outbreak occurred in 1975 involving one primary case, a man who hitch-hiked through Rhodesia, and two women who nursed him. The virus causes a uniformly fatal infection in guinea pigs and monkeys, and can be propagated in a variety of cell cultures such as VERO, BHK-21 and HELA. Diagnosis by EM of blood, or by inoculation of Vero cells which develop eosinophilic inclusions and antigen demonstrable by immunofluorescence. Virus is ether-sensitive and inactivated in 30 min at 56°. It has an outer ENVELOPE and is formed by budding through the cell membrane. There are two structural forms: filamentous and circular. Both have an overall diameter of 70–100 nm and contain an internal helix 40 nm in diameter. Some filaments may be several microns long. Natural reservoir unknown but probably not a primate. The case in Rhodesia had been handling insects and spiders. EBOLA VIRUS is morphologically similar but immunologically different.

SYN: green monkey virus; Marburger Affenkrankheit virus; vervet monkey disease virus.

Marchal bodies INCLUSION BODIES found in cells infected with ECTROMELIA VIRUS.

Marco virus

Monath T.P. *et al.* (1979) *Arch. Virol.* **60**, 1

A species in the family RHABDOVIRIDAE. Isolated from the lizard *Ameiva ameiva ameiva* in Para, Brazil. Pathogenic for new-born mice. Not reported to cause disease in humans. Replicates well with CPE in VERO CELLS at 30°. Not isolated from arthropods but considered to be arthropod-transmitted as it will replicate in experimentally infected mosquitoes.

Marcy virus

Gordon I. *et al.* (1947) *J. exp. Med.* **86**, 409

Obtained from a case of gastroenteritis in an outbreak in New York State. Could be passed in humans, causing anorexia, nausea, vomiting and diarrhoea. This virus is now lost, and hence can no longer be identified.

Mare abortion virus Synonym for equid (alpha) herpesvirus 1.

Marek's disease virus Synonym for gallid herpesvirus 1.

Maridi virus Caused an outbreak of severe fever with haemorrhages and high mortality in the area of Maridi and Nazara in the southern Sudan during 1976. Morphologically indistinguishable from MARBURG VIRUS, but serologically unrelated.

Marituba virus A species in the genus BUNYAVIRUS, and belonging to the C GROUP VIRUSES. Isolated from SENTINEL *Cebus* monkey and mouse in Para, Brazil. Also found in *Culex* sp. Has been associated with a febrile illness in man. Antibodies are frequent in arboreal opossums of *Caluromys* sp. and *Marmosa* sp. but not so common in forest-floor-dwelling rodents and marsupials.

marker rescue *See* reactivation.

Marmoset herpesvirus Synonym for cebid herpesvirus 1.

Marmur method of extracting DNA

Marmur J. (1961) *J. molec. Biol.* **3**, 208

After disruption of the cells, debris and protein are removed by denaturation and centrifugation. RNA is removed by RNase and the DNA selectively precipitated with isopropanol. Degradation of DNA is prevented, and divalent metal ions removed by the action of chelating agents and sodium lauryl sulphate.

Marsupial papilloma virus Synonym for marsupial pox virus.

Marsupial pox virus

Papadimitriou J.M. & Ashman R.B. (1972) *J. gen. Virol.* **16**, 87

Possibly a species in the family POXVIRIDAE. EM studies revealed the presence of poxvirus-like particles in the cytoplasm of cells in the stratum granulosum of papillomata on the dorsum of the tails of quokka *Setonix brachyurus*. The infected population of this marsupial has been isolated for 7,000 years on the small island of Rottnest off the coast of W. Australia.

SYN: marsupial papilloma virus; quokka pox virus.

Masern virus Synonym for measles virus.

Mason–Pfizer monkey virus Probably a TYPE D ONCOVIRUS. Isolated from a spontaneous mammary carcinoma in an 8-year-old rhesus monkey. Can be propagated in human and non-human primate cell cultures. Morphologically similar to MOUSE MAMMARY TUMOUR VIRUS but has no surface spikes. Is intermediate between B and C TYPE VIRUS PARTICLES. Antigenically unrelated to other members of the ONCOVIRINAE. Transforms rhesus foreskin cells in culture but injection into monkeys has not resulted in any mammary tumours. Strains have been isolated from placental tissues of normal rhesus monkeys and from HELA CELL lines. Approximately 20% of the viral genetic sequences are present in rhesus tissue as ENDOGENOUS PROVIRUS. Similar sequences are present in other Old World monkeys but not in RD 114 or SIMIAN SARCOMA VIRUS, or in the cell DNA of New World monkeys, apes of humans.

Mastadenovirus A genus in the family ADENOVIRIDAE comprised of the species isolated from mammals. They share a common antigen. The 12 vertex CAPSOMERES each have a single filament which varies in length in different species. GENOME mol. wt. $20–25 \times 10^6$. G+C CONTENT 48–61%. Many haemagglutinate. The type species is HUMAN ADENOVIRUS TYPE 2. There are many other species all taking their names from their host animal.

Mastomys natalensis papilloma virus

Muller H. & Gissmann L. (1978) *Med. Microbiol. Immunol.* **165**, 93

Muller, H. & Gissmann L. (1978) *J. gen. Virol.* **41**, 315

A species in the genus PAPILLOMAVIRUS. Causes spontaneous papillomas in the skin of inbred line 'GRA Giessen' of multimammate mouse *M. natalensis*. Crystalline arrays of virus particles are present in the upper layers of the thickened stratum granulosum. Antiserum can be prepared in rabbits.

Matariya antigenic group viruses Three unclassified ARBOVIRUSES isolated from birds in Africa:
Burg el Arab
Garba
Matariya

Matariya virus An unclassified ARBOVIRUS. The first member of the MATARIYA ANTIGENIC GROUP. Isolated from birds of *Sylvia* sp. in Egypt. Probably also present in Europe since the birds were viraemic on arrival in Egypt. Not reported to cause disease in the wild.

Matruh virus A species in the genus BUNYAVIRUS and a member of the TETE ANTIGENIC GROUP. Isolated from birds in Egypt and Italy. Not reported to cause disease in the wild.

Matucare virus An unclassified ARBOVIRUS, isolated from the tick *Ornithodoros boliviensis* in the San Joanquin area, Beni, Brazil. Antibodies found in bats. Not reported to cause disease in humans.

Mayaro virus

Casals J. & Whitman L. (1957) *Am. J. trop. med. Hyg.* **6**, 1004

A species in the genus ALPHAVIRUS. Isolated from man and mosquitoes in central and southern America. Associated with an epidemic febrile illness in man in Uruma colony, Bolivia. Antibodies are found in man and monkeys. Present in Surinam, Trinidad, Brazil, Colombia and Bolivia.

MC virus Synonym for Montgomery County virus.

MDCK (NBL-2) cells (CCL 34) A heteroploid cell line derived from the kidney of an apparently normal cocker spaniel.

Measles virus

Morgan E.M. & Rapp F. (1977) *Bact. Rev.* **41**, 636

A species in the genus MORBILLIVIRUS. A natural infection of humans causing measles, an acute febrile illness of children. Onset with prodromal symptoms of cough, coryza and conjunctivitis occurs about 10 days after infection. Prodromal stage 4–5 days, followed by mounting fever, the appearance of Koplik's spots on the buccal mucosa and rash on head and neck spreading to the trunk and limbs. Recovery usually rapid but the disease can be fatal, especially in poorly nourished children. The rash is dependent on the presence of a specific immune response and is absent from certain immunodeficient patients. The patient is most infectious in the prodromal period and transmission is by airborne droplets. Respiratory complications and otitis media due to secondary bacterial infection are common. Encephalitis occurs rarely but is a serious complication with high mortality and incidence of sequelae. Subacute sclerosing panencephalitis, a progressive degenerative disease of the CNS, is associated with chronic infection. VIRION ether-sensitive, roughly spherical, 150 nm in diameter, buoyant density in CsCl about 1·27 g/ml and contains a helical NUCLEOCAPSID of about 17×1100 nm. RNA mol. wt. 6×10^6. Measles virus is related antigenically to DISTEMPER and RINDERPEST VIRUSES and antibodies to them can be demonstrated in patients with measles. Virus haemagglutinates primate erythrocytes only and lacks NEURAMINIDASE. Isolation is easiest in primary human or monkey kidney cell cultures, but the virus can be adapted to growth in a number of cell lines or eggs. Multinuclear giant cells are formed, followed by gradual cell destruction. Changes are most easily seen in stained preparations. Monkeys are susceptible and develop a disease similar to that seen in man, but many monkeys have antibodies and are immune. Virus can be adapted to replicate in mice, ferrets and hamsters. Inactivated and attenuated virus vaccines have been used with success. The attenuated vaccine is recommended after age 1 in the U.K. Though subacute sclerosing panencephalitis can follow measles vaccine it is less likely to do so than after clinical measles. The vaccine appears to be protective whenever given.

SYN: masern virus; morbilli virus; rougeole virus; rubeola virus.

Medical Lake macaque herpesvirus

Blakely G.A. *et al.* (1973) *J. infect. Dis.* **127**, 617

Synonym for cercopithecid herpesvirus 5.

Medoc virus A species in the genus FLAVIVIRUS. Isolated from a mouse mammary gland in California. No known arthropod vector.

Melao virus A species in the genus BUNYAVIRUS, belonging to the CALIFORNIA ANTIGENIC GROUP. Isolated from mosquitoes in Trinidad, and Belem, Brazil. Not reported to cause disease in humans.

Mengo virus A strain of ENCEPHALOMYOCARDITIS VIRUS.

meractinomycin Synonym for actinomycin D.

Mermet virus A species in the genus BUNYAVIRUS, belonging to the SIMBU ANTIGENIC GROUP. Isolated from several different species of birds in Illinois and Texas, U.S.A. Not reported to cause disease in humans.

mesogenic strains Virus strains of average virulence; particularly used to describe strains of NEWCASTLE DISEASE VIRUS.

messenger RNA A single POSITIVE STRAND RNA molecule which carries the information to the RIBOSOMES to make protein. The positive strand of certain RNA viruses can act as mRNA and thus TRANSCRIPTION of the viral NUCLEIC ACID is not necessary.

methisazone

Pearson G.D. & Zimmerman E.F. (1969) *Virology*, **38**, 641

Fox M.P. *et al.* (1977) *Ann. N.Y. Acad. Sci.* **284**, 533

N-methyl-isatin-β-thiosemicarbazone. A synthetic antiviral agent. Mode of action unclear but apparently dependent upon presence of benzene ring and a side-chain containing sulphur. Inhibits TRANSLATION of late viral MRNA. Active in cell culture systems against poxviruses and adenoviruses. Used in the treatment of complicated vaccinia and

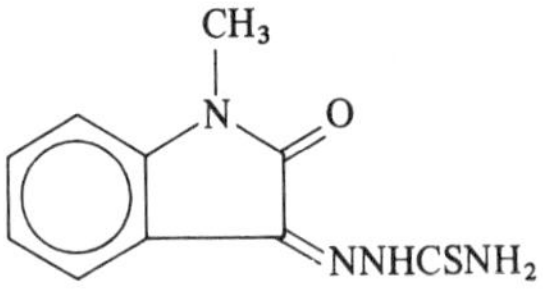

CH_3 N O $NNHCSNH_2$

in the prevention of smallpox, but the eradication of this disease and the change in vaccination policy has rendered the drug obsolete. Various HERPESVIRUSES and TYPE C ONCOVIRUSES are inactivated by extracellular contact with this drug, or with first transition series metals, of which Cu^{2+} is the most effective. Rapid contact inactivation of ARENAVIRUSES requires the presence of the drug and differing concentrations of $CuSO_4$. NEWCASTLE DISEASE VIRUS, VACCINIA VIRUS, VESICULAR STOMATITIS and HUMAN POLIOVIRUS are sensitive to both but not to the drug alone.

8-methoxypsoralen

Oill P.A. *et al.* (1978) *J. infect. Dis.* **137**, 715

A naturally occurring furocoumarin which has photosensitizing properties in the skin of guinea pigs and humans. Albino guinea pigs with cutaneous infection by HUMAN (ALPHA) HERPESVIRUS showed significant favourable response to treatment with this drug and long wave u.v. light. Treatment was effective even after virus multiplication had begun and lesions had appeared.

α-methyl-1-adamantane-methylamine hydrochloride *See* rimantadine hydrochloride.

methylene blue A photoreactive dye. *See* photodynamic inactivation.

N-methyl-isatin-β-thiosemicarbazone *See* methisazone.

1′-methyl spiro (adamantane-2,3′-pyrrolidine) maleate

Beare A.S. *et al.* (1972) *Lancet* **i**, 1039

A derivative of AMANTADINE. A double-blind trial of this drug against a placebo on volunteers infected with influenza virus A/Hong Kong/68 showed that the group receiving the drug, though not entirely protected, showed fewer clinical symptoms, antibody rises or virus secretions than those receiving the placebo. The drug was apparently non-toxic, and routine liver function tests at the end of each trial were uniformly normal.

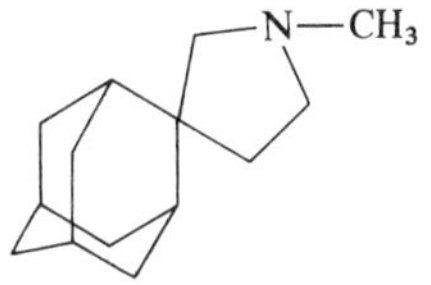

ME virus A strain of encephalomyocarditis virus.

MG virus

Lecarsas G. & Prozesky O.W. (1975) *Arch. Virol.* **47**, 393

Wright P.J. *et al.* (1976) *J. Virol.* **17**, 762

A species in the genus POLYOMAVIRUS. Isolated in primary human foetal fibroblasts, from the urine of a renal allograft patient in S. Africa. Resembles BK VIRUS in replicating in various human cells such as HEK and HEL and agglutinating both human and guinea pig erythrocytes at 4°. However, it may be antigenically distinct from BK and JC viruses. The virus aggregates in infected cells to form spherical masses which appear different from the aggregates of BK and JC VIRUS.

MH_1C_1 cells (CCL 144) A clonal strain of epithelial cells derived from a transplantable Morris hepatoma in a rat.

MH 2 virus Synonym for Mill Hill 2 virus.

microsomes Small particles 16–150 nm in diameter, obtained on cell fractionation. They are fragments of endoplasmic reticulum. On treatment with sodium deoxycholate they are disrupted into two fractions. The first contains most of the protein, phospholipid, pigment and enzymes. The second is a particulate fraction sedimentable at 100,000 ***g***, and containing nearly all the RNA of the cytoplasm. These are the ribosomes.

Middelburg virus

Kokernot R.H. *et al.* (1957) *S. Afr. J. med. Sci.* **22**, 145

A species in the genus ALPHAVIRUS. Isolated in S. Africa from *Aedes* sp. and may be the cause of an EPIZOOTIC in sheep. Found in S. Africa, Senegal, Central African Republic, Cameroon, Kenya and probably Mozambique and Angola. Not reported to cause disease in humans.

Milker's node virus A species in the genus PARAPOXVIRUS. Similar to ORF VIRUS. Causes hemispherical cherry-red papules on the udders of cows and the hands of milkers. Can be propagated in human cell cultures.

SYN: natural cow pox virus; paravaccinia virus; pseudo-cow pox virus.

Milk factor Synonym for Bittner virus.

Milk-pox virus Synonym for variola minor virus. *See* variola virus.

Mill Hill 2 virus

Hu S.S.F. *et al.* (1978) *Virology* **89**, 162

Hu S.S.F. & Vogt P.K. (1979) *Virology* **92**, 278

Alexander R.W. *et al.* (1979) *J. nat. Cancer Inst.* **62**, 359

A subspecies of the species CHICKEN LEUKOSIS SARCOMA VIRUS. Isolated from a 'globular tumour in the ovarian region' in a white leghorn chicken. Causes endotheliomas, leukaemia, kidney carcinomas, hepatocarcinomas in chickens, and haemorrhagic disease

in embryos. It is DEFECTIVE, lacking full function of the GAG, ENV, and POL GENES necessary for replication.
SYN: MH 2 virus.

Minatitlan virus A species in the genus BUNYAVIRUS. Not assigned to an antigenic group. Isolated from a SENTINEL hamster in Veracruz, Mexico. Not reported to cause disease in humans.

Minireovirus Synonym for minirotavirus.

Minirotavirus

Spratt H.C. *et al.* (1978) *J. Pediat.* **93**, 922
Middleton P.J. *et al.* (1977) *Am. J. Dis. Child.* **131**, 733

A name sometimes used for the 32 nm particles seen in faeces. Differ from other small round virus-like particles seen in faeces in being slightly larger.
SYN: minireovirus.

Mink cell focus-inducing virus

Hartley J.W. *et al.* (1977) *Proc. natn. Acad. Sci. U.S.A.* **74**, 789
Vogt M. (1979) *Virology* **93**, 226

A MOUSE TYPE C ONCOVIRUS, which is associated with the development of lymphomas in mice. Replicates in cell cultures of mouse and mink lung fibroblasts. Strains obtained from AKR mice produce cytopathic foci in mink cells but strains from BALB/C (MO) MICE cause foci in mink and mouse cells. The virus may have arisen by recombination between ecotropic and XENOTROPIC mouse viruses.

Mink endogenous type C RNA virus

Barbacid M. *et al.* (1978) *J. Virol.* **25**, 129

A species in the genus TYPE C ONCOVIRUS GROUP. After about 100 generations in culture the mink cell line MV1LU produced sedimentable REVERSE-TRANSCRIPTASE activity. This activity was the result of activation of virus endogenous to the mink cells. The DNA of normal mink cells had extensive NUCLEOTIDE sequence homology with the viral NUCLEIC ACID, demonstrating that the virus was an ENDOGENOUS VIRUS of mink.

Mink enteritis virus

Johnson R.H. (1967) *J. Small Anim. Pract.* **8**, 319

A species in the genus PARVOVIRUS, very similar or identical to FELINE PANLEUKOPENIA VIRUS.

Minnal virus An unclassified ARBOVIRUS. Isolated from *Culex vishnui* in Madras, India. Not known to cause disease in humans.

minus strand Synonym for negative strand.

Minute virus of canines

Binn L.N. *et al.* (1970) *Infect. Immun.* **1**, 503

A species in the genus PARVOVIRUS. Isolated from dog faeces in the Walter-Reed canine cell line. Causes CPE in this cell line but not in primary canine kidney or thymus cell cultures, or in cells of human, simian, porcine, bovine, feline or murine origin. Agglutinates rhesus monkey erythrocytes at 5° but not guinea pig, human, rat or pig erythrocytes. Antibodies are found in the blood of many dogs. It is probably non-pathogenic. Antigenically distinct from H-1 VIRUS, LATENT RAT VIRUS and MINUTE VIRUS OF MICE.
SYN: canine parvovirus.

Minute virus of mice

Crawford L.V. (1966) *Virology* **29**, 605
Siegl G. (1976) *Virology Monographs*, vol. 15
Bourguignon G.J. *et al.* (1976) *J. Virol.* **20**, 290

A species in the genus PARVOVIRUS. Belongs serologically to RODENT PARVOVIRUS group 4. Isolated from a mouse adenovirus preparation. A natural and probably silent infection in wild and laboratory mice. Multiplies on injection into new-born mice, rats and hamsters. In hamsters a disease similar to that caused by LATENT RAT VIRUS is produced

but in mice there is only retarded growth: in rats a silent infection. Replicates in rat or mouse embryo cell cultures with CPE. Agglutinates guinea pig, hamster, rat and mouse erythrocytes between 4 and 37°.
SYN: MVM virus.

Mirim virus A species in the genus BUNYAVIRUS. Not assigned to an antigenic group. Isolated from SENTINEL *Cebus* monkey, and from mosquitoes in Para, Brazil. Not reported to cause disease in humans.

missense mutants Mutants with an altered NUCLEOTIDE sequence which results in the production of proteins unable to perform their function normally.

Mitchell River virus A species in the genus ORBIVIRUS. With WARREGO VIRUS forms the Warrego antigenic group. Isolated from *Culicoides* sp. in Queensland, Australia. Antibodies found in cattle, wallabies and kangaroos. Not reported to cause disease in the wild.

Miyagawanella Synonym for Chlamydia.

Mj virus

Geder L. *et al.* (1976) *Science, N.Y.* **192**, 1134

A strain of human cytomegalovirus isolated from a cell line derived from prostate tissue of a young boy. Transforms human cells without prior inactivation of the virus.

MK virus

Rustigian R. *et al.* (1955) *Proc. Soc. exp. Biol. Med.* **88**, 8

Johnston P. (1961) *J. inf. Dis.* **109**, 1

Synonym for simian foamy virus.

MML virus Very similar to RIO BRAVO VIRUS. Isolated from bats of *Myotis* sp. in Montana, U.S.A.

MM virus A strain of ENCEPHALOMYOCARDITIS VIRUS.

MMV virus

Takemoto K.K. *et al.* (1974) *J. natn. Cancer Inst.* **53**, 1205

A strain of BK VIRUS. Isolated from a reticulum cell sarcoma of the brain of an 11 year old boy with Wiskott-Aldrich syndrome. Isolated by CO-CULTIVATION of brain tissue with human foetal brain cells.

Modoc virus A species in the genus FLAVIVIRUS. Found in California, Oregon, Montana and Colorado, U.S.A. Not known to cause human disease. Isolated from the deer mouse *Peromyscus maniculatus*.

Moju virus A species in the genus BUNYAVIRUS, and a member of the GUAMA ANTIGENIC GROUP. Isolated from SENTINEL mice and forest rats, also mosquitoes in Para, Brazil. Not reported to cause disease in humans.

Mokola virus

Tignor G.H. *et al.* (1973) *J. inf. Dis.* **128**, 471

Kemp G.E. *et al.* (1973) *Am. J. Epidemiol.* **98**, 43

A species in the genus LYSSAVIRUS. Antigenically related to but distinguishable from RABIES VIRUS. Isolated from a shrew of *Crocidura* sp. and from children with CNS disease in Nigeria. Experimental infection often fatal in shrews. Can be transmitted from shrews to mice by biting. Pathogenic for dogs and monkeys given i/c.

Molluscum contagiosum virus

Francis R.D. & Bradford H.B. (1976) *J. Virol.* **19**, 382

A species in the family POXVIRIDAE. An exclusively human infection. Lesions are confined to the skin. Incubation period 14 to 50 days. Pimples develop into nodules 2 mm in diameter which become pearly white and may develop an opening to reveal a white core. Lesions persist for months. Transmission by direct and indirect contact. Does not replicate in eggs but may be isolated from skin lesions in WI-38 CELLS. After passage in these cells it is reported to replicate in FL cells. Not inhibited by vaccinia, cow pox or fowl pox antiserum and does not reactivate heat-inactivated VACCINIA VIRUS. Not inactivated by ether or chloroform but inactivated by exposure to pH3. Causes CPE in

FL cells, and may be titrated by plaque assay. Does not haemagglutinate chick or human erythrocytes.

Moloney leukaemia virus A strain of mouse TYPE C ONCOVIRUS. Obtained from a mouse sarcoma S37. Produces lymphoid leukaemia in 2–3 months. Most active when injected into new-born mice. Also causes leukaemia in rats.

Moloney mouse sarcoma virus

Moloney J.B. (1966) *Natn. Cancer Inst. Monograph* **22**, 139

Isolated from a BALB/C mouse injected with MOLONEY LEUKAEMIA VIRUS. Appears to be a recombinant between the Moloney leukaemia virus and an ENDOGENOUS mouse Type C oncovirus. See TYPE C ONCOVIRUS GROUP and MOUSE SARCOMA VIRUS.

Monkey papilloma virus Synonym for simian papilloma virus.

Monkey pox virus

Cho C.T. & Wenner H.A. (1973) *Bact. Rev.* **37**, 1

Zuckerman A. & Rondle C. (1978) *Nature, Lond.* **276**, 212

A species in the genus ORTHOPOXVIRUS. Has caused outbreaks of disease in captive monkeys, most commonly in cynomolgus and the rhesus monkeys. The animals are not seriously ill except occasionally the very young. Little is known about the infection in the wild, and the natural host is not established. May be isolated from apparently normal monkeys. Isolated from captive monkeys, and from about 36 cases of human disease in W. and Central Africa, 6 of which were fatal. Mortality rate similar to that in VARIOLA VIRUS infections and the disease is similar, but transmission to human contacts is infrequent. Very similar to VACCINIA but pocks on the CAM may have haemorrhagic centres at 34·5° and are not produced above 39°. Inoculation of rabbit skin produces an indurated lesion with purple centre. Adult mice susceptible. Replicates in various cell cultures but CPE variable.

Mono Lake virus A species in the genus ORBIVIRUS and a member of the KEMEROVO ANTIGENIC GROUP. Isolated from the tick *Argas cooleyi* in California, U.S.A. Similar virus isolated from the same species in a swallow's nest in Texas, U.S.A. Not reported to cause disease in humans.

Montana myotis leukoencephalitis virus A species in the genus FLAVIVIRUS. Isolated from a paralysed little brown bat *Myotis lucifugus* in Western Montana, U.S.A. Not known to cause disease in humans.

Montgomery County virus

Thornhill T.S. *et al.* (1977) *J. inf. Dis.* **135**, 20

An unclassified FAECAL VIRUS type 1. Observed by EM in the faeces in a family outbreak of gastroenteritis in Montgomery County, Maryland, U.S.A. Antigenically related to NORWALK VIRUS.

SYN: MC virus.

Morbillivirus (Latin: *morbillus*, diminutive of *morbus* = disease).

Kingsbury D.W. *et al.* (1978) *Intervirology* **10**, 137

A genus of the family PARAMYXOVIRIDAE. Viral ENVELOPE contains haemagglutinin but not NEURAMINIDASE. NUCLEOCAPSID about 18 nm in diameter, with helical pitch of 5–6 nm. All species contain a common antigen, but are readily distinguishable. Type species MEASLES VIRUS. Other species are KATA, DISTEMPER and RINDERPEST VIRUSES.

Morbilli virus Synonym for measles virus.

Moriche virus A species in the genus BUNYAVIRUS and a member of the CAPIM ANTIGENIC GROUP. Isolated from *Culex amazonensis* in Trinidad. Not reported to cause disease in humans.

Mossman virus

Cambell *et al.* unpublished observation reported by Jun M.H. (1977) *Aust. J. exp. Biol. med. Sci.* **55**, 645

A species in the genus PARAMYXOVIRUS. A rodent virus.

Mossuril virus A species of the family RHABDOVIRIDAE. With KAMESE VIRUS forms the Mossuril antigenic group. Isolated from *Culex* sp. in S. Africa, Central African Republic and Mozambique. Not reported to cause disease in humans.

Mount Elgon bat virus A species of the family RHABDOVIRIDAE, isolated from a bat in Kenya. VIRIONS larger than most rhabdoviruses (mean = 226 nm). Propagated in new-born mouse brain, but not in cell cultures. Not reported to cause disease in humans.

Mouse cytomegalovirus Synonym for murid (beta) herpesvirus 1.

Mouse encephalomyelitis virus

Lipton H.L. (1975) *Infect. Immun.* **11**, 1145

A species in the genus ENTEROVIRUS. A common and usually inapparent infection of laboratory and wild rodents. Occasional animals develop flaccid paralysis of the hind limbs. Injection of mice i/c may produce flaccid paralysis after 12–29 days. Mice injected with the virus and recovering may later develop demyelinating disease. Mice from a colony free of infection respond more regularly to injection. Replicates in mouse kidney cell cultures, and after adaptation, produces CPE. Strains vary in the cells in which they will replicate. There are several strains: TO, FA, and GD I–VII; FA and GD VII on i/m injection produce local myositis in mice. FA causes encephalitis. FA and GD VII are antigenically related. There may be some antigenic crossing with TO and GD VII.

Mouse hepatitis virus

Piazza M. *Experimental Viral Hepatitis*. Springfield, Illinois: C.C. Thomas (1969)

Lai M.M.C. *et al.* (1978) *J. Virol.* **26**, 236

A species in the genus CORONAVIRUS. Serologically related to RAT CORONAVIRUS and SIALODACRYOADENITIS VIRUS of rats. Often a silent infection of laboratory mice which may be activated by passage of other viruses such as leukaemia virus, or by cortisone, urethane or enterotoxin from gram-negative bacteria, or by thymectomy. Injection of virus into mice infected with the parasite *Eperythrozoon coccoides* usually produces fatal hepatitis but in its absence there is often no disease. Neurotropic strains infect cotton-rats and hamsters when given i/c. All strains are antigenically similar but vary in pathogenicity, and have been numbered 1–4. Type 1 was the original isolate. Type 2 was activated on mouse leukaemia passage in Princeton mice and produced hepatitis in the absence of *E. coccoides*. Type 3 is also pathogenic for weanling mice in the absence of *E. coccoides*, and causes ascites in older mice. Type 4 causes encephalomyelitis with demyelination and some focal liver necrosis in mice. Virus is present in excreta and highly infectious. Transplacental transmission has not been demonstrated. NUCLEIC ACID is single stranded RNA of mol. wt. $5{\cdot}4 \times 10^6$, which is a POSITIVE STRAND.

SYN: murine coronavirus; murine hepatitis virus.

Mouse leukaemia virus *See* mouse type C oncovirus.

Mouse mammary tumour virus

Morris V.L. *et al.* (1979) *Virology* **92**, 46

Cohen J.C. & Varmus H.E. (1979) *Nature, Lond.* **278**, 418

A species in the genus TYPE B ONCOVIRUS GROUP. There are a number of EXOGENOUS strains (laboratory strains) transmitted via the milk as well as ENDOGENOUS VIRUSES demonstrable after the milk-transmitted virus has been eliminated by foster nursing. As there is no agreed nomenclature, strains are probably best named after the mouse strain from which they were isolated. Often a letter is appended, e.g. MTV-S (S for standard). Other letters are L for low oncogenicity (this was formerly described as nodule-inducing virus and designated NIV), P for plaque-inducing, O for overlooked, and X or Y for irradiation-induced. The endogenous virus will often fail to infect the strain of mouse from which it came, but will infect other strains. Can be propagated in cultures of mammary tumour tissue though the cells often lose their ability to produce mammary tumour virus and start to produce C TYPE VIRUSES. Attempts to infect normal cells in culture have not been very successful. There are 3 classes of laboratory mice (1) those that receive infectious virus in their mothers milk, do not produce antibodies and have a high incidence of tumours, (2) those that do not receive virus in their milk but have an intermediate tumour incidence, presumably due to endogenous virus expression, and (3) those that neither express virus nor develop tumours. The endogenous mammary tumour virus DNA appears to be distributed between at least 3 separate chromosomes.

Mouse papule agent (MPA)

Kraft L.M. & Moore A.E. (1961) *Z. Versuchstierk.* **1**, 66

An unidentified infective agent in mice, causing a self-limiting lesion which heals with no obvious sequelae. The condition can be serially transmitted by injection of extracts of lesions, and there is an incubation period of 4–5 days. Eosinophilic inclusion bodies appear in the cytoplasm of epidermal cells. Infectivity passed a 450 nm Millipore membrane or a Selas 03 filter in 2 of 5 attempts. After 1 hour at 37°, 99% of infectivity is lost. Mice with healed papular lesions are more resistant to challenge with MPA than are controls, though their sera do not neutralize VACCINIA VIRUS. Rabbit anti-vaccinia serum does not neutralize MPA. Mice vaccinated against ECTROMELIA VIRUS are as susceptible to MPA as are controls. Mouse papule agent has neither been visualized nor cultured.

Mouse poliovirus Synonym for mouse encephalomyelitis virus.

Mouse pox virus Synonym for ectromelia virus.

Mouse sarcoma virus

Maisel J. *et al.* (1977) *Virology* **76**, 295

A member of the ecotropic subspecies of MOUSE TYPE C ONCOVIRUS. There are a number of strains, HARVEY, MOLONEY, KIRSTEN, GAZDAR and FBJ OSTEOSARCOMA VIRUS with slightly different properties. They induce sarcomas in mice after a latent period of only a few days and transform fibroblasts in cell culture, but are unable to produce infective progeny virus in the absence of a MOUSE LEUKAEMIA VIRUS which acts as a HELPER. The Harvey and Kirsten strains cause marked erythroblastic splenomegaly and progressively growing sarcomas. The Moloney strain does not affect the erythroid cells and the tumours which it induces usually regress except in very young or immunosuppressed mice.

Mouse thymic virus Synonym for murid herpesvirus 3.

Mouse-tropic strain Synonym for ecotropic murine type C virus.

Mouse type C oncovirus

Rich M.A. & Siegler R. (1967) *Ann. Rev. Microbiol.* **21**, 529

Pasternak G. (1969) *Adv. Cancer Res.* **12**, 1

Stockert E. *et al.* (1979) *J. exp. Med.* **149**, 200

A species of the subgenus MAMMALIAN TYPE C ONCOVIRUS GROUP. There are many strains and all mice probably carry one or more. The first strain was isolated from AKR mice by Gross. Strains can be grouped by their ENVELOPE antigens or the antigens they induce on the surface of infected cells. They vary in the type of leukaemia they induce, but this also depends on the strain and age of the host animal. The Gross, Moloney and Kaplan strains injected into new-born mice cause thymus-dependent lymphocytic leukaemia. Friend and Rauscher strains injected into adult mice cause splenomegaly and erythroblastic leukaemia. Sarcoma-inducing strains can transform cells in culture but are DEFECTIVE for virus replication, requiring a HELPER leukaemogenic virus to provide information for the viral COAT proteins. Laboratory strains and EXOGENOUS VIRUSES are transmitted mainly via the milk, but in nature the ENDOGENOUS VIRUS probably passes to the young via the egg or sperm. There are three subspecies: (1) ECOTROPIC MURINE TYPE C VIRUSES, the laboratory strains of exogenous leukaemia and sarcoma inducing virus. Members of this subspecies show reciprocal viral interference, (2) XENOTROPIC MURINE TYPE C VIRUSES and (3) AMPHOTROPIC MURINE TYPE C VIRUSES.

SYN: murine leukaemia virus.

Mozambique virus Synonym for lassa virus of S.E. Africa.

M'Poko virus An unclassified ARBOVIRUS morphologically like BUNYAVIRUS but serologically unrelated to members of that genus. A member of the TURLOCK ANTIGENIC GROUP. Isolated from *Culex* sp. near Bengui, Central African Republic. Not reported to cause disease in humans.

MS-1 virus

Feinstone S.M. *et al.* (1973) *Science, N.Y.* **182**, 1026

Krugman S. & Giles J.P. (1970) *J. Am. med. Ass.* **212**, 1019

A strain of HEPATITIS A VIRUS. Demonstrated in the sera of hepatitis patients by inoculation into normal human volunteers, in whom the disease could be passaged.

MTV-S virus Synonym for Bittner virus.

Mucambo virus

Scherer W.F. & Pancake B.A. (1970) *Am. J. Epidemiol.* **91**, 225

A species in the genus ALPHAVIRUS, closely related and perhaps a serological type of VENEZUELAN EQUINE ENCEPHALOMYELITIS VIRUS. Isolated from man, rodents, birds and mosquitoes in São Paulo, Para, Brazil; and Trinidad, Surinam and French Guiana. Causes a febrile illness with headache and myalgia in humans.

Mucosal disease virus Synonym for pestivirus diarrhoea virus.

Mudjinbarry virus

Doherty R.L. *et al.* (1978) *Aust. J. Biol. Sci.* **31**, 97

A species in the genus ORBIVIRUS antigenically related to WALLAL VIRUS. Isolated from midges collected in the Northern Territory of Australia. Antibodies have been found in 5 of 30 wallabies, 2 of 12 dingoes, 1 of 30 domestic fowl and in 1 of 53 human sera tested. Not known to cause disease.

Muhlbock virus A highly oncogenic strain of MOUSE MAMMARY TUMOUR VIRUS isolated from GR mice. Also known as GR virus or MTV-P. Differs from other strains of high oncogenicity in being transmitted via the eggs and sperm.

multicomponent viruses

Reijnders L. (1978) *Adv. Virus Res.* **23**, 79

Viruses in which the complete viral GENOME is not present in a single virus particle but is divided between two or more particles. The partial genomes present in separate particles are not completely overlapping. The mixture of particles can replicate but the individual particles cannot. DEFECTIVE VIRUSES and HELPER VIRUSES are thus excluded. There are many examples among the small RNA viruses of plants.

multipartite viruses Synonym for multicomponent viruses.

Multiple sclerosis virus *See* carp virus.

multiploid virus

Simon E.H. (1972) *Prog. med. Virol.* **14**, 36

Virus containing a population of particles, most of which contain a variable number of GENOMES. The number of genomes per particle may depend on the host cell and other cultural conditions, but is independent of the number of genomes contained by the infecting virus, i.e. it is not a genetically determined characteristic.

Mumps virus A species in the genus PARAMYXOVIRUS. A human infection commonly causing fever and parotitis, and occasionally meningo-encephalitis, orchitis, oophoritis or pancreatitis. Incubation period 18–21 days. Virus present in saliva and urine. Patients are infectious 6 days before onset and for 9 days after. Rhesus monkeys are susceptible and develop a similar disease to that seen in humans. Virus can be adapted to hamsters, mice and rats. Isolation is by amnion inoculation, when it takes 4–5 days, or in primary monkey kidney or human cell lines. Multiplication is recognized by syncytia formation or HAEMADSORPTION. Human and fowl erythrocytes are agglutinated. VIRION diameter 150 nm. NUCLEOCAPSID helical with 50S single-stranded RNA. There are 2 CF antigens:

'S' associated with the nucleocapsid and 'V' with the ENVELOPE. Antibodies to 'S' appear first and disappear more rapidly than those to 'V'. Cross-reactions may occur with NEWCASTLE DISEASE and PARAINFLUENZA VIRUSES 1–4.

Murid (beta) herpesvirus 1

Moon H.M. *et al.* (1979) *J. gen. Virol.* **42**, 159

A species in the family HERPESVIRIDAE. A probably ubiquitous SILENT INFECTION of wild mice but present in a minority only of laboratory stocks. Young uninfected mice can be infected by any route, the virus localizing in the salivary glands, in which tissue alone is serial passage possible. Large doses of virus given i/p will kill in 4–7 days. Small doses produce focal hepatitis. Infection of pregnant mice causes foetal infection. Replication occurs in primary mouse fibroblasts with focal CPE in 9–12 days. Virus is released into the medium much more freely than with most CYTOMEGALOVIRUSES.

SYN: mouse cytomegalovirus.

Murid herpesvirus 1 Synonym for murid (beta) herpesvirus 1.

Murid herpesvirus 2

Ashe W.K. (1969) *J. gen. Virol.* **4**, 1

A species in the family HERPESVIRIDAE. Present in the salivary glands of rats and can cause abortion in laboratory rats. Agglutinates rabbit erythrocytes at 4°.

SYN: rat cytomegalovirus, rat submaxillary gland virus.

Murid herpesvirus 3 (number assigned by us)

Houba V. *et al.* (1976) *J. Immunol.* **117**, 635

A species in the family HERPESVIRIDAE. Injection into new-born mice produces extensive necrosis of the thymus resulting in profound suppression of immunological functions mediated by T-cells. However, some T-cell functions such as thymic cell reaction to mitogens appear to be spared, suggesting that virus selectively destroys sub-populations of T-cells. The virus can be obtained from homogenates of mouse thymus during the acute phase of infection. In adult mice there is chronic infection of the salivary glands without cell necrosis. Replication in cell cultures has not been reported, but the virus can be obtained from homogenates of mouse thymus during the acute phase of infection.

SYN: mouse thymic virus.

Murine adenovirus

Van der Veen J. & Mes A. (1974) *Arch. ges. Virusforsch.* **45**, 386

A species in the genus MASTADENOVIRUS. At least 2 serotypes are described. Usually a SILENT INFECTION of mice but may be fatal on injection into new-born mice. Excretion of virus in the urine can continue for a long time. Multiplies with CPE in mouse embryo cell cultures but not in mouse cell lines or rat, monkey or human cells. Some strains do not agglutinate erythrocytes of human, monkey, rabbit, guinea pig, mouse, etc.

Murine coronavirus Synonym for mouse hepatitis virus.

Murine enteroviruses Two species are included under this heading. Each contains a number of strains. (1) ENCEPHALOMYOCARDITIS VIRUS which is a species in the genus CARDIOVIRUS. (2) MOUSE ENCEPHALOMYELITIS VIRUS which is a species in the genus ENTEROVIRUS.

Murine hepatitis virus Synonym for mouse hepatitis virus.

Murine leukaemia virus Synonym for mouse type C oncovirus.

Murine papovaviruses *See* K virus *and* polyoma virus.

Murine polioencephalomyelopathy virus

Brooks B.R. *et al.* (1979) *Infect. Immun.* **23**, 540

An ecotropic strain of MURINE TYPE C VIRUS. Causes a non-inflammatory spongiform degeneration of the CNS which results in paralysis of the limbs. The condition occurs spontaneously in wild mice between the ages of 7 and 18 months. It can be produced in Swiss but not BALB/c (Mo) mice by i/c injection of virus when they are less than 24 hours old. The incubation period is dose-dependent and can be as short as 3 weeks.

SYN: polioencephalomyelopathy of mice virus.

Murivirus Synonym for human rhinovirus.

Murray Valley encephalitis virus A species in the genus FLAVIVIRUS. Natural host probably a bird. The vector is *Culex annulirostris*. Occurs in Northern Territory and Queensland, Australia, and in Papua. After the spring rains the virus is carried south to Victoria, New South Wales and South Australia. In man it causes a mild fever and in some cases encephalitis. There may be troublesome sequelae. Epidemics occur and children are most often infected. Horses may be infected but do not develop encephalitis. Encephalitis follows i/c injection in mice, hamsters, monkeys, sheep and chicks. Rabbits, guinea pigs and birds usually only have VIRAEMIA. Antibody is present in the yolk of eggs laid by infected birds. Virus replicates in eggs, producing pocks on the CAM.
SYN: Australian X-disease virus.

Murutucu virus A species in the genus BUNYAVIRUS and a member of the C GROUP VIRUSES. Has been associated with a febrile illness in man. Isolated from a SENTINEL *Cebus* monkey and mice in Para, Brazil. Has also been isolated from the rodents *Nectomys squamipes* and *Proechimys guyannensis*, the opossums *Didelphis marsupialis* and *Marmosa* sp., and mosquitoes of *Culex* sp.

Mus caroli type C oncovirus

Lieber M.M. *et al.* (1975) *Proc. natn. Acad. Sci. U.S.A.* **72**, 2315

A species in the subgenus MAMMALIAN TYPE C ONCOVIRUS GROUP. An ENDOGENOUS xenotropic C TYPE VIRUS. Found in a cell line derived from the Asian mouse *Mus caroli*, on treatment with BROMODEOXYURIDINE. The REVERSE TRANSCRIPTASE and p30 antigen are more closely related to the WOOLLY MONKEY TYPE C and GIBBON APE TYPE C VIRUSES, than to laboratory mouse viruses.

Mus cervicolor mammary tumour virus

Schlom J. *et al.* (1978) *J. natn. Cancer Inst.* **61**, 1509

A species in the genus TYPE B ONCOVIRUS GROUP. The major ENVELOPE glycoprotein and internal protein are antigenically related to the equivalent proteins in mouse mammary tumour virus. Obtained from the milk. Distinct from MUS CERVICOLOR TYPE C ONCOVIRUSES.

Mus cervicolor type C oncoviruses

Benveniste R.E. *et al.* (1977). *J. Virol.* **21**, 849

Callahan R. *et al.* (1977) *Virology* **80**, 401

Species in the subgenus MAMMALIAN TYPE C ONCOVIRUS GROUP. Isolated from a lung cell line of *Mus cervicolor* cells by treatment with BROMODEOXYURIDINE and CO-CULTIVATION with heterologous cell lines. Two viruses CERV-CI and CERV-CII, and endogenous multiple copies are present in the cellular DNA. CERV-CI replicates in SIRC rabbit cell line and is antigenically related to SIMIAN SARCOMA VIRUS, SIMIAN SARCOMA-ASSOCIATED VIRUS and to the GIBBON APE TYPE C ONCOVIRUS. CERV-CII replicates in *Mus musculus* cell lines. It is related to, but different from, mouse leukaemia viruses of *Mus musculus*. A third virus, M432 is an ENDOGENOUS VIRUS unrelated by morphology, antigenicity or molecular HYBRIDIZATION to other retroviruses except MUS CAROLI TYPE C ONCOVIRUS.

M virus Synonym for cebid herpesvirus 1.

Mv 1 Lu (NBL-7) (CCL 64) A cell line derived from the trypsinized lungs of several nearly full-term unsexed foetuses of the Aleutian mink *Mustela vison*.

MVM virus Synonym for minute virus of mice.

mycoviruses

Hollings M. (1978) *Adv. Virus Res.* **22**, 2

Viruses which replicate in the cells of fungi.

Myeloblastosis-associated virus A name suggested for the AVIAN MYELOBLASTOSIS VIRUSES (AMV) 1 and 2, which are present in 'standard' AMV but are not leukaemogenic. They are CHICKEN LEUKOSIS SARCOMA VIRUSES with surface properties of subgroup A and B respectively. Cause osteopetrosis on injection into day-old chicks.

Myxoma subgroup viruses Synonym for leporipoxvirus.

Myxoma virus The type species of the genus LEPORIPOXVIRUS. Similar to VACCINIA VIRUS but rather more sensitive to inactivation by heat. Ether-sensitive but resistant to sodium desoxycholate. Antigenically similar to RABBIT FIBROMA VIRUS and CALIFORNIA RABBIT FIBROMA VIRUS, yet diffusion tests show a difference. Produces pocks on the CAM, but eggs are 2·5 times less sensitive than rabbit skin. Replicates and produces CPE in tissue culture of rabbit, rat, hamster and human cells; also in cells of other species. Exists naturally in Uruguay and Brazil as a silent or mild infection of wild rabbits *Sylvilagus brasiliensis.* Introduced into wild *Oryctolagus* rabbits it causes at first a severe disease, 99% fatal, with inflammation and swelling of the eye-lids, nose, genital and anal openings. With passage the disease becomes endemic and less severe due to selection of resistant rabbits and ATTENUATED STRAINS of the virus. Hares *Lepus* sp. are rarely naturally infected. The virus has been propagated in suckling mouse brain. Transmission is by contact and by insects, mosquitoes in S. America and Australia, fleas in Britain. Rabbits can be protected by vaccination with rabbit fibroma virus.

Myxovirus multiforme A latinized name for NEWCASTLE DISEASE VIRUS, based on the multiformity of both the disease picture and the virus particles.

Myxovirus pestis-galli *See* influenza virus A avian.

NAD Nicotinamide adenine dinucleotide. An old name for diphosphopyridine nucleotide, DPN, coenzyme 1 or cozymase.

$NADH_2$ Reduced NAD.

Nagata strain of faecal virus A strain of virus found in Japan, probably related to NORWALK VIRUS.

Nairobi sheep disease antigenic group viruses All tick-borne. All cause disease in humans. Morphologically similar to BUNYAVIRUS but antigenically unrelated to members of that genus.

Nairobi sheep disease (I,H)
Ganjam (C,I,H)
Dugbe (C,I,Cu,H)

Isolated from:
(I) Ixodid ticks
(C) Culicine mosquitoes
(Cu) Culicoides
(H) Humans

Nairobi sheep disease virus

Davies F.G. *et al.* (1978) *J. comp. Path.* **88**, 519

An ARBOVIRUS morphologically like BUNYAVIRUS but serologically unrelated to members of that genus. Belongs to NAIROBI SHEEP DISEASE ANTIGENIC group. Found in Kenya, Uganda, Congo, Ethiopia, Somalia and Tanzania. Causes a haemorrhagic gastro-enteritis in sheep and goats with high mortality. There is splenic enlargement and involvement of the female genital tract. Nephritis and myocardial degeneration occur. Causes encephalitis in mice inoculated i/c. Transmitted by the tick *Rhipicephalus appendiculatus.* Virus replicates in cell cultures of lamb and goat tissue with CPE. One human case of infection with fever and arthralgia is reported, and two cases of serological conversion without disease.

naked viruses Viruses without a lipoprotein ENVELOPE.

NANB virus Synonym for hepatitis C virus.

Nandi virus A strain of MOUSE MAMMARY TUMOUR VIRUS, of low oncogenicity, isolated from C_3H mice. Also known as MTV-L and NIV.

Nariva virus

Tikasingh E.S. *et al.* (1966) *Am. J. trop. Med. Hyg.* **15**, 235

Isolated from forest rodents in Trinidad. Morphologically and biologically similar to viruses of the family PARAMYXOVIRIDAE. Kills new-born mice on i/c injection. Hamsters and guinea pigs produce antibodies but develop no disease. No isolations from arthropods. Not reported to cause disease in humans.

nascent cleavage Cleavage of a polyprotein occurring at the same time as it is being synthesized by cell ribosomes.

nascent RNA RNA in process of being synthesized.

Natural cow pox virus Synonym for milker's node virus.

Navarro virus A species of the family RHABDOVIRIDAE. Isolated from the turkey-vulture *Cathartes aura* in Colombia. Not reported to cause disease in humans.

NCTC 3526 cells (CCL 7·2) A heteroploid cell line derived from LLC-MK_2 CELLS and adapted to grow in a chemically defined medium.

NCTC clone 929 L cells (CCL 1) L strain is a heteroploid cell line derived from subcutaneous areolar and adipose tissue of a normal 100 day old male C3H/An mouse, and was one of the first cell lines to be established in continuous culture. Clone 929 was established from the 95th passage.

Ndumu virus

Kokernot R.H. *et al.* (1961) *Am. J. trop. Med. Hyg.* **10**, 383

A species in the genus ALPHAVIRUS. Isolated from mosquitoes in S. Africa. No known association with disease. Kills new-born mice on injection.

nearest-neighbour sequence analysis A method of characterizing DNA molecules. Any deoxyribonucleotide can be linked to another by its 3′ or 5′ carbon to form a dinucleotide molecule. There are thus two different ways of forming the link. Since there are four different deoxyribonucleotides *viz.*: adenine, guanine, cytosine and thymine 5′ triphosphates there are 16 possible dinucleotides. When the DNA chain is being made, each nucleotide added has the chance of joining any of the four nucleotides and the frequency with which each of these unions occurs is characteristic of the particular DNA. The frequency of each of the 16 possible combinations can be determined by incubating a DNA template with *Esch. coli* polymerase and the four deoxyribonucleotides, one of which, say dATP, is labelled with ^{32}P in the innermost phosphate. The ^{32}P becomes the bridge between the labelled NUCLEOTIDE (containing the base A in the diagram) and the nearest-neighbour nucleotide (containing the base Z in the diagram). After synthesis is complete, the DNA is isolated and degraded with micrococcal DNase and spleen phosphodiesterase to give deoxyribonucleoside 3′ monophosphates. The ^{32}P is now on the 3′ carbon of the neighbouring nucleoside, the one with which the labelled triphosphate reacted. The four deoxyribonucleoside 3′ monophosphates are isolated by paper electrophoresis and their radioactivities measured to give the frequency with which the originally labelled nucleotide locates itself next to the other nucleotides. The process is repeated using the remaining three labelled deoxyribonucleotides. Thus the frequency of the 16 dinucleotides is determined.

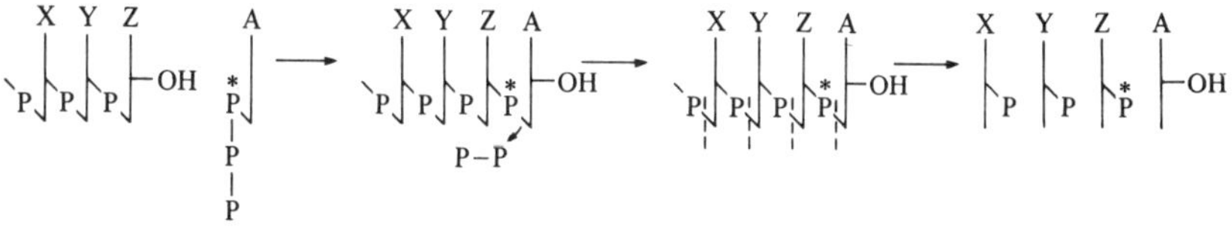

Illustration of the method of nearest-neighbour sequence analysis

Nebraska calf diarrhoea virus

Fauvel M. *et al.* (1978) *Intervirology* **9**, 95

A strain of CALF ROTAVIRUS. Associated with gastroenteritis in calves. Has been propagated in bovine embryonic kidney cell cultures, where it is cell-associated. Agglutinates human O erythrocytes.

Necrotic rhinitis virus Synonym for bovid herpesvirus 1.

Neethling virus Synonym for lumpy skin disease virus.

negative staining Not a form of staining. A method for visualizing virus particles by drying them in a film of electron-dense material which outlines the particle and reveals surface structures.

negative strand The RNA strand complementary to the POSITIVE STRAND. It forms the GENOME of several families of RNA viruses, jointly termed 'negative strand viruses'. These are ARENAVIRIDAE, BUNYAVIRIDAE, ORTHOMYXOVIRIDAE, PARAMYXOVIRIDAE and RHABDOVIRIDAE.

Negishi virus

Okuno T. *et al.* (1961) *Jap. J. med. Sci. Biol.* **14**, 51

A tick-borne species in the genus FLAVIVIRUS. Isolated from two fatal cases of human encephalitis in Japan.

Negri bodies Intracytoplasmic acidophilic INCLUSION BODIES seen in the brain cells of animals with rabies.

Nelson Bay virus

Gard G. & Compans R.W. (1970) *J. Virol.* **6**, 100

A species in the genus ORBIVIRUS isolated from the heart blood of a flying fox in New South Wales, Australia. Passage i/c in suckling mice causes paralysis and death. Causes cell fusion and CPE in a line of pig kidney cells.

neo-antigen Antigens which appear in cells after TRANSFORMATION. They are coded for by the transforming virus. Often called tumour antigens or T antigens.

Neonatal calf diarrhoea coronavirus

Mebus C.A. *et al.* (1973) *Am. J. vet. Res.* **34**, 145

Woode G.N. & Bridger J.C. (1975) *Vet. Rec.* **96**, 85

Hajer I. & Storz J. (1979) *Arch. Virol.* **59**, 47

A species in the genus CORONAVIRUS. Causes severe diarrhoea, usually in calves less than 5 days old. Replicates in bovine kidney cell cultures producing syncytia. Some strains such as the highly pathogenic strain LY-138 have not been propagated *in vitro* and are replicated by passage in calves. The strains can then be purified from the contents of the small intestines. Serial passage resulted in attenuation and this virus can induce resistance to virulent virus. A similar disease is caused by CALF ROTAVIRUS.

SYN: bovine coronavirus.

Nephropathia epidemica virus

Lee H.W. *et al.* (1979) *Lancet* **i**, 186

Synonym for Korean haemorrhagic fever virus.

Nepuyo virus An unclassified ARBOVIRUS morphologically similar to BUNYAVIRUS but antigenically unrelated to members of that genus. Belonging to the C GROUP VIRUSES. Isolated from bats and mosquitoes in Trinidad, Honduras, Mexico, Panama, and Belem, Brazil. Not associated with disease in humans.

neuraminic acid *See* neuraminidase.

neuraminidase An enzyme which splits the *N*-acetylneuraminic acid from the glycoprotein viral receptors on the cell membrane. Neuraminidase activity is carried by one of the two types of glycoprotein PEPLOMER on the surface of ORTHOMYXOVIRIDAE. The second type is a haemagglutinin or ATTACHMENT site by which the virus is joined to the cell receptor site. This can be destroyed by the neuraminidase, releasing the virus. In PARAMYXOVIRIDAE, both neuraminidase and haemagglutinin activity are carried on the same peplomer. (*See* figure facing.)

Neurocytes hydrophobiae

Calkins G.N. (1909) *Protozoology*. New York: Lea and Febiger

Name given to a supposed protozoan aetiological agent of rabies. The structure is now known as the NEGRI BODY.

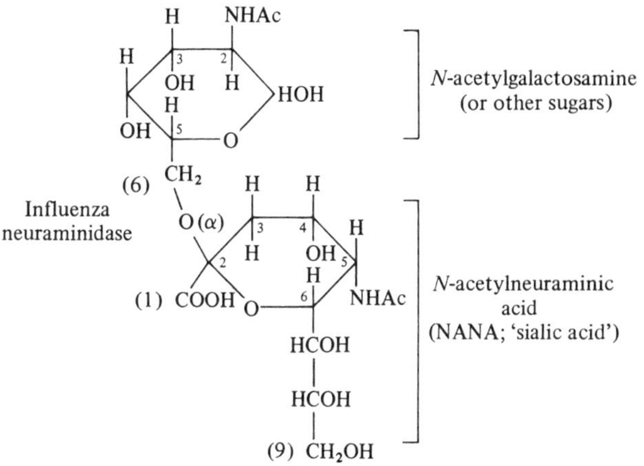

See neuraminidase opposite.

Neurolymphomatosis of fowls virus Synonym for gallid herpesvirus 1.

Neurovaccinia virus A strain of VACCINIA VIRUS, more virulent than others. Produces flat, ulcerated pocks on the CAM, with a tendency to haemorrhage.

neutralization

Mandel B. (1978) *Adv. Virus Res.* **23**, 205

Della-Porta A.J. & Westaway E.G. (1977) *J. gen. Virol.* **38**, 1

Usually understood to mean neutralization of infectivity by combination with specific antibody. On the surface of the virus particle there may be several antigens, and antibodies to some of these can combine without causing loss of infectivity. However, such an infective antigen-antibody complex may be neutralized if either complement or an antibody against the first antibody binds to the complex. In such a case the neutralization may be due to VIROLYSIS of an enveloped virus, or to steric hindrance due to the build up of protein molecules. This type of neutralization is described as 'extrinsic' in contrast to 'intrinsic' neutralization in which there is a direct inactivation reaction between antibody and a vital site on the virus. Virus particles may be agglutinated without losing infectivity, but this will result in a fall in the titre of infectivity units. This process is described as 'pseudoneutralisation'. The initially formed virus-antibody union is dissociable, but with time the binding becomes firmer though some dissociation of a small amount of infective virus can still occur.

See also non-neutralizable fraction *and* neutralization test.

neutralization test Used to measure infectivity neutralizing capacity, usually of specific antibody. Virus and antiserum are mixed and surviving infectivity, if any, is tested for by inoculation of animals, eggs, or cell cultures. The amount of virus or antibody is kept constant, but the other component is varied to obtain a titre of neutralizing activity which will be expressed as serum dilution required to neutralize a certain number of infective doses of virus, or as the number of infective doses of virus neutralized by a certain amount of antiserum. A virus control with no antiserum is required, and the test is read when the control becomes positive because the virus may later break through the neutralizing action of the antibody, and the apparent titre of the antiserum will fall.

See also non-neutralizable fraction.

neutral red A photoreactive dye. *See* photodynamic inactivation.

neutroseron A name proposed for any group of viruses which cross-react in NEUTRALIZATION TESTS.

New-born pneumonitis virus Synonym for parainfluenza virus type 1 human.

Newbury virus

Woode G.N. & Bridger J.C. (1978) *J. med. Microbiol.* **11**, 441

A strain of a bovine species in the family CALICIVIRIDAE.

Newcastle disease virus A genus of the family PARAMYXOVIRIDAE. A natural infection of fowls, turkeys and other species of birds. Strains have antigenic differences and vary in virulence. Disease produced is primarily respiratory but signs of nervous system involvement may been seen. The eyes are closed, there is nasal discharge and watery diarrhoea. Spasms and paralysis may occur. Mild strains cause low mortality but reduce egg production. Infection of the conjunctiva has been reported in poultry and laboratory workers. Experimental i/c injection in hamsters and mice causes encephalitis which is not transmissible. Transmission is through drinking water or inhalation of dust. Control is by slaughter or use of vaccine. Most strains replicate readily in eggs or chick cell cultures in which they produce CPE. Replication also occurs in many species of mammalian cells. Cultures may remain latently infected for long periods. All strains agglutinate fowl erythrocytes; some agglutinate a variety of avian and mammalian cells. Human erythrocytes treated with some strains are agglutinated by serum from infectious mononucleosis patients.

SYN: Atypischen Geflügelpestvirus; avian pneumo-encephalitis virus; ranikhet disease virus.

New Jersey virus A strain of VESICULAR STOMATITIS VIRUS.

New Minto virus

Ritter D.G. *et al.* (1978) *Canad. J. Microbiol.* **24**, 422

A species of the family RHABDOVIRIDAE. Isolated from the tick *Haemaphysalis leporis-palustris* removed from snowshoe hares *Lepus americanus* in central Alaska. Sensitive to sodium deoxycholate. Kills suckling mice on i/c but not on i/p injection. Weaned mice do not die after i/c injection. Produces plaques in VERO CELLS but not in Pekin duck embryo cells. Antigenically related to SAWGRASS VIRUS.

Ngaingan virus An unclassified ARBOVIRUS. Isolated from *Culicoides* sp. in Queensland, Australia. Antibodies present in wallabies, kangaroos, and cattle. Not reported to cause disease in humans.

Nicolau bodies Intranuclear or intracytoplasmic INCLUSION BODIES found in cells infected with HUMAN HERPESVIRUS 1, 2 OR 3.

Nigerian horse virus

Porterfield J.S. *et al.* (1958) *Brit. vet. J.* **114**, 425

A species in the genus LYSSAVIRUS isolated from the brain of a horse with sporadic meningo-encephalomyelitis (staggers) by i/c inoculation of suckling mice. Probably the cause of staggers in horses in Nigeria. Non-pathogenic for rabbits but probably pathogenic for *Cercocebus torquatus torquatus* monkeys given i/c. Not known to cause disease in man.

Nigg's virus Not a virus. Synonym for mouse pneumonitis agent. A chlamydia of sub-group A.

Niigata virus

Kojima S. *et al.* (1948) *Jap. med. J.* **1**, 467

A virus isolated from an outbreak of gastroenteritis in Japan. Could be passed in humans.

Nique virus An unclassified ARBOVIRUS morphologically like BUNYAVIRUS but serologically unrelated to members of that genus. A member of the PHLEBOTOMUS FEVER ANTIGENIC GROUP. Isolated from *Lutzomyia panamensis* in Panama. Not reported to cause disease in humans.

Nkolbisson virus An unclassified ARBOVIRUS. Isolated from mosquitoes near Yaounde, Cameroon. Not reported to cause disease in humans.

NK virus A member of the genus POLYOMAVIRUS, similar to MG VIRUS.

Nodamura virus

Scherer W.F. & Hurlbut H.S. (1967) *Am. J. Epidemiol.* **86**, 271

Newman J.F.E. *et al.* (1978) *J. Virol.* **25**, 78

A small RNA-containing virus but not a picornavirus because it has a segmented GENOME. Although shown to multiply in arthropods, it may not be considered an ARBOVIRUS. Isolated from *Culex tritaeniorhynchus* in Japan. Antibodies found in pigs, young herons and egrets. Not reported to cause disease in humans. Epidemiological surveys suggest it is natural infection of swine. Multiples in a number of insects. No disease produced in mosquitoes, ticks, or larvae of the moth *Plodia interpunetella*, but kills honey bees and wax moth larvae. Resembles PICORNAVIRIDAE in morphology, stability at pH 3, and density in CsCl. Disease produced in suckling mice similar to that caused by group A COXSACKIE VIRUS. However, it contains equimolar amounts of 2 RNA species: RNA 1, a 22S species of mol. wt. $1{\cdot}1 \times 10^6$ which codes for a protein of mol. wt. 105,000, RNA 2 a 15S species of mol. wt. $0{\cdot}46 \times 10^6$ which codes for a protein mol. wt. 43,000, probably the viral COAT protein. Both RNA's are in the same VIRION and are required for infectivity. It is a novel ribovirus.

Nodule-inducing mouse mammary tumour virus A strain of virus found in mice freed from BITTNER VIRUS by foster nursing. These mice develop mammary tumours late in life. The virus is morphologically identical to Bittner virus but induces only hyperplastic nodules with low neoplastic potential.

Nola virus A species in the genus BUNYAVIRUS. Belongs to the SIMBU ANTIGENIC GROUP. Isolated from *Culex perfuscus* in Central African Republic. Not known to cause disease in humans.

nonallelic complementation *See* complementation.

Non-A non-B hepatitis virus Synonym for hepatitis C virus.

Non-bacterial regional lymphadenitis virus Synonym for cat-scratch disease virus.

non-genetic reactivation *See* reactivation *and* complementation.

nonidet P 40 A detergent used to break up virus particles.

non-neutralizable fraction NEUTRALIZATION by antibody is often not complete, a small fraction of the original infectivity resisting neutralization. This may be due to dissociation of the virus-antibody union or to the formation of infective complexes. The addition of anti-antibody neutralizes such complexes.

See neutralization.

non-permissive cells Cells in which a virus will not replicate. They may be permissive for one virus but not for another. The fact that they are non-permissive for virus replication may make them very suitable for demonstrating TRANSFORMATION.

non-producer cells Cells usually transformed, carrying all or part of a viral GENOME but not producing infective virus particles. In the case of ROUS SARCOMA VIRUS-transformed NP cells, non-infective virus may be produced. Such cells are called L-R CELLS.

nonsense codons Codons which do not code for an amino acid. They are UAA, UAG and UGA. UAA, UAG and UGA are sometimes referred to as the 'ochre', 'amber' and 'opal' codons respectively. They are chain terminating signals.

non-structural viral proteins Proteins coded for by the viral GENOME but not incorporated into the viral particle. They probably have a functional role during viral replication.

Northway virus A species in the genus BUNYAVIRUS. A member of the BUNYAMWERA ANTIGENIC GROUP. Isolated from *Aedes* sp. in Alaska. Not known to cause disease in humans.

Norwalk virus

Schreiber D.S. *et al.* (1977) *Gastroenterology* **73**, 174

Kapikian A.Z. *et al.* (1972) *J. Virol.* **10**, 1075

An unclassified FAECAL VIRUS of type 1. Possibly a species in the genus PARVOVIRUS. Causes acute gastroenteritis. A filtrate from a rectal swab from a patient in Norwalk, Ohio, was given to volunteers and caused gastroenteritis. Could be serially passaged. Virus particles 27 nm in diameter were seen in stool filtrates by immune electron microscopy. Acid-stable. Ether-resistant. BUOYANT DENSITY (CsCl) 1·37–1·41 g/cm^3.

NP cells *See* non-producer cells.

Ntaya virus A species in the genus FLAVIVIRUS. Isolated from mosquitoes in Uganda, Cameroon and Central African Republic. Not known to cause disease in man or other animals.

nucleases Enzymes which break down NUCLEIC ACID molecules by hydrolysis of phosphodiester bonds. They are present in almost all biological systems. Some are specific for RNA or DNA and are called ribonucleases or deoxyribonucleases respectively, while a third group are non-specific. Nucleases can attack the POLYNUCLEOTIDE chain in two ways: at points within the chain or stepwise from one end of the chain. Enzymes acting by the first method are called endonucleases and work endolytically. They produce OLIGONUCLEOTIDES and cause a rapid change in physical properties such as viscosity. Enzymes

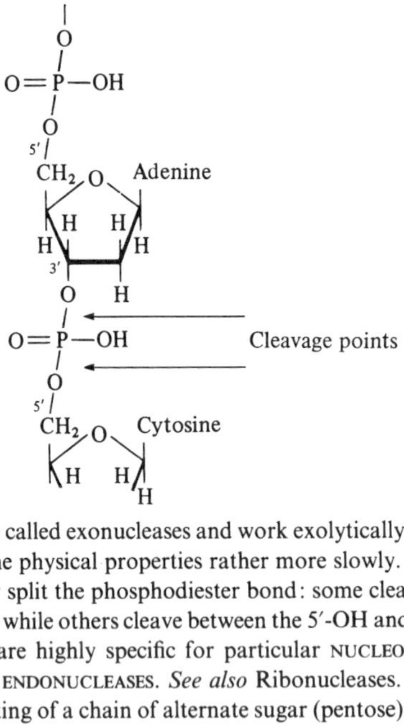

Adenine

Cleavage points

Cytosine

acting by the second method are called exonucleases and work exolytically. They produce mononucleotides and change the physical properties rather more slowly. Nucleases also differ in the point at which they split the phosphodiester bond: some cleave between the 3′-OH and the phosphate group while others cleave between the 5′-OH and the phosphate group. Certain endonucleases are highly specific for particular NUCLEOTIDE sequences and are known as RESTRICTION ENDONUCLEASES. *See also* Ribonucleases.

nucleic acid A compound consisting of a chain of alternate sugar (pentose) and phosphate molecules with one purine or pyrimidine base attached to each sugar molecule. The basic

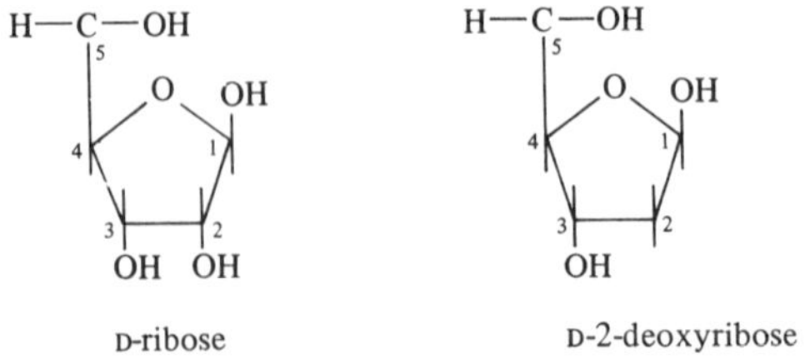

D-ribose

D-2-deoxyribose

unit is thus a NUCLEOTIDE molecule. There are two types: DNA in which the sugar molecules are D-2-deoxyribose and RNA in which they are D-ribose.

In both types of nucleic acid the sugar phosphate chain is through the 3′ and 5′ carbons in the sugar. Thus the chain has a 3′ and a 5′ end.

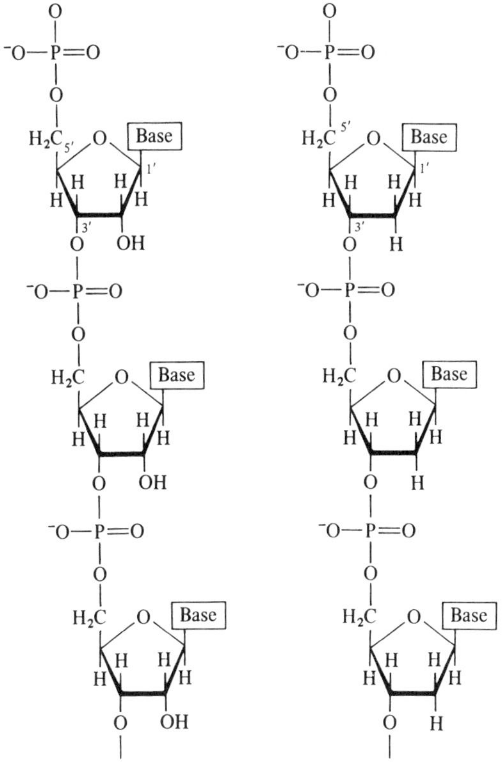

Structure of part of an RNA chain

Structure of part of a DNA chain

nuclein The first name given to an unusual phosphorus compound isolated in the last century from the nuclei of pus cells. Now known as NUCLEOPROTEIN.

nucleocapsid The viral NUCLEIC ACID directly enclosed by the CAPSID. This simple arrangement is usual in the rod-shaped plant viruses and a few isometric VIRIONS, but with most viruses the capsid encloses a more complex structure, the CORE.

nucleoid A term used by electron microscopists to describe the electron-dense centrally placed region observed in certain viruses. *See* C type virus particles.

nucleoprotein A complex of NUCLEIC ACID and protein. The form in which DNA exists in the nucleus of eukaryotic cells and virus particles.

nucleosides Units composed of a PURINE or PYRIMIDINE BASE combined to a pentose or deoxypentose sugar. Adenine forms adenosine, guanine guanosine, cytosine cytidine and uracil uridine. They may be formed on partial hydrolysis of RNA. The nucleosides derived from 2 deoxyribose are known as deoxyadenosine, deoxyguanosine etc.

nucleosomes Units of NUCLEIC ACID and histone joined by protein-free stretches of nucleic acid. The NUCLEOPROTEIN of the CHROMATIDS is probably of nucleosomes.

nucleotide phosphohydrolase An enzyme which converts NUCLEOTIDE diphosphates. Present in VIRIONS of REOVIRIDAE. May play a role in inhibition of host cell DNA synthesis or in formations of the 5′ terminal cap structure on mRNA.

nucleotides Phosphoric esters of NUCLEOSIDES. Those derived from ribonucleosides are called ribonucleotides, and those from deoxyribose nucleosides as deoxyribonucleotides. Sometimes the abbrevations riboside, ribotide, deoxyriboside and deoxyribotide are incorrectly used. Since the ribonucleosides have three free hydroxyl groups on the sugar ring, there are 3 possible ribonucleoside monophosphates; for example adenosine 2′, 3′, or 5′ monophosphate. The adenosine 5′ monophosphate is present in muscle and was formerly known as muscle adenylic acid, while the 3′ monophosphate obtained by hydrolysis of yeast RNA was called yeast adenylic acid. In the same way guanosine,

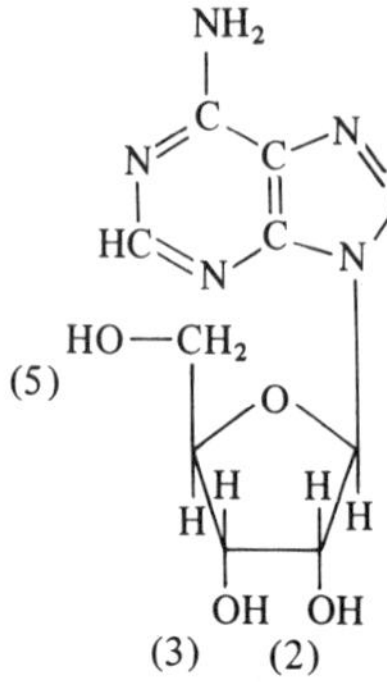

Adenosine

cytidine and uridine yield guanylic acids, cytadylic acids and uradylic acids. The adenosine 5′ monophosphate (AMP) can be further phosphorylated at position 5′ to give 5′ di- and triphosphates. Thus AMP becomes ADP and ATP. The triphosphates are used as precursor molecules for the synthesis of NUCLEIC ACIDS by virus or cellular polymerases.

Nugget virus A species in the genus ORBIVIRUS and a member of the KEMEROVO ANTIGENIC GROUP. Isolated from nymphs of *Ixodes uriae* collected at Macquarie Island, 800 miles S.E. of Tasmania, in tussock grass and under planks on the shore near a rookery of Royal Penguins, *Eudyptes chrysalophus schlegeli*. Antibodies are found in these birds. Not known to infect man.

Nyamanini virus An unclassified ARBOVIRUS. Isolated from *Bubulcus ibis*, and other birds, and ticks of *Argas* sp. in S. Africa, Egypt and Nigeria. On injection kills new-born mice. Not reported to cause disease in humans.

Nyando virus An unclassified ARBOVIRUS of the NYANDO ANTIGENIC GROUP. Isolated from mosquitoes in Kenya and Central African Republic. Probably present in Uganda. Isolated from, but not known to cause disease in humans.

Obodhiang virus

Bauer S.P. & Murphy F.A. (1975) *Infect. Immun.* **12**, 1157

A species in the genus LYSSAVIRUS isolated from *Mansonia uniformis* mosquitoes in Sudan and Ethiopia. Antigenically related to KOTONKAN VIRUS and MOKOLA VIRUS, but not to EPHEMERAL FEVER VIRUS.

ochre mutant Virus with mutation resulting in a chain termination codon UAA. *See* amber.

Odocoileus hemionus type C virus

Aaronson S.A. *et al.* (1976) *Cell* **9**, 489

A species in the subgenus MAMMALIAN TYPE C ONCOVIRUS GROUP. An ENDOGENOUS VIRUS isolated from the Columbian black-tailed deer, *Odocoileus hemionus* (*Dama hemionus columbiana*). The distribution of DNA sequences related to the ENDOGENOUS VIRUS in various species of deer is compatible with the closeness of the relationship between the different species in the family *Cervidae*.

O'Higgins disease virus Synonym for junin virus.

Okhotskiy virus

Lvov D.K. *et al.* (1973) *Arch. ges. Virusforsch.* **41**, 160

A species in the genus ORBIVIRUS. A member of the KEMEROVO ANTIGENIC GROUP. Isolated from the tick *Ixodes putus* collected from several islands in the sea of Okhotsk in the N. of the Soviet Far East. Antibodies are found in guillemots *Uria aalge*, fulmars *Fulmarus glacialis* and cormorants *Phalacrocorax pelagicus*. Pathogenic for suckling mice. Not reported to cause disease in humans.

Okola virus An unclassified ARBOVIRUS. Isolated from the mosquito *Eretmapodites chrysogaster* in Cameroon. Not reported to cause disease in humans.

Olifantsvlei virus A species in the genus BUNYAVIRUS. With BOBAYA VIRUS forms the Olifantsvlei antigenic group. Isolated in suckling mice from a pool of female mosquitoes *Culex pipiens* trapped at Olifantsvlei, Johannesburg, S. Africa. Also isolated from *Mansonia uniformis* in the Sudan and from *Culex poicilipes* in Ethiopia. Not reported to cause disease in humans.

oligonucleotides Small polynucleotides containing fewer than about 20 NUCLEOTIDES.

OLV virus Synonym for H 3 virus.

Omsk haemorrhagic fever virus

Netzky G.I. (1967) *Jap. J. med. Sci. Biol.* (suppl.) **20**, 141

A tick-borne species in the genus FLAVIVIRUS. There are two antigenic subgroups. Vectors are ticks *Dermacentor pictus* and *D. marginatus* in which transovarian transmission is reported. Man may also be infected by direct contact with muskrats. Causes a biphasic illness in man with fever, enlargement of lymph nodes, gastro-intestinal symptoms, and haemorrhages from nose, stomach and uterus but little or no CNS involvement. Mortality 1–2%. Disease occurs in central U.S.S.R. Causes fever in rhesus monkeys injected i/p. On first isolation does not infect adult mice.

Onc gene A synonym for Src gene.

oncogenic Tumour producing.

Oncogenic RNA virus Old name for group of RNA tumour viruses, now included in the family RETROVIRIDAE as the subfamily ONCOVIRINAE.

Oncornaviruses Old name for group of RNA tumour viruses, now included in the family RETROVIRIDAE as the subfamily ONCOVIRINAE.

Oncovirinae A subfamily of the family RETROVIRIDAE. A large and complex group of tumour-producing viruses and a few antigenically related viruses which are probably non-oncogenic. Viral RNA has mol. wt. 6×10^6. Sediments at 70 S, and on heating to 68° dissociates into 35 S pieces which appear to be complete GENOMES. The NUCLEIC ACID shows some homology with the cellular DNA of the host species. The VIRION also contains some 4 S tRNA which is probably host-coded. There are 6 virion proteins, 2 of which are glycoproteins and form PEPLOMERS on the ENVELOPE. The CORE shell proteins have antigens specific to the host animal species and others specific to groups such as the birds or mammals. There are two genera: TYPE C ONCOVIRUS GROUP (the leukaemia and sarcoma viruses) and TYPE B ONCOVIRUS GROUP (the mammary tumour viruses).

one-hit kinetics In systems where one particle can initiate infection, the number of plaques appearing is directly proportional to the first power of the concentration of the inoculum. If this concentration is doubled, the number of plaques will be doubled.

one-step growth curve An experiment in which all the cells in a particular culture are infected simultaneously, so that events in individual cells can be inferred from events in the whole population.

Ontario encephalomyelitis virus Synonym for porcine haemagglutinating encephalitis virus.

O' Nyong-Nyong virus

Chanas A.C. *et al.* (1979) *Arch. Virol.* **59**, 231

A species in the genus ALPHAVIRUS. In man it causes a febrile illness with lymphadenitis, severe joint pains and rash. Epidemic spread occurs with anopheline mosquitoes as vector. Occurs in Uganda, Kenya, Tanzania, Malawi and Senegal. Pathogenic for suckling mice given i/c: older mice are resistant. Infant mice which survive the infection are stunted and show patchy alopecia. Virus is propagated in chick embryo fibroblast cell cultures.

opal mutant Virus with mutation resulting in a chain termination codon UGA. *See* amber.

Opossum adenovirus

Morales-Ayala F. *et al.* (1964) *Bact. Proc.* p. 117

A species in the genus MASTADENOVIRUS. Isolated from an opossum *Didelphis marsupialis marsupialis* primary kidney cell culture showing spontaneous CPE. Did not replicate in rabbit, hamster, human or rhesus monkey kidney cell cultures or in HELA or HEP-2 CELLS.

Opossum herpesvirus

Hurst E.W. *et al.* (1943) *Aust. J. exp. Biol. med. Sci.* **21**, 149

Inclusions have been described in the kidney cells of Australian opossums *Trichiurus* sp., but only in animals which had been in the laboratory for some time.

Opossum viruses A and B Not viruses. Chlamydiae.

Orbivirus (Latin: *Orbis* = a ring)

Gorman B.M. (1979) *J. gen. Virol.* **44**, 1

Borden E.C. *et al.* (1971) *J. gen. Virol.* **13**, 261 and 273

A genus of the family REOVIRIDAE. All multiply in insects and several also in vertebrates. VIRION 65 to 80 nm in diameter, has a double protein shell, the outer one without readily definable CAPSOMERES, the inner with 32 seemingly ring-shaped capsomeres arranged with ICOSAHEDRAL SYMMETRY and visible in the presence of the outer shell. Only slightly sensitive to lipid solvents, inactivated at pH 3. The double-stranded RNA consists of 10 pieces of mol. wt. between 0·3 and $2{\cdot}7 \times 10^6$ with the total weight of 12×10^6. The single-shelled NUCLEOCAPSID having lost the outer shell has TRANSCRIPTASE activity with an optimum temperature of 28 °C. They replicate with CPE in BHK21 cells. Kill new-born mice but not adults on i/c injection. Do not kill mice of any age on i/p injection. The type species is BLUE-TONGUE VIRUS. They have no common antigen but are divided into 10 groups on the basis of antigenic cross-reactions.

Oregon sockeye disease virus

Yasutake W.T. *et al.* (1965) *Ann. N.Y. Acad. Sci.* **126**, 520

A species in the genus VESICULOVIRUS. Causes necrosis of haematopoietic tissues of spleen and anterior kidney in trout and salmon. Occurs as epidemic disease in fish hatcheries. There is abdominal swelling and haemorrhages at fin bases. Stomach is full of milky fluid and the intestines contain watery straw-coloured fluid. Can be propagated in fathead minnow and other fish tissue cell lines with CPE. Closely related to INFECTIOUS HAEMOTOPOIETIC NECROSIS VIRUS.

SYN: sockeye salmon virus

Orf subgroup viruses Synonym for parapoxvirus.

Orf virus

Falk E.S. (1978) *Brit. J. Derm.* **99**, 647

The type species of the genus PARAPOXVIRUS. Causes disease predominantly in lambs and kids. There are vesicles on the lips and nose, progressing to pustules, ulcers and warty scabs. Malignant aphtha is a severe form of the disease which may be fatal. Papilloma of chamois is caused by orf virus. Man may be infected from animals but man-to-man infection is very rare. Does not naturally infect cattle but they can be infected experimentally as can rabbits, horses, dogs and monkeys. VIRION 252×158 nm and the surface has the appearance of a ball of yarn. Inactivated by chloroform, but ether may not inactivate. Dried scabs retain infectivity at room temperature for years. Does not replicate on the CAM but multiplies in ovine and bovine cell cultures. An active vaccine applied by scarification has been used.

SYN: contagious pustular dermatitis of sheep virus; contagious pustular stomatitis of sheep virus; ecthyma contagiosum of sheep virus; infectious labial dermatitis virus; scabby mouth virus; sore mouth virus.

organ culture *See* tissue culture.

Oriboca virus

Karabatsos N. & Shope R.E. (1979) *J. med. Virol.* **3**, 167

Causey O.R. *et al.* (1961) *Am. J. trop. Med. Hyg.* **10**, 227

A species in the genus BUNYAVIRUS, belonging to the C GROUP. Isolated from the opossum *Didelphis marsupialis*, rodents *Proechimys* sp. and *Oryzomys capito*. Mosquito-borne. Found in Brazil, Surinam, French Guiana and Trinidad. Can cause a febrile illness in humans.

Oropouche virus

Anderson C.R. *et al.* (1961) *Am. J. trop. Med. Hyg.* **10**, 574

A species in the genus BUNYAVIRUS and a member of the SIMBU ANTIGENIC GROUP. First isolated from a febrile patient in Trinidad in 1955. In 1960 it caused an outbreak of fever affecting 7,000 people near Belem in Brazil. In some cases there was myalgia, arthralgia and leukopenia. A mosquito-borne infection. Has been isolated from the three-toed sloth *Bradypus tridactylus*.

orphan virus Any virus which has not been identified as the cause of a disease.

Orthomyxoviridae

Kilbourne E.D. (1975) *The Influenza Viruses and Influenza.* London: Academic Press.

A family of RNA viruses consisting of 2 genera: INFLUENZAVIRUS and INFLUENZAVIRUS TYPE C. They are 80–120 nm in diameter, spherical or slightly elongated, but filamentous forms several microns in length occur. They are enveloped viruses with glycosylated protein surface projections of two types: one type is a haemagglutinin and the other is a receptor-destroying enzyme, NEURAMINIDASE in INFLUENZA VIRUS A and B. The NUCLEOCAPSID has HELICAL SYMMETRY, 9 nm in diameter, and is probably in 8 pieces. The RNA is NEGATIVE STRAND, linear, in 8 pieces of mol. wt. 0·89, 0·89, 0·86, 0·66, 0·56, 0·48, 0·28 and $0{\cdot}21 \times 10^6$. The seven largest RNA pieces each code for one virus structural protein; the smallest RNA piece codes for two non-structural virus proteins. The GENOME RNA is transcribed by a VIRION polymerase into complementary RNA molecules which act as mRNA's. This process is host-cell dependent, and replication, which occurs partly in the cell nucleus, is inhibited by ACTINOMYCIN D or α-AMANITIN added during the first 2 hours after infection. Virus matures at the cell surface from which it buds. The 7 virion polypeptides form 60–75% of the viral mass. The most abundant is the M protein (membrane or matrix protein). Together with the NP protein (nucleocapsid protein) in the viral CORE, these two antigenic proteins provide the basis for division of the family into genera. The other three core proteins, P_1 P_2 and P_3 (polymerase proteins), are minor constituents and their antigenicity has not been demonstrated. The haemagglutinin and neuraminidase are species-specific within the genera. The receptor-destroying enzyme of influenzavirus C is not a neuraminidase. The virion contains 18–37% lipid and 5–9% carbohydrate. Infectivity is lost in 30 minutes at 56° and on exposure to lipid solvents, formalin, detergents and oxidizing agents.

Orthopoxvirus A genus of the subfamily CHORDOPOXVIRINAE. Consists of viruses of mammals, most of which cause generalized infections with a rash. Ether-resistant. Different species undergo genetic RECOMBINATION and exhibit serological cross-reactivity and NUCLEIC ACID homology. A haemagglutinin is produced by infected cells; it is serologically specific and is a lipid-rich pleomorphic particle 50–65 nm in diameter, separate from the VIRION. They all produce pocks on the CAM but some strains may be more easily isolated in animals or cell cultures. They replicate in chick embryo fibroblasts, VERO CELLS and HELA CELL cultures. Because of the close serological relationship within the genus, species are identified by biological characters. Type species is VACCINIA VIRUS.

Other species are VARIOLA VIRUS, BUFFALO POX, CAMEL POX, COW POX, ECTROMELIA VIRUS, MONKEY POX, RACCOON POX, and RABBIT POX VIRUSES.
SYN: vaccinia subgroup viruses.

Orthopoxvirus bovis Name proposed for COW POX VIRUS, but not adopted.

Orthopoxvirus commune Name proposed for VACCINIA VIRUS, but not adopted.

Orthopoxvirus officinale Name proposed for VACCINIA VIRUS, but not adopted.

Orthopoxvirus simiae A name proposed for MONKEY POX VIRUS, but not adopted.

Orthoreoviruses A term used to describe the classical or original isolates. There are three mammalian and several avian serotypes. A synonym for the genus REOVIRUS.

Orungo virus

Tomori O. *et al.* (1976) *Arch. Virol.* **51**, 285
Tomori O. *et al.* (1977) *Arch. Virol.* **55**, 181
Tomori O. (1977) *Microbios* **19**, 157

A species in the genus ORBIVIRUS. First isolated from the mosquito *Anopheles funestus* in Uganda, and *Aedes dentatus* mosquitoes and man in Nigeria. Can be passed in new-born mice by i/c injection. Replicates with CPE in BHK 21 CELLS. Develops in the cytoplasm associated with a specific viral granular matrix and accompanying filaments. VIRION diameter 63 nm, CORE diameter 34 nm. Released from the cells by lysis or BUDDING through membranes. Found in Uganda, Nigeria, Central African Republic and Senegal. Has been isolated from human blood and causes a febrile illness in man, with headache, conjunctivitis, myalgia, vomiting and rash. Antibodies are found in man, other primates, sheep and cows in Nigeria.

Ossa virus

Rodaniche E. de *et al.* (1964) *Am. J. trop. Med. Hyg.* **13**, 839

A species in the genus BUNYAVIRUS, belonging to the C GROUP. Isolated from man, the spiny rat *Proechimys semispinosus*, and *Culex* sp. in Panama. Associated with a febrile illness in humans.

Osteopetrosis virus

Campbell J.G. *et al.* (1964) *J. comp. Path.* **74**, 263
Young D. (1966) *J. comp. Path.* **76**, 45
Paterson R.W. & Smith R.E. (1978) *Infect. Immun.* **22**, 891

A strain of CHICKEN LEUKOSIS SARCOMA VIRUS which can cause osteopetrosis, a disease which occurs naturally in fowls, and is characterised by enlargment of the bones, especially the leg bones. There is an increase of hard bone due to hypertrophic activity of the periostium. It can be transmitted by inoculation of day-old chicks or the amnion of chick embryos with blood from birds with osteopetrosis or from some cases of lymphomatosis. Osteopetrosis is often accompanied by soft tissue tumours. Turkeys do not naturally develop the disease but it can be transmitted to them. *See* AVIAN MYELOBLASTOSIS VIRUS.
SYN: big bone disease virus; marble bone disease virus; thick leg disease virus.

ouabain

Tomita Y. & Kuwata T. (1978) *J. gen. Virol.* **38**, 223

A cardiac glycoside. Obtained from the seeds of *Strophanthus gratus* or the wood of *Acokanthera schimperi* or *A. ouabio*. An inhibitor of Na^+- and K^+- dependent adenosine triphosphatase. Reduces synthesis of cellular protein and rate of growth of cells. Markedly inhibits the growth of mouse cell lines K_3b and JLS-V9, and the production in them of MOUSE TYPE C ONCOVIRUS. It has been reported that low concentrations of ouabain will inhibit the growth of some enveloped viruses such as INFLUENZA VIRUS A AVIAN and PARAINFLUENZA VIRUS TYPE 1 MURINE in chick embryo cells. However, it will also block the anti-viral action of primate INTERFERONS in green monkey cells, and that of mouse interferon on the replication of VESICULAR STOMATITIS VIRUS.

Ouango virus An unclassified ARBOVIRUS. Isolated from a bird *Sitagra melanocephala* in Central African Republic. Not reported to cause disease in humans.

Oubangui virus An unclassified ARBOVIRUS. Isolated in suckling mice from a pool of female mosquitoes *Culex guiarti* collected in Bangui, Central African Republic from human bait. Infectivity resistant to chloroform. Haemagglutinates goose erythrocytes. Not reported to cause disease in humans.

Ovine adeno-associated virus

Clarke J.K. *et al.* (1979) *Arch. Virol.* **60**, 171

A species in the genus ADENO-ASSOCIATED VIRUS. Isolated in association with an adenovirus in lamb kidney cell cultures from ovine faeces. Agglutinates guinea pig and human erythrocytes. Replicates in association with the cell nucleus and requires the presence of an adenovirus.

Ovine adenovirus

Sharp J.M. (1977) *Vet. Rec.* **101**, 524

A species in the genus MASTADENOVIRUS. Five serotypes are identified and associated with pneumoenteritis in lambs. Because few sheep give a positive reaction in the gel diffusion test for precipitating antibodies it was suggested that the infection was not common, but the majority of sheep in Scotland have neutralizing antibodies to 4 serotypes of this virus. The infection must therefore be common and as the virus can be recovered from the faeces of normal sheep, its isolation from disease outbreaks must be viewed with caution. Multiplies in sheep kidney cell cultures. Agglutinates rat erythrocytes.

Ovine catarrhal fever virus A synonym for blue tongue virus.

Ovine encephalomyelitis virus Synonym for louping-ill virus.

'O' virus (O for Offal)

Malherbe H.H. & Strickland-Cholmley M. (1967) *Archiv ges. Virusforsch.* **22**, 235

A species in the genus ROTAVIRUS. Isolated from the waste water which had been used to wash the intestines of slaughtered cattle and sheep. Indistinguishable from SIMIAN VIRUS SA-11 and HUMAN ROTAVIRUS by CFT, but electrophoresis of viral RNA reveals differences. Replicates in monkey kidney cell cultures producing eosinophilic inclusions and cell destruction.

Owl herpesvirus Synonym for strigid herpesvirus 1.

Owl monkey herpesvirus Synonym for cebid herpesvirus 4.

PAA *See* phosphonoacetic acid.

Pacheco's disease of parrots virus Synonym for psittacid herpesvirus 1.

Pacora virus An unclassified ARBOVIRUS. Isolated from *Culex dunni* in Panama. Not reported to cause disease in the wild.

pactamycin Selectively inhibits INITIATION of protein synthesis. Interferes with firm ATTACHMENT of initiator tRNA to the initiation complex. Polypeptides already in the making are completed. This drug has proved very useful experimentally in mapping the gene order of PICORNAVIRIDAE and TOGAVIRIDAE, since after drug addition, the first polypeptides to be affected will be coded close to the 5′ end, the least affected near the 3′ end, of the GENOME.

Pacui virus An unclassified ARBOVIRUS morphologically like BUNYAVIRUS but serologically unrelated to members of that genus. Belongs to the PHLEBOTOMUS FEVER ANTIGENIC GROUP. Isolated from rodents of *Oryzomys* sp. in Para, Brazil, and Trinidad. Not reported to cause disease in humans.

Pahayokee virus A species in the genus BUNYAVIRUS. Belongs to the PATOIS ANTIGENIC GROUP. Isolated from mosquitoes in Florida, U.S.A. Not known to cause disease in humans.

Palyam antigenic group viruses Four antigenically related viruses belonging to the genus ORBIVIRUS.

D'aguilar (Cu)	Palyam (C)
Kasba (C)	Vellore (C)

Isolated from:
(Cu) Culicoides
(C) Culicine mosquitoes

Palyam virus A species in the genus ORBIVIRUS. A member of the PALYAM ANTIGENIC GROUP. Isolated from *Culex vishnui* in Tamil Nadu, India, from *Culicoides* sp. in Australia and from *Culicoides* sp. and mosquitoes in Abadina, Nigeria.

papilloma of chamois An orf virus infection.

Papillomavirus

Le Bouvier G.L. (1966) *J. gen. Microbiol.* **45**, 497
Coggin J.R. *et al.* (1979) *Cancer Res.* **39**, 545

A genus of the family PAPOVAVIRIDAE, 55 nm in diameter. Mol. wt. of DNA, 5×10^6; G+C CONTENT 41–45%. Cause papillomas in various species (cattle, dog, man, rabbit, horse, monkey, sheep, goat and birds) and are species-specific. Rarely cause TRANSFORMATION in cell cultures or CPE. Type species RABBIT PAPILLOMAVIRUS.

Papovaviridae A family of DNA viruses, 45 to 55 nm in diameter with ICOSAHEDRAL SYMMETRY and 72 CAPSOMERES, resistant to lipid solvents and to heating for 30 min at 56°–65 °C. In the VIRION the DNA is a double-stranded covalently closed ring with a variable degree of supercoiling. Mol. wt. $3–5 \times 10^6$; G+C CONTENT 41–49%. BUOYANT DENSITY (CsCl) 1·34 g/ml. Replication occurs in the nucleus. Infectious DNA can be extracted. Most members are ONCOGENIC. Several species haemagglutinate by reacting with NEURAMINIDASE-sensitive receptors. The family consists of two genera: PAPILLOMAVIRUS and POLYOMAVIRUS.

Papova viruses An old name for the species first included in the family PAPOVAVIRIDAE. They were *PA*pilloma virus, *PO*lyoma virus and *VA*cuolating virus.

Pappataci fever viruses Synonym for phlebotomus fever viruses.

Papular stomatitis of cattle virus Synonym for bovine papular stomatitis virus, though other viruses may cause the same clinical picture.

PARA Particle aiding replication of adenovirus. *See* adenovirus – SV_{40} hybrids.

Parainfluenza virus type 1 human A species in the genus PARAMYXOVIRUS. Causes a febrile respiratory illness, most often in children in autumn or early winter. The commonest cause of croup. Causes a symptomless infection in mice, ferrets, hamsters and rhesus monkeys. Isolated from the respiratory tract, optimally in primary monkey kidney or human embryo cells. CPE is slight or absent on isolation but infected cells haemadsorb guinea pig or human O erythrocytes. Some newly isolated strains will replicate in embryonated eggs, the amniotic cavity being most sensitive. Strains can be adapted to replicate in HELA CELLS which may form persistent carrier cultures. Closely related to PARAINFLUENZA VIRUS TYPE 1 MURINE, but can be differentiated by haemagglutination inhibition or NEUTRALIZATION TESTS.

SYN: haemadsorption virus 2, new-born pneumonitis virus.

Parainfluenza virus type 1 murine

Ishida N. & Homma M. (1978) *Adv. Virus Res.* **23**, 349

A species in the genus PARAMYXOVIRUS. Can be isolated in embryonated eggs, the allantoic cavity being the most sensitive, or in primary cultures of mouse, human, chick and other species. Less exacting in requirements for replication and causing a more definite CPE than PARAINFLUENZA VIRUS TYPE 1 HUMAN. Produces plaques in human, bovine and simian cells. Inactivated virus is used experimentally to cause cell fusion. On mouse to mouse passage there is an increase in virulence resulting in pneumonia. An inactivated chick embryo vaccine is available to protect laboratory mice. Not generally accepted as causing

human infection. Injected i/c in mice it causes a fatal infection but serial passage by this route is not possible. Causes inapparent infection in ferrets, monkeys and pigs and occurs as a latent infection of laboratory mice, rats and guinea pigs.
SYN: haemagglutinating virus of Japan, sendai virus.

Parainfluenza virus type 2 A species in the genus PARAMYXOVIRUS. There are strains with a human or simian origin. Antibodies are common in man, and in monkeys who have been in contact with humans. A human strain causes acute laryngo-tracheitis (croup) in young children and occasionally mild upper respiratory tract infections in older children and adults. There may be more than one type of the virus. It is best isolated in primary human or monkey kidney cell cultures or diploid human cell lines. Replication is poor in eggs. CPE may be slight at first but becomes more marked on passage. Syncytia are formed which float off leaving holes in the cell sheet. HAEMADSORPTION is better with chick than human cells, but may not be demonstrable until the 10th day on primary isolation. Hamsters and guinea pigs can be infected with the virus but no pathological changes are produced. Simian strains (SIMIAN VIRUS 5 and 41) are sometimes classified as PARAINFLUENZA VIRUS TYPE 5.
SYN: acute laryngo-tracheo-bronchitis virus; croup-associated virus.

Parainfluenza virus type 3 A species in the genus PARAMYXOVIRUS consisting of human, bovine and ovine strains which can be differentiated by NEUTRALIZATION, haemagglutination inhibition, CF and immunodiffusion tests. Isolation is most efficient in primary human or monkey kidney cell cultures but the virus will replicate in cell lines such as HELA and HEP2. CPE on isolation may be minimal and HAEMADSORPTION is used. On passage the cell sheet is disrupted, the cells becoming long and narrow. Bovine strains replicate in calf, goat, buffalo and camel kidney cell cultures. The human virus causes pharyngitis, bronchiolitis and pneumonia in young children, especially in nursery schools. Uncommon cause of 'colds' in adults. Inoculation into young hamsters causes inapparent infection or small lung lesions. Bovine strains are normally harmless but under conditions of stress, cause shipping fever. Inoculation of calves causes fever, conjunctivitis and rhinitis. Transmission to man is doubtful.
SYN: haemadsorption virus 1, shipping fever virus.

Parainfluenza virus type 4 A species in the genus PARAMYXOVIRUS. Isolation best in primary monkey kidney cell cultures but HAEMADSORPTION may not be demonstrable for 3–4 weeks. Agglutinates guinea pig and rhesus monkey cells better than human cells. CPE poor in early passages. Common infection of young children causing mild respiratory disease but the virus not easily isolated. No evidence of virus replication in eggs. Two antigenic types A and B recognized by haemagglutination inhibition tests. Not pathogenic for laboratory animals but produces high antibody levels in guinea pigs.

Parainfluenza virus type 5 A species in the genus PARAMYXOVIRUS, consisting of SIMIAN VIRUSES 5 and 41. Often found in cultures of 'normal' monkey kidney cells, but not known to cause disease. Though a common infection in laboratories, antibodies are rarely present in wild monkeys. Vervet monkeys and baboons can be infected intranasally and transmit infection to contacts. Strains similar to SV5 have been isolated from dogs with upper respiratory disease. A virus related to but distinct from SV41 has been isolated from bats. Human infection may occur, but it is uncommon and the disease produced uncertain.

Paramaribo virus

Young N.A. & Johnson K.M. (1969) *Am. J. Epidemiol.* **89**, 286

A strain of VENEZUELAN EQUINE ENCEPHALOMYELITIS VIRUS, antigenic group III. First isolated in Paramaribo, Surinam.

Paramushir virus

Lvov D.K. *et al.* (1976) *Arch. Virol.* **51**, 157

An unclassified ARBOVIRUS. Isolated from the ticks *Ixodes signatus* and *I. putus* collected on Tyuleniy, Bering and Paramushir Islands in the N. of the Soviet Far East, where there are colonies of guillemots *Uria aalge* and cormorants *Phalacrocorax pelagicus*. Pathogenic for suckling mice on i/c injection, replicates without CPE in chick embryo fibroblasts, human and BHK-21 CELLS. Virus diameter between 50 and 100 nm, sensitive to lipid solvents and contains RNA. Not reported to cause disease in humans.

Paramyxoviridae

Kingsbury D.W. *et al.* (1978) *Intervirology* **10**, 137

A family of large RNA viruses. Similar to the ORTHOMYXOVIRIDAE except that (1) they contain a larger helical NUCLEOCAPSID, up to 18 nm by 1000 nm (2) they have a GENOME consisting of a single continuous RNA molecule, and (3) their replication is not inhibited by ACTINOMYCIN D. VIRIONS consist of a helical ribonucleo-protein nucleocapsid contained in an approximately spherical ENVELOPE 150–200 nm in diameter. Larger virions 500–600 nm in diameter and filamentous forms are occasionally observed. The surface is covered with projections 8–12 nm in length which can be removed by treatment with PRONASE, which abolishes the haemagglutinating and NEURAMINIDASE activity of the virion but does not disrupt it. Both activities appear to be functions of one protein. The RNA is a single NEGATIVE STRAND molecule of mol. wt. $5–6 \times 10^6$. Can be propagated in tissue cultures, usually with CPE, HAEMADSORPTION and syncytium formation. Most species replicate in embryonated eggs. Replication occurs entirely in the cytoplasm. Inactivated by lipid solvents. Paramyxoviruses cause a wide spectrum of disease in man and other animals. They can cause persistent infection in cultured cells and probably in animals, as well as cell fusion and lysis of erythrocytes. The ability to fuse cells and produce hybrids is used in cell genetics and in the study of cellular regulation of growth. There are three genera: PARAMYXOVIRUS, MORBILLIVIRUS and PNEUMOVIRUS.

Paramyxovirus

Kingsbury D.W. (1978) *Intervirology* **10**, 137

A genus of the family PARAMYXOVIRIDAE. VIRIONS contain haemagglutinin and NEURAMINIDASE. NUCLEOCAPSID is 18 nm in diameter with helical pitch of 5 to 6 nm, PEPLOMERS 8 nm long, spaced 8 to 10 nm from each other. Type species is NEWCASTLE DISEASE VIRUS. Other species are MUMPS VIRUS, PARAINFLUENZA 1, 2, 3 and 4 and a variety of species isolated from domestic and wild animals.

Parana virus A species in the genus ARENAVIRUS. One of the AMERICAN HAEMORRHAGIC FEVER VIRUSES. Belongs to the TACARIBE ANTIGENIC GROUP. Isolated from the rodent *Oryzomys buccinatus* in Paraguay. Not reported to cause disease in humans.

Parapoxvirus

Wittek R. *et al.* (1979) *J. gen. Virol.* **43**, 231

A genus of the subfamily CHORDOPOXVIRINAE. Consists of viruses of ungulates which may infect man. Infectivity ether-sensitive. VIRION ovoid, 220–300 × 140–170 nm. External COAT and filaments are thicker than in VACCINIA and are arranged in a regular spiral coil consisting of a single thread. Species show serological cross-reactivity. Haemagglutinin not produced. Type species ORF VIRUS. Other species are BOVINE PUSTULAR STOMATITIS VIRUS, CONTAGIOUS ECTHYMA VIRUS, and MILKER'S NODE VIRUS.

SYN: orf subgroup viruses.

Paravaccinia virus Synonym for milker's node virus.

Parma wallaby herpesvirus Synonym for macropodid herpesvirus 1.

Parramatta virus

Christopher P.J. *et al.* (1978) *Med. J. Aust.* **i**, 121

A virus seen by EM in faecal extracts from 14 patients with gastroenteritis during an outbreak in a primary school near Parramatta, Australia. Diameter 23–26 nm, morphologically like a PARVOVIRUS.

Parvoviridae (Latin: *parvus* = small)

Bachmann P.A. *et al.* (1979) *Intervirology* **11**, 248

A family of small DNA viruses. VIRION diameter 18–26 nm, non-enveloped, with 32 CAPSOMERES of diameter 3–4 nm and ICOSAHEDRAL SYMMETRY. BUOYANT DENSITY (CsCl)

1·39–1·42 g/cm³. GENOME consists of one molecule of single-stranded DNA of mol. wt. $1{\cdot}5$–$2{\cdot}2 \times 10^6$. G+C CONTENT 41–53%. In some genera the single strands from virions are complementary, and after extraction come together to form a double strand. Infectivity ether-resistant and relatively heat-stable. Replication occurs in the nucleus and is dependent on either certain functions of the host cell, or on a HELPER VIRUS. There are three genera: PARVOVIRUS, ADENO-ASSOCIATED VIRUS, and DENSOVIRUS.

Parvovirus (Latin: *parvus* = small)

Siegl G. (1976) *Virology Monographs*, vol. 15. Berlin: Springer-Verlag.
Tinsley T.W. & Longworth, J.F. (1973) *J. gen. Virol.* **20**, (suppl.) 7, 15
Hallaver C. *et al.* (1971) *Arch. Virol.* **35**, 80

A genus of the family PARVOVIRIDAE. Type species LATENT RAT VIRUS. Parvoviruses replicate in susceptible cell cultures without a HELPER VIRUS. Mature virus particles contain only POSITIVE STRANDS of DNA which have a hairpin structure at both the 5′ and 3′ ends of the otherwise single-stranded molecule. There are many species infecting a variety of vertebrates and most are host-specific. A number of parvoviruses have been isolated from cell lines, and their origins are therefore doubtful. Only the feline and related viruses are known to cause disease in the wild. The pathogenicity of the rodent viruses in the laboratory suggests parvoviruses may cause non-acute disease in man and other animals. Replication in cell culture is best in rapidly-dividing cells derived from tissues of the natural host, but usually produces only slight or transient CPE, making detection difficult. However, some species haemagglutinate, and infected cells haemadsorb. No group antigen and no antigenic relationship to other DNA viruses.

Paschen bodies ELEMENTARY BODIES found in cells infected with VARIOLA or VACCINIA VIRUSES. *See also* Buist bodies.

passenger virus Any non-pathogenic virus. When isolated from diseased tissue it has no causal relationship to the disease process.

Patas monkey virus

McCarthy K. *et al.* (1968) *Lancet* **ii**, 856

Synonym for cercopithecid herpesvirus 5.

Pata virus A species in the genus ORBIVIRUS. With EUBENANGEE VIRUS forms the Eubenangee antigenic group. Isolated from *Aedes palpalis* in Central African Republic. Not reported to cause disease in humans.

pathogens, viral: classification of *Code of practice for the Prevention of Infection in Clinical Laboratories and Post-mortem Rooms*, London: H.M. Stationery Office, 1978.

Category A: Viruses which are extremely hazardous to laboratory workers and cause serious epidemic disease. They require the most stringent conditions for their containment and work on them requires the endorsement of the Dangerous Pathogens Advisory Group of the D.H.S.S. They are:

Cercopithecid herpesvirus 1	Machupo virus
Crimean haemorrhagic fever virus	Marburg fever virus
Ebola virus	Rabies virus
Junin virus	Variola virus
Lassa virus	Venezuelan equine encephalomyelitis virus

Category B1: Viruses which present special hazards to laboratory workers and for which special conditions for containment must be provided. They are:

'Arboviruses' except Semliki Forest, Uganda S, Langat, Yellow fever 17D vaccine strain and Sindbis viruses

Hepatitis B virus when deliberately introduced into the laboratory

Creutzfeldt–Jakob disease virus in brain tissue

Multiple sclerosis virus in brain tissue

Coxiella burneti
Chlamydia psittaci } not viruses, but often handled in virus laboratories.

Category B2: Viruses which require special conditions for containment, but not special accommodation. They are:

Hepatitis virus A, B and C in pathological specimens

Creutzfeldt–Jakob disease virus in specimens other than brain tissue

Category C: Viruses offering no special hazards, provided high standards of safety are observed. They are:

Viruses not listed in A, B or C

Pathum Thani virus An unclassified ARBOVIRUS. Belongs to the DERA GHAZI KHAN ANTIGENIC GROUP. Isolated from a tick *Argas robertsi* in Thailand. Not reported to cause disease in humans.

Patois antigenic group viruses Four serologically related viruses in the genus BUNYAVIRUS. Found only in N. America.

Pahayokee (C)
Patois (C,R)
Shark River (C,A,R)
Zegla (R)

Isolated from:
(C) Culicine mosquitoes
(A) Anopheline mosquitoes
(R) Rodents

Patois virus A species in the genus BUNYAVIRUS. First member of the PATOIS ANTIGENIC GROUP. Isolated from cotton-rats *Sigmodon hispidus* and mosquitoes of *Culex* sp. in Panama and Mexico. Not reported to cause disease in humans.

Paul–Bunnell–Davidsohn test The Paul-Bunnell test as originally described consisted of a simple titration of the patient's serum for sheep erythrocyte-agglutinating antibodies. In order to distinguish between infectious mononucleosis, Forssman and serum-sickness antibodies (all of which agglutinate sheep cells) Davidsohn introduced an absorption step into the test, the patient's serum being absorbed with (*a*) guinea pig kidney tissue and (*b*) ox cells before titration of agglutinins. Guinea pig kidney absorbs both Forssman and serum-sickness antibodies; whole ox cells absorb serum-sickness and infectious mononucleosis antibodies, so that it is possible to distinguish between the three agglutinins.

	Sheep cells agglutinated		
		Serum absorbed with:	
Serum from patient with:	Serum unabsorbed	Guinea pig kidney	Ox cells
Infectious mononucleosis	+	+	–
Forssman antibodies	+	–	+
Serum-sickness antibodies	+	–	–

The test may be positive for only a short period, and if negative should be repeated at weekly intervals. It may not become positive until late in the disease, and becomes negative again in a few weeks. A very useful diagnostic test.

Paver virus

Paver W.K. *et al.* (1973) *Lancet* **i**, 237

Paver W.K. *et al.* (1974) *J. gen. Virol.* **22**, 447

A small virus 22 nm in diameter, seen by IMMUNO-ELECTRON MICROSCOPY in the faeces of patients with gastroenteritis and in normal subjects. Very similar in morphology and density on CsCl gradients to PORCINE PARVOVIRUS and MINK ENTERITIS VIRUS.

penetration

Lonberg-Holm K. & Philipson L. (1974) *Monogr. Virology*, vol. 9, Basel: S. Karger

The second stage of infection of a cell by a virus. After ATTACHMENT to a receptor area on the cell surface, the virus is taken into the cell either by fusion with the plasma membrane or by VIROPEXIS. The mechanism probably differs from one virus/cell system to another. With BACTERIOPHAGES the COAT remains outside the cell and only the NUCLEIC ACID is taken in.

pentons Groups of five protein units at the vertices of an icosahedral CAPSOMERE. In ADENOVIRIDAE the pentons are complex structures with base, fibre and knob.

peplomers Knob-like structures (spikes) projecting from the surface of a virus particle. They may have haemagglutinating activity and act as cell receptors, or have enzyme activity such as NEURAMINIDASE. They are surface antigens.

peplos (Greek: *peplos* = an outer robe or cloak as worn by women in ancient Greece.) Synonym for envelope.

peptidyl transferase Enzyme, part of the 50S subunit of the ribosome which forms the peptide bonds between amino acids.

permissive cells Cells in which replication of a particular virus can take place.

Peromyscus virus

Morris A.J. *et al.* (1963) *Proc. Soc. exp. Biol. Med.* **113**, 276

A species in the genus PARAMYXOVIRUS. Isolated from the pooled tissues of 4 wild white-footed mice *Peromyscus leucopus* trapped in Virginia, U.S.A. Replicates in embryonated eggs and a variety of cell cultures with CPE. Infected cells haemadsorb guinea pig erythrocytes. Kills suckling mice on i/c injection and hamsters on i/c or i/p injection. Antibodies are found in some humans and in wild *Peromyscus* sp. but not in laboratory mice or other wild animals.

persistent fraction Synonym for non-neutralizable fraction.

persistent infection

Mims C.A. (1974) *Prog. med Virol.* **18**, 1

Jack I. (1974) *Prog. med. Virol.* **18**, 160

The term encompasses a wide range of pathological processes in cell cultures and whole animals. In general the term is best described as including infections in which a degree of equilibrium is established between the virus and the host. In an animal host the chronic pathological process may or may not progress, with or without fluctuation in severity. Infective virus is intermittently or always recoverable. In cell cultures there are three types of persistent infection: CARRIER CULTURES, STEADY-STATE INFECTION, and a third in which the viral GENOME is integrated with the cell genome, as in cells transformed by tumour viruses.

Peste des petits ruminants virus Synonym for Kata virus.

pesticins BACTERIOCINS produced by *Yersinia pestis*.

Pestivirus A genus of the family TOGAVIRIDAE. Antigenically unrelated to viruses in other genera of the family. No invertebrate host. Type species PESTIVIRUS DIARRHOEA VIRUS. Other species in the genus: HOG CHOLERA VIRUS and BORDER DISEASE VIRUS.

Pestivirus bovis Synonym for pestivirus diarrhoea virus.

Pestivirus diarrhoea virus

Harkness J.W. *et al.* (1978) *Res. vet. Sci.* **24**, 98

A species in the genus PESTIVIRUS. Infection appears to be confined to artiodactyls – cattle, sheep, pigs, buffaloes, moose and deer. Causes mucosal disease with diarrhoea, fever and oral ulceration. Necrotic lesions are found in mucosa, hooves and lymph nodes. If primary infection occurs during pregnancy the virus may cross the placenta, causing abortion or foetal abnormalities. The disease is often mild and antibodies may be present in most members of a herd. Antibodies not found in man or horses. A related virus occurs in sheep in southern Germany and pigs in Australia. Serial passage in rabbits leads to attenuation of virulence for cattle and this virus may be used as a vaccine. There are probably at least 7 antigenically distinguishable types of the virus. It is spherical, 57 nm in diameter with a 24 nm wide CORE, and ENVELOPE without projections. Infectivity sensitive to lipid solvents, exposure to 56°, and to pH 3 or below. Replicates in bovine cell cultures without CPE.

SYN: bovine diarrhoea virus, diarrhoea virus of bovines, mucosal disease virus, pestivirus bovis.

Pestivirus ovis Synonym for border disease virus.

Pestivirus suis Synonym for hog cholera virus.

Pferdestaupe virus Synonym for equine infectious arteritis virus.

phage *See* bacteriophage.

Phalacrocorid herpesvirus 1 A species in the family HERPESVIRIDAE. Isolated on the CAM from a young little pied cormorant *Phalacrocorax melanoleucos*. Other birds and rodents are resistant. No evidence of pathogenicity for cormorants. Replicates on the CAM, producing pocks.

SYN: cormorant herpesvirus 1.

Phasianid herpesvirus 1 Synonym for gallid herpesvirus 3.

Phasianid herpesvirus 2 Synonym for gallid herpesvirus 1.

Pheasant leukosis virus

Fujita D.J. *et al.* (1974) *Virology* **60**, 558

A species in the subgenus AVIAN TYPE C ONCOVIRUS. ENDOGENOUS VIRUSES present in pheasant cells and capable of acting as HELPER VIRUS for defective ROUS SARCOMA VIRUS. ENVELOPE-characterised specificities of the virus from ring-necked pheasants *Phasianus colchicus* were group F, while those of the virus from golden pheasants *Chrysolophus pictus* were group G.

phenotypic mixing

Boettiger D. (1979) *Prog. med. Virol.* **25**, 37

Závada J. (1976) *Arch. Virol.* **50**, 1

The production, in a mixed infection, of progeny virus with phenotypic characters from two genetically different viruses, but with a GENOME derived from only one of them. The phenomenon is particularly common in viruses which mature by budding through the cell membrane. The DEFECTIVE avian and mammalian sarcoma viruses are always phenotypically mixed since their ENVELOPE proteins are coded for by a HELPER VIRUS. In an extreme case, where the genome of one virus is enclosed in a CAPSID coded for by another, it is described as transcapsidation (see adeno-SV_{40} hybrids) or genomic masking. Phenotypic mixing has also been accomplished artificially by physical encapsidation of the genome of MOUSE SARCOMA VIRUS with the envelope of CAT LEUKAEMIA VIRUS by ultracentrifugation of a mixture of the two viruses. (Fischinger, P.J. and O'Connor, T.E. (1969) Science, N.Y. **165**, 714)

n-phenylacetoaminomethylene-DL-*p*-nitrophenylanine

Fujita H. *et al.* (1979) *J. natn. Cancer Inst.* **62**, 565

An anti-viral agent. An amino acid-related compound. Prolongs survival time and reduces splenomegaly in mice injected with FRIEND LEUKAEMIA VIRUS. Reduces the yield of Friend and MOLONEY LEUKAEMIA VIRUS in mouse cell cultures. Mechanism of action not clear.

$$O_2N\text{-}C_6H_4\text{-}CH_2 \cdot CH(NH \cdot CH_2 \cdot NH \cdot CO \cdot CH_2\text{-}C_6H_5) \cdot COOH$$

Phlebotomus fever antigenic group viruses

Tesh R.B. *et al.* (1975) *Am. J. trop. Med. Hyg.* **24**, 135

Twenty-four serologically related viruses, all morphologically like BUNYAVIRUS but serologically unrelated to members of that genus.

Aguacate (P)
Anhanga
Arumowot (C,R)
Bujaru (R)
Cacao (P)
Caimito (P)
Candiru*
Chagres* (C)
Chilibre (P)
Frijoles (P)
Gordil (R)
Icoaraci (C,A,P,R,B)
Itaporanga (C,B,M)
Karimabad (P)
Nique (P)
Pacui (P, R)
Punta Toro* (P)
Rio Grande (R)
Salehabad (P)
Sandfly fever (Naples)* (P)
Sandfly fever (Sicily)* (P)
Urucuri (R)

**Cause disease in man.*

Isolated from:

(C) Culicine mosquitoes
(P) Phlebotomine flies
(B) Birds
(A) Anopheline mosquitoes
(R) Rodents
(M) Marsupials

Phlebotomus fever virus Five viruses (CANDIRU, CHAGRES, PUNTA TORO and SANDFLY FEVER VIRUSES of NAPLES and SICILY types) can cause phlebotomus fever in man, though only SF-Naples and SF-Sicily have caused large outbreaks. Both are antigenically distinct from each other and from other ARBOVIRUSES. Isolated from man in Italy, Egypt, Iran and Pakistan. Causes short, sharp fever after an incubation period of 2–4 days. Fever may be recurrent. Injection of the conjunctivae. There is pain in the eyes, head, back and limbs. Gastro-intestinal symptoms occur. There is leucopenia. Mortality nil. Not known to cause disease except in man. The sandfly *Phlebotomus papatasi* is the vector. Mouse-adapted virus given i/d to man produces immunity but no disease. However, prevention is usually by control of the vector. Replicates in human, mouse and hamster kidney cell cultures with CPE. Diagnosis confirmed by rising antibody titre or by virus isolation from blood in early stages of disease.
SYN: hundskrankheitvirus; pappataci fever viruses.

Phnom-Penh bat virus A species in the genus FLAVIVIRUS. Isolated from bats in Cambodia. Not reported to cause disease in humans.

phosphonoacetic acid (PAA)

Felsenfeld A.D. *et al.* (1978) *Antimicrobial Agents Chemother.* **14**, 331

An anti-viral agent, used as the disodium salt. Not VIRUCIDAL, does not block ATTACHMENT, PENETRATION or RELEASE, but inhibits replication by blocking DNA synthesis. When WI-38 CELLS are infected with HUMAN HERPESVIRUS 1 there is specific inhibition of the virus-induced DNA POLYMERASE (as compared to normal DNA polymerase). Also active against HUMAN HERPESVIRUS 2 and 5, EQUID HERPESVIRUS 1, MOUSE HERPESVIRUS 1, VACCINIA VIRUS, and to some extent HUMAN ADENOVIRUS 2. May have a future use in the treatment of herpes encephalitis.

```
        OH  H
        |   |
Na—O—P—C—C—O—Na
        ||  |  ||
        O   H  O
```

Disodium phosphonoacetate

phosphonoformate *See* trisodium phosphonoformate.

photodynamic inactivation

Kaufman R.H. *et al.* (1973) *Am. J. Obstet. Gynecol.* **117**, 1144
Myers M.G. *et al.* (1975) *New Eng. J. Med.* **293**, 945
Yen G.S.L. & Simon E.H. (1978) *J. gen. Virol.* **41**, 273

Inactivation of viruses by visible light in the presence of certain photoreactive dyes: acridine orange, acriflavine, brilliant cresyl blue, methylene blue, neutral red, proflavine and toluidine blue. The dye is able to pass through the cell membrane and become associated with the DNA. The anti-viral effect is seen when light energy absorbed by the dye causes photochemical oxidation of any viral DNA with which it has become associated. Limited clinically to treatment of superficial herpetic lesions. The partially denatured DNA could, in theory, be carcinogenic.

photoreactivation

Pfefferkorn E.R. & Boyle M.K. (1972) *J. Virol.* **9**, 474

The repair of u.v.-inactivated viral DNA by cellular enzymes activated by exposure to long-wave light. Such enzymes are found in the cells of bacteria, birds and frogs but not placental mammals.

Photo-Shootur virus Synonym for camel pox virus.

phycoviruses Synonym for cyanophages.

Phytoreovirus A genus of the family REOVIRIDAE containing species which infect plants and insects.

Pichinde virus

Leung W.C. *et al.* (1979) *J. Virol.* **30**, 98

A species in the genus ARENAVIRUS. One of the AMERICAN HAEMORRHAGIC FEVER VIRUSES. A member of the TACARIBE ANTIGENIC GROUP. Isolated from the rodents *Oryzomys albigularis* and *Thomasomys fuscatus*, mosquitoes of *Ixodes* sp. and mites of *Gigantolaelaps* sp. in Colombia. Not reported to cause disease in humans.

Picodna virus A name proposed but not adopted for the family PARVOVIRIDAE.

Picornaviridae

Cooper P.D. *et al.* (1978) *Intervirology* **10**, 165

A family of naked, ether-resistant viruses with icosahedral CAPSIDS 22–30 nm in diameter. The capsid is composed of several different polypeptides whose apparent size can vary between closely related strains, but whose aggregate mol. wt. lies between 80,000 and 120,000. Typically there are equal amounts of 4 major capsid polypeptides, 3 of mol. wt. 20,000–40,000 and one of mol. wt. 5,000–10,000. One molecule of each probably makes up the capsid structural unit. The capsid is composed of 60 structural units. There is one piece of linear single-stranded RNA of about $2{\cdot}5 \times 10^6$ which is infectious. It is the message for protein TRANSLATION and carries a polyadenylate tract at the 3′ end added transcriptionally. Virus multiplication occurs in the cytoplasm and functional proteins are mainly produced by processing and POST-TRANSLATIONAL CLEAVAGE of a nascent precursor. There are 4 genera: ENTEROVIRUS, CARDIOVIRUS, RHINOVIRUS and APHTHOVIRUS, distinguished by sensitivity to acid, BUOYANT DENSITY of the VIRION and clinical features of infection in susceptible hosts.

Picornavirus epidemic conjunctivitis virus

Lim K.H. & Yin-Murphy M. (1977) *Singapore med. J.* **18**, 41

A name proposed for ACUTE HAEMORRHAGIC CONJUNCTIVITIS VIRUS since the severity and frequency of the subconjunctival haemorrhages is very variable. This term would also include conjunctivitis due to COXSACKIE VIRUS A24.

Pig cytomegalovirus Synonym for suid herpesvirus 2.

Pigeon herpesvirus Synonym for columbid herpesvirus 1.

Pigeon pox virus *See* avipoxvirus.

Pig herpesvirus 1 Synonym for suid (alpha) herpesvirus 1.

Pig herpesvirus 2 Synonym for suid herpesvirus 2.

Pig infertility virus May be the same as PORCINE PARVOVIRUS.

Pig papilloma virus

Newman J.T. & Smith K.O. (1972) *Infect. Immun.* **5**, 961

A species in the genus PAPILLOMAVIRUS. Isolated from swine pancreatic trypsin in a line of pig kidney cells. Causes a slowly developing CPE over three weeks. Infected cells can be identified by immunofluorescence using guinea pig antiserum. Antiserum to SV 40 or POLYOMA VIRUS did not react with infected cells. VIRION diameter 36 to 44 nm. Replicates in primary embryo pig kidney and a pig kidney cell line.

Pig pox virus Synonym for swine pox virus.

Pike fry rhabdovirus

de Kinkelin P. *et al.* (1973) *Nature, Lond.* **241**, 465

A species in the genus VESICULOVIRUS. Causes haemorrhagic lesions in the muscles and kidneys of young pike *Esox lucius* and red swollen areas are visible on the trunk, usually above the pelvic fins. Causes a severe fatal disease in Dutch fish hatcheries. Isolated from diseased pike fry in FHM cells. CPE evident in 40 h. Pathogenic on injection into young pike. Not neutralized by antiserum to RHABDOVIRUS CARPIO.

SYN: red disease virus.

Pike type C oncovirus

Sonstegard R.A. (1976) *Prog. exp. Tumor Res.* **20**, 141

Sonstegard R.A. (1976) *Nature, London.* **261**, 506

A species in the genus TYPE C ONCOVIRUS. The Northern pike *Esox lucius* suffers EPIZOOTICS of lymphosarcoma. There are cutaneous lesions, and there is evidence of horizontal transmission during spawning. A C TYPE VIRUS and REVERSE TRANSCRIPTASE have been demonstrated in the tumour cells. Tumours often regress during the summer season.

Pink-eye virus Synonym for equine infectious arteritis virus.

pinocytosis *See* viropexis.

Piry virus A species in the genus VESICULOVIRUS. Antigenically related to VESICULAR STOMATITIS VIRUS. Isolated from an opposum in Para, Brazil. Laboratory infections have resulted in a febrile illness with myalgia, arthralgia and abdominal tenderness.

Pixuna virus

Shape R.E. *et al.* (1964) *Am. J. trop. Med. Hyg.* **13**, 723

A species in the genus ALPHAVIRUS. Closely related to and perhaps a serological type of VENEZUELAN EQUINE ENCEPHALOMYELITIS VIRUS. Isolated from rodents *Proechimys guyannesis oris* and mosquitoes in Brazil. No known association with disease.

PK (15) cells (CCL 33) A heteroploid cell line from the kidneys of a pig *Sus scrofa.*

plaque mutants Mutants producing plaques different in size or appearance from those produced by the WILD TYPE. Plaque size may be affected by speed of replication, sensitivity or resistance to inhibitors in the agar, and pH.

plasmids Genetic elements composed of DOUBLE-STRANDED circular DNA which replicate separately from the bacterial chromosome within the bacterial cell wall. Some can induce their direct transmission to other bacteria, though they differ from viruses in having no extracellular infective particle. Some plasmids are under stringent control and as little as one copy is replicated per GENOME. Others, under more relaxed control, replicate many copies per cell. They may carry genetic determinants which can be translocated from the plasmid to the bacterial chromosome. Some of these determinants mediate antibiotic resistance. *See also* episomes.

plating efficiency *See* efficiency of plating.

pleurodynia Synonym for Bamble disease.

plus strand Synonym for positive strand.

PML-2 virus Synonym for SV 40-PML virus.

Pneumonia of mice virus A species in the genus PNEUMOVIRUS. A common latent or mild respiratory virus infection of laboratory mice. Can be activated by serial intranasal passage of lung tissue in uninfected mice at 7- to 9-day intervals. Causes dense accumulations of mononuclear cells around the bronchi and blood vessels. Lung lesions are produced in hamsters but the virus cannot be serially passaged. VIRIONS 80–120 nm in diameter but filamentous forms occur. ENVELOPE covered with projections. There is a helical NUCLEOCAPSID 12–15 nm in diameter containing single-stranded RNA. Agglutinates mouse and hamster erythrocytes. Replicates in hamster kidney cell cultures and BHK_{21} CELLS, recognized by HAEMADSORPTION. Antigenically related viruses have been isolated from hamsters, cotton rats and rabbits.

pneumonia of rats

Brennan P.C. *et al.* (1969) *Lab. Anim. Care* **19**, 360

This very common chronic pulmonary disease of old laboratory rats probably has no specific cause, but a multiple aetiology in which Mycoplasma play a part. The many descriptive names given to chronic lung disease in rats do not describe specific diseases but rather clinical findings. Disease starts as a silent pneumonia and progresses slowly, often with the formation of pus-filled cavities and fibrosis. The nose and middle ears may be mainly involved. Pleuropneumonia-like organisms and bacteria as well as Mycoplasma are regularly isolated.

SYN: atypical pneumonia of rats; endemic pneumonia of rats; enzootic bronchiectasis of rats.

Pneumovirus

Kingsbury D.W. (1978) *Intervirology* **10**, 137

A genus of the family PARAMYXOVIRIDAE. VIRIONS contain neither haemagglutinin nor NEURAMINIDASE. NUCLEOCAPSID about 14 nm in diameter with a helical pitch of 6·5 nm. Type species HUMAN RESPIRATORY SYNCYTIAL VIRUS. Other species are BOVINE RESPIRATORY SYNCYTIAL VIRUS and PNEUMONIA OF MICE VIRUS.

pock assay Viruses which replicate on the CAM often produce local lesions called pocks, visible to the naked eye. Each one originates from an infected cell, so a count of the pocks produced is a measure of the infective dose applied to the membrane.

Pol gene

Sawyer R.C. *et al.* (1979) *J. Virol.* **29**, 856

One of the genes in the GENOME of the AVIAN TYPE C ONCOVIRUS. Codes for the REVERSE TRANSCRIPTASE of the virus: the *pol*ymerase, hence the name.

Polioencephalomyelopathy of mice virus Synonym for murine polioencephalomyelopathy virus.

Poliomyelitis virus type 4

Chumakov M.P. *et al.* (1956) *Probl. Virol.* **1**, 16

A name used at one time for coxsackie virus A7.

Poliovirus hominis Synonym for human poliovirus.

Polka fever virus Synonym for dengue virus.

poly (A) Polyadenylic acid. A stretch of polyadenylic acid up to 300 bases long occurs at the 3′ end of mRNA (histone mRNA is an exception) of all virus mRNAs which have been studied, including VIRION RNA of POSITIVE STRAND viruses.

poly (AU) A synthetic double-stranded POLYNUCLEOTIDE. Under the influence of polynucleotide phosphorylase, adenosine diphosphate molecules polymerise to form a polyribonucleotide containing only adenine bases. This is usually referred to as poly (A). Similarly, using uridine diphosphate, poly (U) can be obtained. If equimolar amounts of poly (A) and poly (U) are mixed in dilute aqueous solution they form a complex in which the adenine and uridine bases link together to make a double strand, known as poly (AU).

poly (C) Polycytidylic acid. A stretch of polycytidylic acid about 100 NUCLEOTIDES long, of unknown function, is found in the GENOME RNA of some picornaviruses.

polycistronic Carrying many CISTRONS. All viral GENOMES are polycistronic.

polyheads Abnormal T-even BACTERIOPHAGE heads produced by mutants lacking glycoprotein 20. They are of normal transverse diameter but of exaggerated length.

polyhedral cytoplasmic deoxyribovirus Synonym for Iridoviridae.

poly I poly C A duplex of polyriboinosinic acid and polycytidylic acid, formed in the same way as POLY (AU). A potent INTERFERON inducer.

polymerase *See* DNA *and* RNA polymerase.

polynucleotide A polymer of NUCLEOTIDE units. The phosphodiester linkage is through the 3 and 5 positions on the sugar ring. Long polynucleotides are NUCLEIC ACIDS.

polynucleotide kinase

Lockard R.E. *et al.* (1978) *Nucleic Acids Res.* **5**, 37

An enzyme isolated from BACTERIOPHAGE T4-infected *Esch. coli* which phosphorylates the 5′-OH termini of RNA or DNA chains. Used experimentally to label RNA prior to sequencing.

Polyomavirus A genus of the family PAPOVAVIRIDAE. The 72 CAPSOMERES are arranged in a right handed skew icosahedral lattice (polyomavirus and BK VIRUS confirmed) 45 nm in diameter. Mol. wt. of DNA 3×10^6; G+C CONTENT 41–48%. Several species haemagglutinate by reacting with NEURAMINIDASE-sensitive receptors. No antigenic relationship between most species in the genus. In their natural hosts most species cause SILENT INFECTION, but on injection into new-born animals (hamsters, mice etc.) most are oncogenic. Type species POLYOMA VIRUS.

Polyoma virus

Eddy B.E. (1969) *Virology Monographs*, vol. 7

Consigli R.A. & Center M.S. (1978) *C.R.C. Critical Reviews in Microbiol.* **6**, 263

Type species of the genus POLYOMAVIRUS. A natural infection of wild and laboratory mice. Causes no disease under natural conditions but if injected into new-born mice or hamsters it is highly oncogenic. Replicates with marked CPE in mouse embryo cell cultures. Hamster cell cultures are not permissive for virus replication but are transformed by the virus. Haemagglutinates erythrocytes of several species, e.g. guinea pig, at 4° by reacting with the NEURAMINIDASE-sensitive receptors, and non-enzymic elution occurs at room temperature.

polyoma virus transformation

Rassoulzadegan M. *et al.* (1978) *J. Virol.* **28**, 421

Type A transformed cells are those whose transformed state is temperature-independent although transformed by ts mutant virus. Type N transformed cells are temperature-dependent, reverting to normal at 39·5°.

polyploid virus Synonym for multiploid virus.

polyprotein A large polypeptide that gives rise to two or more proteins by enzymatic cleavage. For example, the HUMAN POLIOVIRUS GENOME codes for a protein of mol. wt. 250,000 which is subsequently cleaved to produce all the virus structural and non-structural proteins.

polyribosomes Synonym for polysomes.

polysomes RIBOSOMES attached to mRNA at intervals of 5–10 nm. In the process of protein synthesis the ribosomes pass along the mRNA strand, each forming a polypeptide chain as it goes.

poly (U) Polyuridylic acid. *See* poly (AU).

Pongola virus A species in the genus BUNYAVIRUS. With BWAMBA VIRUS forms Bwamba antigenic group. Isolated from mosquitoes in S. Africa, Uganda, Ethiopia, Kenya, Mozambique and Central African Republic. On injection kills new-born mice. Natural hosts sheep, cattle and donkeys. Antibodies found in humans but disease not reported.

Ponteves virus An unclassified ARBOVIRUS morphologically like BUNYAVIRUS but serologically unrelated to members of that genus. A member of the UUKUNIEMI ANTIGENIC GROUP. Isolated from a tick *Argas reflexus* in southern France. Not reported to cause disease in humans.

Porcine adenovirus

Bibrack B. (1969) *Zentbl. Vet. Med.* **16**, 327

A species in the genus MASTADENOVIRUS. There are at least 4 serological types. Some strains agglutinate erythrocytes of several species. Replicates in a wide range of cell cultures (pig, cattle, dog, hamster and man). Commonly found in the digestive tract of pigs. On inoculation intranasally into colostrum-deprived new-born pigs, the tonsils and lower intestine become infected but no symptoms or disease are produced.

Porcine enterovirus

Dunne H.W. *et al.* (1971) *Infect. Immun.* **4**, 619

A species in the genus ENTEROVIRUS. Usually a harmless inhabitant of the intestinal tract, but virulent strains can cause diarrhoea or Teschen or Talfan disease, which may be sporadic or occur in outbreaks. There is fever, convulsions, and paralysis which may be permanent in survivors. There is a diffuse encephalomyelitis. Disease is produced in no other species. A vaccine has been used successfully. There are at least 8 serological types. Strains causing significant disease are all in one serological group which can be divided into 3 subgroups: (1) includes Konratice and Bozen strains, (2) includes Talfan and Tyrol strains and (3) includes Reporyje strain. The serological subgroups are not correlated with virulence. Virus replicates with CPE in pig kidney cell culture and strains can be types T or V according to the type of CPE. In general does not replicate in cells from other species. Does not haemagglutinate.

SYN: Ansteckende Schweinelahmung virus; enteric cytopathic porcine orphan virus; enteric cytopathic swine orphan virus; infections porcine encephalomyelitis virus; porcine poliomyelitis virus; Talfan disease virus; Teschen disease virus.

porcine enzootic pneumonia

Jericho K.W.F. (1977) *Vet. Bull. Weybridge* **47**, 887

The clinical features and histopathology do not appear to define one disease. There may be more than one agent and the cause must be identified from each outbreak.

Porcine haemagglutinating encephalitis virus A species in the genus CORONAVIRUS. Found in Canada and the United Kingdom, associated with outbreaks of encephalomyelitis in suckling pigs. There is high mortality in young animals but older animals may survive though they grow less well. Adults may vomit and eat poorly but recover or merely have a silent infection. Virus is found in the respiratory tract but not in other tissues. It may be excreted for up to 10 days. No evidence of infection *in utero*. Virus replicates in primary pig kidney cell cultures causing the formation of multi-nucleate giant cells. Agglutinates rat, chicken, turkey, mouse and hamster erythrocytes at 22°.

SYN: Canadian vomiting and wasting disease of pigs virus; haemagglutinating encephalomyelitis virus of pigs; Ontario encephalomyelitis virus; vomiting and wasting disease virus of piglets.

Porcine parvovirus

Cartwright S.F. *et al.* (1969) *J. comp. Path.* **79**, 371

Joo H.S. & Johnson R.H. (1976) *Vet. Bull. Weybridge* **46**, 653

Mengling W.L. (1978) *Canad. J. comp. Med.* **43**, 106

A species in the genus PARVOVIRUS. A natural infection of pigs. Has been recovered from infertile pigs and aborted piglets. May be a cause of reproductive failure causing prenatal death without maternal clinical disease. Surviving piglets have virus in various organs up to 9 weeks of age. Has been isolated from cell cultures of kidney tissue from normal pigs. Pathogenicity doubtful. Agglutinates chick, rat, guinea pig, cat, rhesus, patas monkey and human O erythrocytes. Replicates in pig kidney cell cultures. Very similar or identical to KBSH VIRUS. Antigenically different from all other parvoviruses.

Porcine poliomyelitis virus Synonym for porcine enterovirus.

Porcine rotavirus

Lecce J.G. & King M.W. (1978) *J. clin. Microbiol.* **8**, 454

Bohl E.H. (1979) *J. Am. vet. med. Ass.* **174**, 613

A species in the genus ROTAVIRUS. Causes diarrhoea in young pigs.

Porcine transmissible gastroenteritis virus

Hamilton J.R. (1976) *Ciba Foundation Symp.* **42**, 209

Woode, G.N. *et al.* (1978) *Vet. Rec.* **102**, 15

A species in the genus CORONAVIRUS, with world-wide distribution. Causes a commonly fatal disease of young pigs. There is diarrhoea, vomiting, dehydration and death after 5–7 days. In pigs over 3 weeks there is more chronic diarrhoea but recovery is usual. Virus replicates in the small intestine and can be demonstrated in the faeces by EM. Infectivity survives drying at room temperature for 3 days. Spread by direct and indirect contact: starlings may play a role in the mechanical spread. Replicates in pig kidney cell cultures. An inactivated vaccine prepared in dog cell cultures has been used. Colostrum from recovered sows protects the young. There appears to be only one antigenic type.

SYN: transmissible gastro-enteritis of pigs virus.

Porcine type C oncovirus A species in the subgenus, MAMMALIAN TYPE C ONCOVIRUS. Identified in a cell line, originating from a lymph node of a leukaemic pig, after treatment with 5-BROMODEOXYURIDINE and DIMETHYL SULPHOXIDE. The porcine lymphoma cell particle (PLCP) is serologically distinct from mouse and cat oncoviruses but contains mammalian interspecies antigen b only. It is thus more like WOOLLY MONKEY and GIBBON APE TYPE C ONCOVIRUSES than the cat and mouse oncoviruses. It is ENDOGENOUS and the DNA sequences are present in the cellular DNA of domestic pigs and other species of the family *Suidae*.

Portillo virus A species in the genus ARENAVIRUS. A member of the TACARIBE ANTIGENIC GROUP viruses, and closely related antigenically to JUNIN VIRUS. Has been isolated from infants in Buenos Aires with haemolytic-uraemic disease.

positive strand One of the two possible RNA strands. The one which functions as mRNA is known as the 'positive strand': the complementary strand is called the 'negative strand'. *See* genome.

post-transcriptional modification Alterations in the structure of RNA transcripts prior to utilisation as mRNA. These may include SPLICING, CAPPING with a blocked methylated structure at the 5′ end, addition of POLY(A) at the 3′ end, or METHYLATION of certain bases internally in the RNA, particularly adenylic and cytidylic acids. These modifications all occur in most species of eukaryotic cell mRNA, and are apparently accomplished by enzymes in the cell nucleus. Viral RNA transcripts synthesised within the cell nucleus (e.g. RETROVIRIDAE, PAPOVAVIRIDAE, ADENOVIRIDAE, HERPESVIRIDAE) may be modified by these cell enzymes. Viruses replicating wholly in the cytoplasm (e.g. PARAMYXOVIRIDAE, RHABDOVIRIDAE, PICORNAVIRIDAE, TOGAVIRIDAE and POXVIRIDAE) carry similar enzymes in the VIRION or induce their synthesis in infected cells.

post-translational cleavage Division of a large protein molecule (POLYPROTEIN) after TRANSLATION from the viral GENOME. The polyprotein is cleaved at specific sites to produce smaller functional proteins; this may involve a series of cleavages as with HUMAN POLIOVIRUS (Jacobson M.F. & Baltimore D. (1968), *Proc. natn. Acad. Sci. U.S.A.* **61**, 77). Post-translational cleavage is a necessary feature of the replication of POSITIVE-STRAND RNA viruses, since it appears that eukaryotic RIBOSOMES only recognise one initiation site on these polycistronic genomes. Most other viruses induce the formation of monocistronic mRNAs during replication, so that functional proteins may be formed directly. Cleavage may also occur within the assembled VIRION. Cleavage of the surface glycoproteins appears to increase virulence in the case of PARAMYXOVIRIDAE (Nagai Y. *et al.* (1976) *Virology* **72**, 494).

Powassan virus

Wilson M.S. *et al.* (1979) *Canad. med. Ass. J.* **121**, 320

A tick-borne species in the genus FLAVIVIRUS. Isolated from a human case of fatal encephalitis in Ontario, Canada. The virus has been recovered from ticks *Ixodes marxi* and *I. cookei* in California, Colorado and New York State, U.S.A. Antibodies occur in squirrels and chipmunks in Ontario. Newborn mice can be infected experimentally, but not adults.

Poxviridae

Baxby D. (1975) *Prog. med. Virol.* **19**, 215

Fenner F. (1979) *Intervirology* **11**, 137

A family of large double-stranded DNA viruses. Brick-shaped or ovoid VIRIONS, 300–450 nm × 170–260 nm, with external COAT containing lipid and tubular or globular protein structures, enclosing one or two lateral bodies, and a CORE which contains the GENOME. There are more than 30 structural proteins and several viral enzymes, including a DNA-DEPENDENT RNA POLYMERASE. The genome is a single molecule of DNA of $130–240 \times 10^6$ mol. wt. G+C CONTENT of vertebrate species is 35–40% and of ENTOMOPOXVIRUSES about 26%. Genetic recombination occurs within genera; non-genetic reactivation occurs both within and between genera of vertebrate species. There are about 10 major antigens in the virion, one of which cross-reacts with most vertebrate species, and there is extensive serological cross-reactivity within genera. Replication occurs in the cytoplasm with type B (viral factories) and type A (cytoplasmic accumulation) inclusion bodies. Virus is released from microvilli or by cellular disruption. Ether-sensitivity varies between genera. A haemagglutinin separate from the virion is produced by ORTHOPOXVIRUS. There are two subfamilies: CHORDOPOXVIRINAE (poxviruses of vertebrates) and ENTOMOPOXVIRINAE (poxviruses of insects) and six genera: Orthopoxvirus, AVIPOXVIRUS, CAPRIPOXVIRUS, LEPORIPOXVIRUS, PARAPOXVIRUS and Entomopoxvirus.

Poxvirus avium Synonym for fowl fox virus.

Poxvirus officinalis Name proposed for VACCINIA VIRUS, but not adopted.

Pretoria virus An unclassified ARBOVIRUS belonging to DERA GHAZI KHAN ANTIGENIC GROUP. Isolated from the tick *Argas africolumbae* in S. Africa. Not reported to cause disease in humans.

Primate adeno-associated viruses

Hoggan M.D. (1971) In *Comparative Virology*, p. 43. Ed. Maramorosch K. & Kurstak E.

Four species in the genus ADENO-ASSOCIATED VIRUS referred to as Types 1, 2, 3 and 4. Antigenically distinguishable by NEUTRALIZATION, CF and precipitin tests. There is some antigenic relationship between type 2 and 3. Type 3 species has strains K, H and T, distinguishable by neutralization. Unrelated antigenically to BOVINE or AVIAN ADENO-ASSOCIATED VIRUSES. The presence of antibodies suggests that types 2 and 3 are human viruses and that types 1 and 4 are monkey viruses. No evidence of pathogenicity.

primer *See* DNA polymerase.

procapsid A stage or perhaps an artifact in VIRION formation. A viral CAPSID without NUCLEIC ACID.

Procyonid herpesvirus 1

Barahona H.H. *et al.* (1973) *Lab. Anim. Sci.* **23**, 830

A species in the family HERPESVIRIDAE. Isolated from kinkajou *Potos flavus* skin and kidney cell culture showing spontaneous CPE. Replicates in a narrow range of cell cultures; kinkajou, owl monkey and VERO CELLS with CPE. Produces A-type intranuclear INCLUSION BODIES. Probably non-pathogenic for kinkajou, rabbit and owl monkey. SYN: kinkajou herpesvirus; kinkajou kidney virus.

productively infected cell Cell in which complete virus particles are being formed.

proflavine A photoreactive dye. *See* photodynamic inactivation.

Progressive interstitial pneumonia virus Synonym for progressive pneumonia virus.

Progressive multifocal leukoencephalopathy (PML) virus

Meulen V. ter & Hall W.W. (1978) *J. gen. Virol.* **41**, 1

PML is a rare, slowly progressive, fatal and non-inflammatory demyelinating disease of the human CNS and probably an opportunistic infection by one of the PAPOVAVIRIDAE in patients with immunodeficiency due to disease or therapy. Two papovaviruses, JC VIRUS and SV 40-PML have been isolated from patients' brain tissue.

Progressive pneumonia virus A species in the subfamily LENTIVIRINAE. Causes a chronic

pulmonary disease in sheep. Affects older ewes and consists of slowly progressive loss of weight and dysphagia over a period of 3–12 months. There is nodular proliferation of lymphocytes in the lungs and thickening of interalveolar septa. First reported affecting sheep in Montana in 1923. Virus very similar to, or a strain of MAEDI VIRUS and the disease produced is similar or identical to maedi but may be confused with pulmonary adenomatosis. Transmission requires close contact indoors. The cough in maedi is dry and irritating while in adenomatosis there is hypersecretion. Transplacental spread does not occur but in ZWOEGERZIEKTE virus is present in the milk and lambs become infected.
SYN: progressive interstitial pneumonia virus.

proliferative ileitis of hamsters *See* hamster enteritis.

pronase

Huppert J. & Semmel M. (1965) *Biochim. biophys. Acta* **108**, 501

A non-specific proteolytic enzyme isolated from a fungus *Streptomyces griseus.* Useful as a preliminary treatment during extraction of intact RNA molecules from cells or virus because of its strong inhibitory action on ribonuclease.

prophage The BACTERIOPHAGE genome integrated into the GENOME of a LYSOGENIC bacterial cell.

prop-pox Synonym for scrum-pox.

protamines Simple basic proteins rich in arginine but lacking tyrosine and tryptophan. Present in cell nuclei. *See* histones.

protein kinase

Rubin C.S. & Rosen O.M. (1975) *Ann. Rev. Biochem.* **44**, 831

An enzyme which catalyses the phosphorylation of proteins, usually in the presence of a cyclic NUCLEOTIDE, cyclic AMP or cyclic GMP, though kinases utilizing ATP or GTP are known. Evidence is accumulating that the transforming gene of RNA sarcoma-inducing viruses (SRC GENE) codes for a protein kinase, which may play a crucial role in cell TRANSFORMATION (Levinson A.D. *et al.* (1978) *Cell* **15**, 561). The T antigen of PAPOVAVIRUSES has also been reported to have protein kinase activity.

protomers Protein units which polymerise to form a CAPSOMERE.

provirus The viral GENOME integrated into the cell genome with which it replicates. Can be activated spontaneously or in response to certain stimuli to produce complete virus. Analogous to a PROPHAGE and can provide the information for TRANSFORMATION of the host cell.

Pseudo-aphthous stomatitis of cattle virus Synonym for bovine papular stomatitis virus, though other viruses may cause the same clinical picture.

Pseudo-cow pox virus Synonym for milker's node virus.

Pseudo-lymphocytic choriomeningitis virus Synonym for ectromelia virus.

Pseudorabies virus Synonym for suid (alpha) herpesvirus 1.

Pseudorinderpest virus Synonym for Kata virus.

pseudo-type virus

Sengupta S. & Rawls W.E. (1979) *J. gen. Virol.* **42**, 141

A virus which may result from a mixed infection. The GENOME of one virus is enclosed in an outer covering coded for by the other.

Psittacid herpesvirus 1

Simpson C.F. *et al.* (1975) *J. infect. Dis.* **131**, 390

A species in the family HERPESVIRIDAE. Isolated in Brazil in 1931 from parrots especially of the genus *Amazona*, in which it causes weakness, diarrhoea, coma and death in 3–7 days. Budgerigars (*Melopsittacus*) are also highly susceptible. Disease is not produced on experimental inoculation of guinea pigs, mice, pigeons, chickens or turkeys. The virus has also been isolated from aviary birds in U.S.A. It can be propagated on the CAM where it produces white plaques and kills the embryo. Replicates with CPE in chick kidney cell cultures.
SYN: Pacheco's disease of parrots virus.

Pt K1 (NBL-3) cells (CCL 35) A cell line derived from the kidney of an apparently normal adult female potoroo *Potorous tridactylis*. Perhaps the first permanent marsupial cell line to be established.

Pt K2 (NBL-5) cells (CCL 56) A cell line derived from the kidney of an apparently normal adult male potoroo *Potorous tridactylis*.

Puchong virus An unclassified ARBOVIRUS. With MALAKAL VIRUS forms the Malakal antigenic group. Isolated from the mosquito *Mansonia uniformis* in Malaysia. Not reported to cause disease in humans.

puffinosis

Stoker M.G.P. & Miles J.A.R. (1953) *J. Hyg. Camb.* **51**, 195

An avian disease, probably caused by a virus, which is characterized by blisters on the foot-web of some sea-birds, particularly shearwaters. Occurs in U.K. as an EPIZOOTIC in late August to mid-September. Species of POXVIRIDAE and CORONAVIRIDAE have been isolated from infected birds but the causative agent has not been definitely established.

Pullet disease virus Synonym for infectious enteritis virus. *See also* blue comb virus.

Pulmonary adenomatosis of sheep virus A species in the family RETROVIRIDAE and probably in the subfamily ONCOVIRINAE. Causes a natural contagious disease of sheep in which there are multiple pulmonary adenocarcinomas which sometimes metastasize. The disease develops slowly and is most common in the 3rd year of life. In the terminal stages there is copious secretion of tracheo-bronchial fluid. The disease can be transmitted by a cell-free filtrate of this fluid or tumour extracts which contain REVERSE TRANSCRIPTASE activity associated with particles which have a BUOYANT DENSITY typical of Retroviridae. The viral NUCLEIC ACID is distinct from that of MAEDI VIRUS.

pulse-chase analysis An experiment in which a radioactivity-labelled precursor compound is added to cells or a cell extract *in vitro* for a short period (pulse), after which a large excess of unlabelled compound is added to dilute and prevent further significant incorporation of radioactivity. Samples are taken at various times to follow the course of the radioactive precursor as it is metabolised (chase period).

Punta Salinas virus An unclassified ARBOVIRUS belonging to the HUGHES ANTIGENIC GROUP. Isolated from the tick *Ornithodoros amblus* in Peru. Not reported to cause disease in humans.

Punta Toro virus

Robeson G. *et al.* (1979) *J. Virol.* **30**, 339

An unclassified ARBOVIRUS morphologically like BUNYAVIRUS but serologically unrelated to members of that genus. A member of the PHLEBOTOMUS FEVER ANTIGENIC GROUP. Isolated from *Lutzomyia* sp. and from man in Panama and Colombia. In man it can cause a febrile illness with myalgia, enlarged liver and spleen and increased protein in the CSF.

purine bases Bases derived from purine:

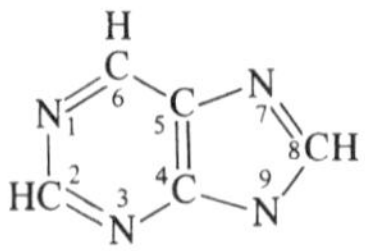

```
          H
          C
     N1 //6 \ 5C — N7
     |        ||      \
     |        ||       8CH
    HC2      4C — N9  /
       \\ 3 /
          N
```

They are adenine and guanine present in RNA and DNA. There are certain others found in small amounts in some NUCLEIC ACIDS. tRNA contains a wide variety of methylated bases including thymine. The unusual bases comprise less than 5% of the total in tRNA and vary in relative amount from species to species.

puromycin

Bablanian R. (1968) *J. gen. Virol.* **3**, 51

6-dimethylamino-9-[3-(*p*-methoxy-L-β-phenylalanylamino)-3-deoxy-β-D-ribofuranosyl]-purine. A NUCLEOSIDE antibiotic produced by *Streptomyces albo-niger*, and an inhibitor of protein synthesis. Can act as acceptor of the nascent polypeptide chain of RIBOSOME-bound peptidyl-tRNA which is then released prematurely. It can inhibit the replication of a variety of RNA and DNA viruses, and can also prevent the production of INTERFERON.

Pustular dermatitis of camels virus

Roslyakov A.A. (1972) *Vop. Virus* **17**, 26

A species in the genus PARAPOXVIRUS. Causes pustular dermatitis in camels.

P1-1-Ut (NBL-9) cells (CCL 74) A heteroploid cell line derived from trypsinized uterine tissue of an adult racoon *Procyon lotor*. Developed for studies of canine and feline viruses, since the racoon is one of the few animals known to be susceptible to both groups.

pyocins BACTERIOCINS produced by *Pseudomonas aeruginosa*.

pyran co-polymer A random co-polymer of maleic anhydride and divinyl ether. Protects mice against ENCEPHALOMYOCARDITIS VIRUS and VESICULAR STOMATITIS VIRUS. Toxic for man, causing fever and thrombocytopenia.

pyrimidine bases Bases derived from pyrimidine:

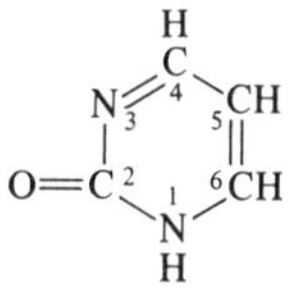

```
          H
          C
      N3 //4 \ 5CH
      |        ||
 O = C2   1   6CH
        \ N /
          H
```

They are:

cytosine, found in DNA and RNA
uracil, found in RNA
thymine, found in DNA
5-methylcytosine, found in DNA
5-hydroxymethylcytosine, which replaces cytosine in certain strains of coliphage.

Qalyub virus An unclassified ARBOVIRUS. With BANDIA VIRUS forms the Qalyub antigenic group. Isolated from the tick *Ornithodoros erraticus* in Egypt. Not reported to cause disease in humans.

Quail adenovirus

Aghakhan S.M. (1974) *Vet. Bull.* **44**, 531

A species in the genus AVIADENOVIRUS. Causes an often fatal respiratory disease of quail in U.S.A. The signs are coughing, sneezing and a sudden fall in egg production. Chickens and turkeys are also susceptible to infection. Inoculation into embryonated chicken eggs causes death of the embryo, with necrotic foci in the liver. In chicken cell cultures typical CPE is produced. Although quail adenovirus isolates may not be distinguishable in NEUTRALIZATION TESTS from strains of CELO VIRUS, they differ in pathogenicity.

SYN: quail bronchitis virus.

Quail bronchitis virus Synonym for quail adenovirus.

Quail parvovirus Synonym for a strain of avian adeno-associated virus.

Quail pox virus *See* avipoxvirus.

Quaranfil virus An unclassified ARBOVIRUS. With JOHNSTON ATOLL VIRUS forms the Quaranfil antigenic group. Isolated from the cattle egret *Bubulcus ibis*, and from pigeons in Egypt and S. Africa, but probably tick-borne. Has been associated with a febrile illness in man.

Quokka pox virus Synonym for marsupial pox virus.

Rabbit fibroma virus A species in the genus LEPORIPOXVIRUS. Antigenically closely related to MYXOMA VIRUS. Can be propagated on the CAM but no lesions are produced and the embryo is not infected. In cultures of rabbit, guinea pig, rat and human cells, replication occurs with CPE. The natural host is the wild cotton-tail rabbit in which the virus causes benign fibromas, commonly on the feet. Virus can be extracted from the tumours and produces fibromas in wild and domestic rabbits on injection. *See* Berry Dedrick phenomenon.

SYN: fibroma virus of rabbits, shope fibroma virus.

Rabbit herpesvirus Synonym for leporid herpesvirus 1.

Rabbit kidney vacuolating virus Synonym for rabbit vacuolating virus.

Rabbit oral papilloma virus

Parsons R.J. & Kidd J. (1943) *J. exp. Med.* **77**, 233

A species in the genus PAPILLOMAVIRUS. Appears to be antigenically different from RABBIT PAPILLOMA VIRUS. A natural infection of domestic rabbits causing papillomas, usually beneath the tongue, which regress in a month or two. On inoculation into the oral mucosa, papillomas appear in 6–38 days. Will not produce skin warts. *Sylvilagus* and *Lepus* can be infected.

Rabbit papilloma virus

Stevens J.G. & Wettstein F.O. (1979) *J. Virol.* **30**, 891

Bryan W.R. & Beard J.W. (1940) *J. natn. Cancer Inst.* **1**, 607

Type species of the genus PAPILLOMAVIRUS. The 72 CAPSOMERES are arranged with a left hand skew lattice. A natural infection of cotton-tail rabbits *Sylvilagus floridanus*. Domestic rabbits *Oryctolagus*, and several species of *Lepus* can be infected by scarification into the skin. Skin warts appear and regress but may become malignant, more often in domestic rabbits than in cotton-tails. Serial propagation in cell cultures has not been reported. Though rabbit erythrocytes adsorb the virus they are not agglutinated.

SYN: shope papilloma virus.

Rabbit parvovirus

Matsunaga Y. *et al.* (1977) *Infect. Immun.* **18**, 495

A species in the genus PARVOVIRUS, isolated from rabbit faeces. Replicates and produces CPE in rabbit kidney cell cultures. Agglutinates human group 0 erythrocytes at 4°. Stable at pH 3, resistant to chloroform and to 60° for 30 minutes. No cross-reaction with LATENT RAT VIRUS in HI tests. Probably a common non-pathogenic infection of laboratory rabbits.

SYN: lapine parvovirus.

Rabbit plague virus Synonym for rabbit pox virus.

Rabbit pox virus A species in the genus ORTHOPOXVIRUS. Very similar to VACCINIA VIRUS but more virulent for rabbits. After infection by the respiratory route causes generalized disease.

SYN: rabbit plague virus.

Rabbit type C endogenous virus

Bedigian H.G. *et al.* (1978) *J. Virol.* **27**, 313

A species in the subgenus MAMMALIAN TYPE C ONCOVIRUS GROUP. When primary lymphosarcoma cell cultures from WH/J rabbits were treated with IDOXURIDINE, C TYPE VIRUS PARTICLES were produced which contained RNA-DEPENDENT DNA POLYMERASE and a p30 structural protein. These proteins shared antigenic homologies with other mammalian type C oncoviruses but also possessed unique antigenic determinants. There was evidence that viral genetic information was present in the WH/J rabbit cells. These rabbits develop spontaneous lymphosarcomas.

Rabbit vacuolating virus

Hartley J.W. & Rowe W.P. (1964) *Science, N.Y.* **143**, 258

A species in the genus POLYOMAVIRUS. A natural and latent infection of cotton-tail rabbits

Sylvilagus floridanus. Not known to be pathogenic in any species. Agglutinates guinea pig erythrocytes at 4 and 20°, by reacting with NEURAMINIDASE-sensitive receptors. Replicates, producing cell vacuolation, in domestic and cotton-tail rabbit kidney cell cultures but not in other species.

SYN: rabbit kidney vacuolating virus.

Rabies virus

Debbie J.G. (1974) *Prog. med. Virol.* **18**, 241

Schneider L.G. & Diringer, H. (1976) *Current Top. Microbiol. Immunol.* **75**, 153

Turner G.S. (1977) *Recent Adv. clin. Virol.* **1**, 79

A species in the genus LYSSAVIRUS. The natural hosts are almost all terrestrial carnivores, but most animals can be infected. In dogs the incubation period is from 10 days to more than 6 months; in man from 15 days to 5 months but may be as long as a year. Dogs at first show excitement with salivation and often bite (furious rabies), later depression and paralysis (dumb rabies) and soon die. The same two stages are seen in man. In vampire bats only the paralytic stage occurs. In cattle and horses the signs are variable and diagnosis may be difficult. In some animals such as skunks, rats and mice the disease may be more chronic. In all species recovery is rare. The saliva of infected animals is highly infectious, and bites are the usual means of transmission though infection through superficial skin lesions also occurs. The natural reservoir of infection varies: in Europe the fox is the most important. After the second world war foxes became much more numerous and the virus was able to spread slowly from Poland across Europe. In U.S.S.R. the wolf, in S. Africa the mongoose, in India the jackal, and in S. and Central America the vampire bat are important reservoirs of infection. In the U.S.A. skunks, foxes, bats and raccoons spread rabies. Various vaccines have been used in man and other animals with some success. However, vaccines prepared from animal nervous system tissue are dangerous and egg or tissue culture vaccines are safer. An inactivated vaccine prepared from a diploid human lung fibroblast cell line is usually used. Britain and Australia are kept free of rabies by a 6-month quarantine of imported cats and dogs. On passage by i/c injection in laboratory rabbits the wild virus ('street' virus) becomes lethal in 4–6 days, but attenuated for man. This is now called 'fixed' virus and can cause a fatal encephalomyelitis in man, the 'rage de laboratoire'. All laboratory animals including chicks can be infected and die. There is encephalitis with degeneration, especially of the mid-brain and medulla. NEGRI BODIES are present in nerve cells and are a useful diagnostic finding. The virus can be replicated in most tissues of the embryonated egg and in a wide range of primary and continuous cell cultures. CPE may or may not be seen. Haemagglutination of goose erythrocytes occurs at 4° and pH 6 but is very sensitive to inhibitors in serum. The virus contains a number of protein antigens. Diagnosis in man depends primarily on a history of a bite from an animal proved to have rabies. The virus replicates in other tissues besides the brain and can be isolated in newborn mice and demonstrated by fluorescent antibody or by direct EM in saliva, urine, CSF, tears and skin biopsy.

SYN: hydrophobia virus; lyssa virus; rage virus; Tollwut virus; Wut virus.

Raccoon pox virus

Thomas E.K. *et al.* (1975) *Arch. Virol.* **49**, 217

A species in the genus ORTHOPOXVIRUS. Isolated from raccoons in Maryland, U.S.A. Experimental inoculation of raccoons resulted in a silent infection and antibody production. Injection into the footpads of suckling mice caused swelling and paralysis of the hind legs. Replicates on the CAM producing pinpoint white pocks, but growth decreased on passage. Replicates in VERO CELLS with CPE.

Rage virus Synonym for rabies virus.

Raji cells (CCL 86) A lymphoblastoid cell line established from a Burkitt's tumour of the maxilla in an 11-year-old negro boy. Grows in suspension. The majority of the cells in culture contain the EBNA ANTIGEN.

Ranid herpesvirus 1

Rafferty K.A. (1963) *Cancer Res.* **24**, 169

Granoff A. (1973) In *The Herpesviruses*, p. 627. Ed. A.S. Kaplan. London: Academic Press.

A species in the family HERPESVIRIDAE. A natural infection in *Rana pipiens* in N., Central and N. eastern parts of the U.S.A. and adjacent southern Canada. Probably the cause of renal carcinoma in these frogs. Replication occurs in frog cell cultures at 35°. G+C CONTENT 45%.

SYN: Lucké virus

Ranid herpesvirus 2 A species in the family HERPESVIRIDAE. Isolated from the urine of Lucké tumour-bearing frogs, but genetically and antigenically distinct from RANID HERPESVIRUS 1. Not oncogenic. G+C CONTENT 54%.

SYN: frog virus 4.

Ranikhet disease virus Synonym for Newcastle disease virus.

Rat coronavirus

Parker J.J. *et al.* (1970) *Arch. ges. Virusforsch.* **31**, 293

A species in the genus CORONAVIRUS. A common and usually silent pulmonary infection of laboratory and probably wild rats. Intranasal inoculation of new-born rats results in pneumonia and death after 6–12 days. Older rats are resistant but develop antibodies. Replicates in primary rat kidney cell cultures with CPE but not in mouse cell cultures. Does not agglutinate erythrocytes of mice, chickens, humans, guinea pigs or sheep. Antigenically related to MOUSE HEPATITIS VIRUS.

Rat cytomegalovirus Synonym for murid herpesvirus 2.

rate zonal centrifugation A form of DENSITY GRADIENT CENTRIFUGATION. As the particles begin to sediment under the influence of centrifugal force, they become separated into different *zones*, each containing particles of similar sedimentation *rate*. Particles studied by this technique should have a density greater than that at any point in the supporting gradient column, and the run should be brought to an end before any separate zone reaches the bottom. *See also* isopycnic gradient centrifugation.

Rat mammary tumour-derived virus (RMTDV) A RAT TYPE C ONCOVIRUS. Isolated from a rat mammary tumour induced by 7,12-dimethylbenz[*a*]anthracene.

Rat mammary tumour virus R-35 C TYPE VIRUS PARTICLES are present in a transplantable mammary fibroadenoma (R-35) which arose spontaneously in a Sprague–Dawley rat. The virus is also produced by a cell line in a culture derived from R-35. Purified virus injected into neonatal rats results in an increased incidence of mammary tumours which appear earlier in life than in control rats.

Rat sarcoma virus

Rasheed S. *et al.* (1978) *Proc. natn. Acad. Sci. U.S.A.* **75**, 2972

A RAT TYPE C ONCOVIRUS. A stable transforming virus of rat origin formed by the combination of a rat ecotropic type C virus with SRC GENES.

Rat submaxillary gland virus Synonym for murid herpesvirus 2.

Rat type C oncovirus

Bronson D.L. *et al.* (1976) *Proc. Soc. exp. Biol. Med.* **152**, 116

A species in the subgenus MAMMALIAN TYPE C ONCOVIRUS GROUP. An ENDOGENOUS non-oncogenic virus designed WF-1 was spontaneously released by a cell line WF-1 derived from a normal Wistar-Furth rat embryo. Closely related to two viruses (R-35 and RNTDV) produced by cell lines derived from rat mammary tumour tissue. All three are morphologically and antigenically similar but only RAT MAMMARY TUMOUR-DERIVED VIRUS (RMTDV) causes leukaemia on injection into rats. Can provide COAT proteins which renders MOUSE SARCOMA VIRUS oncogenic for the rat.

Rat virus Synonym for latent rat virus.

Rauscher leukaemia virus A strain of mouse leukaemia virus similar to FRIEND LEUKAEMIA VIRUS. Obtained by passage of filtrates of leukaemia mouse tissue in new-born BALB/c mice. A DEFECTIVE VIRUS requiring a HELPER leukaemia virus for replication. GENOME contains specific leukaemia-producing sequences very like or identical to those in Friend virus SPLEEN FOCUS-FORMING VIRUS and other sequences related to a different helper virus.

RAV Rous-associated virus.

RAV-O An ENDOGENOUS chicken virus which replicates in some chicken cells, but very poorly, and does not cause any known disease. Belongs to subgroup E of CHICKEN LEUKOSIS SARCOMA VIRUS. Recombination with horizontially transmitted wild strains of virus leads to a very virulent virus, suggesting that the endogenous virus may have accumulated defects during its residence in the chicken GENOME. Indistinguishable from RAV-60 in its ENVELOPE properties.

RAV-60

Hanafusa T. *et al.* (1970) *Proc. natn. Acad. Sci. U.S.A.* **67**, 1797

A ROUS-ASSOCIATED VIRUS isolated when fowl cells with the CHICK HELPER FACTOR were infected with an avian leukaemia virus RAV-1 or RAV-2. It belongs to subgroup E of the CHICKEN LEUKOSIS SARCOMA VIRUS. Propagates very much more rapidly in quail cells than RAV-O does but is indistinguishable from RAV-0 in its ENVELOPE properties. Unlike RAV-0 it causes leukosis in chickens.

Razdan virus An unclassified ARBOVIRUS. Isolated in suckling mice from a pool of female ticks *Dermacentor marginatus* collected from sheep in Razdansk Region, Armenian S.S.R. Diameter 100 nm by EM. Infectivity not sensitive to 5-BROMO-2-DEOXYURIDINE but sensitive to ether. Haemagglutinates goose erythrocytes. Not reported to cause disease in humans.

R.D.E. Receptor destroying enzyme. NEURAMINIDASE.

RD 114 virus A MAMMALIAN TYPE C ONCOVIRUS isolated when a human rhabdomyosarcoma cell line (RD) was passed in cat foetuses developing *in utero*. One kitten at birth contained RD tumour cells which were producing a type C oncovirus. Differs in major species-specific protein and REVERSE TRANSCRIPTASE from exogenous cat type C oncovirus, but very similar or identical to CCC CAT ENDOGENOUS TYPE C ONCOVIRUS. It is a XENOTROPIC VIRUS unable to infect cat cells and was at first thought to be a human virus.

reactivation A special type of RECOMBINATION. When one or more of the virus particles involved in a multiple infection is inactivated, and unable alone to initiate a productive cycle, it nevertheless can contribute to the production of progeny virus with the assistance of the other viruses, i.e. it is 'reactivated'. When the virus particles involved differ genetically, the process is known as cross-reactivation or marker rescue. If they are genetically identical and all are inactivated, the process is known as multiplicity reactivation. 'Non-genetic reactivation' is in fact not a case of reactivation, but a special example of COMPLEMENTATION of a virus inactivated by damage to its proteins rather than its GENOME NUCLEIC ACID. *See* Berry-Dedrick Phenomenon.

reannealing The coming together of complementary strands of NUCLEIC ACID after separation by melting. *See* hybridization.

reassortants Hybrid viruses which have derived parts of their GENOMES from two viruses involved in a mixed infection. This process is particularly likely to occur with viruses which have fragmented genomes, such as ORTHOMYXOVIRIDAE and REOVIRIDAE.

receptor-destroying enzyme NEURAMINIDASE.

recognizate

Madeley C.R. & Kay, C.J. (1978) *Lancet* **ii**, 733

A term proposed to describe the demonstration of the presence of a virus, and its recognition without it having been cultivated in pure culture. Cf. isolate.

recombinants Viruses containing NUCLEIC ACID sequences from two or more different virus GENOMES. They may be formed in either of two ways: intramolecular recombination, which involves transfer of sequences within single molecules of nucleic acid, or genetic reassortment, in which viruses whose genomes are fragmented into a number of pieces (ORTHOMYXOVIRIDAE or REOVIRIDAE) exchange whole pieces.

recombination The reassortment of genetic material from two or more virus particles into recombinant progeny virus during a mixed infection.

Red disease of pike virus Synonym for pike fry rhabdovirus.

Red nose virus Synonym for bovid herpesvirus 1.

Reoviridae (acronym: *R*espiratory, *E*nteric, *O*rphan)

Wood H.A. (1973) *J. gen. Virol.* **20**, 61

A family of unenveloped double-stranded RNA viruses infecting vertebrates, invertebrates, higher plants, bacteria and fungi. VIRION has an isometric two-layered CAPSID with ICOSAHEDRAL SYMMETRY, 60 to 80 nm in diameter, usually naked but pseudomembranes probably of host origin, are described. BUOYANT DENSITY (CsCl) 1·31–1·38 g/ml. 630 S. Virion contains an RNA-DEPENDENT RNA POLYMERASE. The RNA GENOME is in 10 to 12 pieces of total mol. wt. 10 to 16×10^6, all within a single virion. G+C CONTENT 42–44%. Resist lipid solvents. Genetic recombination occurs readily within genera. Viral synthesis and maturation occur in the cytoplasm. Inclusion bodies with crystalline arrays of virus particles are often seen. The vertebrate species are in three genera: REOVIRUS, ORBIVIRUS and ROTAVIRUS. The insect species are in two genera: PHYTOREOVIRUS and FUJIVIRUS.

Reovirus

Lee E.B. *et al.* (1979) *J. Virol.* **30**, 863

Stanley N.F. (1974) *Prog. med. Virol.* **18**, 257

A genus of the family REOVIRIDAE. Strains have been isolated from man and many other mammals and birds. The mammalian viruses are of 3 serological types of which type 2 can be divided into 4 subtypes. Human isolates of each of the 3 types are indistinguishable from those isolated from other mammals. The bovine isolate described as type 4 is probably type 2. The avian viruses are of 5 serological types. There are a number of group-and type-specific antigens. Reoviruses have been isolated from humans and other animals with a variety of febrile, enteric and respiratory diseases, but the evidence that they cause disease is not strong. They can often be isolated from the respiratory tract or faeces of normal humans and other animals. Injection of new-born mice with type 3 causes oily hair, jaundice and stunted growth though often with recovery. Types 1 and 2 more often cause cardiac and pulmonary lesions. Virus has been isolated from mosquitoes but replication probably does not occur in insects. Virus particle diameter 60–75 nm, BUOYANT DENSITY 1·38 g/ml, contains 14·6% RNA and 86% protein. RNA is mostly double-stranded and in 10 segments, but there is also single-stranded adenine-rich RNA making up 25% of the total encapsulated NUCLEIC ACID. Single-stranded RNA is not required for infectivity and its function is unknown. Surrounding the nucleic acid CORE are two protein shells with ICOSAHEDRAL SYMMETRY, but the detailed structure remains to be elucidated. The outer shell can be removed with trypsin leaving a subviral particle of diameter 40–45 nm. Mammalian strains but not avian agglutinate human group O erythrocytes. Infectivity is stable between pH 2·2–8, resists ether, 1% phenol, 3% formalin and 20% lysol but is inactivated by 70% ethanol. Mammalian strains replicate with CPE in primary and continuous cell lines derived from a wide range of animal species. Avian strains replicate with CPE in chick embryo cell cultures. Type species reovirus type 1. SYN: orthoreovirus.

Reovirus-like agent Synonym for rotavirus.

replicase An RNA-DEPENDENT RNA POLYMERASE catalysing the formation of new VIRION RNA from a COMPLEMENTARY STRAND template. *See* RNA-dependent RNA polymerase.

replicative form *See* RNA-dependent RNA polymerase.

replicative intermediate *See* RNA-dependent RNA polymerase.

Reptilian type C oncovirus group A subgenus of the genus TYPE C ONCOVIRUS GROUP. Natural host range restricted to reptiles. Type species VIPER TYPE C ONCOVIRUS.

reptilian viruses

Lunger P.D. & Clark H.F. (1978) *Adv. Virus Res.* **23**, 159

1 Green lizard papillomavirus	7 Viper type C oncovirus
2 Gecko virus	8 Elaphe virus
3 Elapid herpesvirus 1	9 Chaco virus
4 Iguanid herpesvirus 1	10 Marco virus
5 Chelonid herpesvirus 1	11 Vesicular stomatitis virus
6 Fer-de-lance virus	12 Togaviruses

Serological evidence of infection with several species has been found in snakes, alligators, lizards and turtles. It is suggested JAPANESE B VIRUS and WESTERN EQUINE ENCEPHALOMYELITIS VIRUS over-winter in snakes and turtles, and that EASTERN EQUINE ENCEPHALOMYELITIS VIRUS does so in lizards.

rescue *See* reactivation.

resistance-inducing factor (RIF) A fowl leukaemia virus which interferes with the growth of ROUS SARCOMA VIRUS.

Respiratory syncytial virus of bovines Synonym for bovine respiratory syncytial virus.

Respiratory syncytial virus of humans Synonym for human respiratory syncytial virus.

Respirovirus Synonym for human rhinovirus.

Restan virus A species in the genus BUNYAVIRUS belonging to the C GROUP VIRUSES. Isolated from *Culex* sp. in Trinidad and Surinam. Can cause a febrile illness in man.

restriction Host cell modification of viral DNA which restricts the virus to replication in the host strain. *See* restriction endonuclease.

restriction endonucleases

Roberts R.J. (1978) *Nature, Lond.* **271**, 502

Bacterial enzymes with a role in the host specificity of BACTERIOPHAGES. They are highly specific, recognising a particular sequence of 4–6 NUCLEOTIDES, where they attach and cut the NUCLEIC ACID chain. Thus they can inactivate foreign, incoming DNA. Host cell DNA is not cut because the specific sites have been methylated, and thus protected, by a methylase also present in the bacterial cell. This enzyme may also rarely methylate, and thus protect, incoming DNA molecules. The result of this is that an occasional cell will replicate a foreign bacteriophage whose DNA will then be methylated on formation and protected. The bacteriophage is thus adapted to the new host. There are two classes of restriction enzyme: Class 1 enzymes are complex multifunctional proteins which in the presence of SAM, ATP and Mg^{2+}, cleave DNA unmodified by methylation. They also function as methylases and ATPases. If the specific binding site is methylated in both strands the enzyme does not recognize it. If it is methylated in only one strand, the enzyme methylates the other. If neither strand is methylated the enzyme functions as an endonuclease, though it does not cut the chain at the binding site. Other sites are cut apparently at random. The endonuclease function occurs once only, after which the enzyme becomes an ATPase. Class 2 enzymes are simpler and only require Mg^{2+} for activation. They are neither methylases nor ATPases. They recognize a specific site on the DNA and if this is unmethylated it is cut. If one strand is methylated at the site, it is not cut, but the specific complementary methylase, also present in the cell, recognises the same specific nucleotide sequence and methylates the other, unmethylated strand. Class 2 enzymes are useful tools for the biochemist because they can be used to cut nucleic acid chains at specific sites. The resulting pieces can be separated by polyacrylamide gel electrophoresis, giving a characteristic pattern. In this way viruses can be differentiated, though by other tests they may appear identical. They can also be used as the first step in the sequencing of DNA and in the isolation of specific genes or analysis of the GENOME. Endonucleases are named after the bacterium producing them. e.g. EcoRI, HpaII etc. The first three letters identify the name of the bacterium. Where present the fourth letter identifies the strain. The final number indicates the particular enzyme.

restriction fragments Fragments of viral or cellular DNA produced by non-random cleavage of the DNA with specific endonucleases. The fragments of a particular DNA are characteristic. *See* restriction endonucleases.

Reticuloendotheliosis virus Synonym for avian reticuloendotheliosis virus.

Retroviridae

Coffin J.M. (1979) *J. gen. Virol.* **42**, 1

A family of large single-stranded RNA viruses which have RNA-DEPENDENT DNA POLYMERASE. VIRION about 100 nm in diameter. Lipoprotein ENVELOPE encloses an icosahedral CORE shell within which there is a helical NUCLEOCAPSID. The GENOME is one molecule of single-stranded RNA, mol. wt. 6×10^6, which dissociates readily into 2. Viral RNA is transcribed into a covalently-linked circle of double-stranded DNA (PROVIRUS) which is integrated into the cellular DNA. Viral RNA serving as mRNA and virion RNA for progeny particles is transcribed from the integrated DNA provirus. Replication is sensitive to inhibitors of DNA synthesis during the first 6 hours after infection, and to ACTINOMYCIN D at any time. Maturation occurs by budding from the cytoplasmic membranes. Provirus DNA extracted from infected cells is infective. There are three subfamilies: ONCOVIRINAE, SPUMAVIRINAE and LENTIVIRINAE.

SYN: ribodeoxy virus.

reverse transcriptase Synonym for RNA-dependent DNA polymerase.

Reye's syndrome

Griffin N. *et al.* (1979) *Archs Dis. Child.* **54**, 74

An acute encephalopathy with fatty degeneration of the viscera. Occurs in children and has a fatality rate of about 20%. Cause is uncertain but some cases have an association with various drugs or chemicals. There are often symptoms and signs of upper respiratory tract infection and an association with various viruses has been suggested, but the evidence is not very strong and environmental or constitutional factors may be important. The viruses which may be involved are INFLUENZA VIRUS B, INFLUENZA VIRUS A, PARAINFLUENZA VIRUS, HUMAN ADENOVIRUS, HUMAN HERPESVIRUS 3 and HUMAN RESPIRATORY SYNCYTIAL VIRUS.

RF virus

Dougherty R.M. & DiStefano H.S. (1974) *Proc. Soc. exp. Biol. Med.* **145**, 481

Miao R. & Dougherty R.M. (1977) *J. gen. Virol.* **35**, 67

A species in the genus POLYOMAVIRUS. Isolated in human embryo kidney cell culture from the urine of a renal transplant patient. Antigenically indistinguishable from BK VIRUS and their DNAs have an 88% homology. Both haemagglutinate, grow better in human monkey cells, are oncogenic in hamsters *in vivo* and transform hamster cells *in vitro*, but RF virus is more oncogenic in new-born hamsters.

Rhabdoviridae

Brown F. *et al.* (1979) *Intervirology* **12**, 1

A family of RNA NEGATIVE STRAND VIRUSES comprising at least 4 genera and 75 species which infect vertebrates, invertebrates and plants. Many species are pathogenic and transmitted by arthropods. Rhabdoviruses are rod-shaped, varying in length 130–380 nm but more uniform in diameter (60–95 nm). The animal species are bullet-shaped, being flattened at one end and pointed at the other whereas the plant species are rounded at both ends. They all have a membranous ENVELOPE with spikes 5–10 nm long. The envelope is disrupted by lipid solvents. Wound inside the envelope is a helical NUCLEOCAPSID with a diameter of 50 nm. There is one molecule of SINGLE-STRANDED RNA which is not infective and is transcribed into several RNA species. There is an RNA-DEPENDENT RNA POLYMERASE in the nucelocapsid which makes it infective in the absence of the envelope. Most of the species which have been studied contain 5 proteins designated L (large) G (glycoprotein) N (nucleoprotein) NS (non-structural) and M (matrix). Defective truncated VIRIONS (T virions) with a segment of RNA deleted and non-infective, occur in most species. Two genera, LYSSAVIRUS and VESICULOVIRUS, have been set up to accommodate some of the animal species.

Rhabdovirus carpio

Roy P. & Clewley J.P. (1978) *J. Virol.* **25**, 912

Bucke D. & Finlay J. (1979) *Vet. Rec.* **104**, 69

A species in the genus VESICULOVIRUS. Causes disease and death in fish farms in America and Europe. Primarily a pathogen of carp but can infect pike. Replicates in FHM CELLS, most rapidly at 20–22°, but can replicate at 31°. Antigenically related to SWIM-BLADDER INFLAMMATION VIRUS.

SYN: infectious dropsy of carp virus; spring viraemia of carp virus.

Rhinoceros pox virus Probably an AVIPOXVIRUS. Causes disease in captive rhinoceroses. Can be propagated in chick embryos.

Rhinovirus A genus of the family PICORNAVIRIDAE. Distinguished from ENTEROVIRUS by (1) being unstable below pH 6, (2) density of 1·39–1·45 g/ml and (3) the disease produced. Species are HUMAN RHINOVIRUS, EQUINE RHINOVIRUS, and BOVINE RHINOVIRUS. They infect the respiratory tract and transmission is by air-borne droplets or contamination with respiratory tract secretions. Type species HUMAN RHINOVIRUS 1A.

ribavirin

Oxford J.S. (1975) *J. gen. Virol.* **28**, 409

Stephen E.L. & Jahrling P.B. (1979) *Lancet* **i**, 268

1-β-D-ribofuranosyl-1,2,4-triazole-3-carboxamide. An antiviral agent. A synthetic NUCLEOSIDE analogue of guanosine. Interferes with biosynthesis of guanylic acid NUCLEOTIDES. Active against DNA and RNA viruses including INFLUENZA, PARA-INFLUENZA, MURINE HEPATITIS and LASSA FEVER VIRUSES. As good *in vitro* as CYTARABINE HYDROCHLORIDE, ADENINE ARABINOSIDE, and IDOXURIDINE against DNA viruses. It is superior to AMANTADINE both *in vitro* and *in vivo* against influenza virus A, A2 and B, and parainfluenza virus. Placebo-controlled studies of hepatitis A patients in Brazil showed that the drug accelerated the return to normal of elevated serum bilirubin and of liver enzymes in the serum. A comparable study in U.S.A. of hepatitis B patients revealed no such beneficial effect. Animal studies suggest that ribavirin can produce anaemia, immunosuppression and, in rodents, teratogenesis.

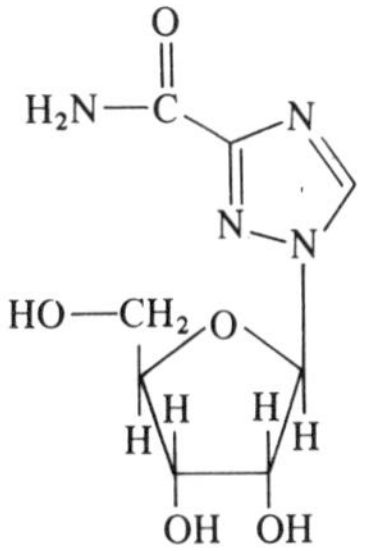

SYN: Virazole.

Ribodeoxy virus Synonym for the family Retroviridae.

3-(β-D-ribofuranosyl)-pyrazolo[4,3,-*d*]-6(H)-7-pyrimidone *See* formycin B.

1-β-D-ribofuranosyl-1,2,4-triazole-3-carboxamide *See* ribavirin.

ribonuclease A The principal active component of bovine pancreatic ribonuclease; cleaves phosphodiester bonds between pyrimidines and adjacent NUCLEOTIDES. Pure purine polymers are relatively resistant to attack by RNase A, but sufficiently high enzyme concentrations will degrade POLY(A), for example.

ribonuclease B A component of bovine pancreatic ribonuclease which can be separated from RIBONUCLEASE A by ion-exchange chromatography, and is present in ten-fold lower concentration.

ribonuclease from *B. cereus* A ribonuclease which cleaves the 3′-phosphodiester bonds after pyrimidine residues. Used in RNA sequence analysis (Lockard R.E. *et al.* (1978) *Nucleic Acids Res.* **5**, 37).

ribonuclease H

Robertson H.D. *et al.* (1975) *J. biol. Chem.* **250**, 3030

A ribonuclease which specifically cleaves the RNA strand present in a RNA-DNA hybrid, but does not digest free single-stranded or double-stranded RNA. Can be isolated from *Esch. coli*; also present as part of the VIRION-contained enzyme complex of retroviruses. Used experimentally to remove POLY(A) tails from mRNA after HYBRIDIZATION with poly(dT).

ribonuclease P A processing enzyme, involved in tRNA biosynthesis in *Esch. coli*, which cleaves tRNA precursor molecules, removing 5′ proximal NUCLEOTIDES to generate the 5′ termini of mature tRNA molecules.

ribonuclease Phy 1

Simoncsits A. *et al.* (1977) *Nature, Lond.* **269**, 833

A ribonuclease isolated from a slime mould *Physarum polycephalum.* Preferentially cleaves the phosphodiester bonds between guanine, adenine and uracil and adjacent residues. Used in RNA sequence analysis to discriminate between cytosine and uracil.

ribonuclease S A preparation of RIBONUCLEASE A in which the main peptide chain has been cleaved with subtilisin (proteinase from *B. subtilis*). The enzyme activity of RNase S is very similar to that of RNase A.

ribonucleases Phosphodiesterases that attack internucleotide bonds in RNA.

ribonuclease T_1 A ribonuclease isolated from TAKA-DIASTASE which splits phosphodiester bonds between 3′ guanylic acid groups and the 5′ hydroxyl groups of adjacent NUCLEOTIDES. It has also been termed guanyloribonuclease.

ribonuclease T_2 A ribonuclease isolated from TAKA-DIASTASE which splits phosphodiester bonds between any pair of NUCLEOTIDES, but displays a preference for adenylic acid bonds.

ribonuclease U_2 A ribonuclease found in culture broth of the smut fungus *Ustilago sphaerogena* which cleaves an RNA molecule at the phosphodiester bonds of purine NUCLEOTIDES to yield 3′ nucleotides with intermediary formation of purine NUCLEOSIDE 2′–3′ cyclic phosphates.

ribonucleic acid A polymer of ribonucleotides. Three of the bases, adenine, guanine and cytosine are the same as in DNA but uracil replaces thymine and a few minor or modified bases are present especially in tRNA. Complementarity of the bases seen in DNA is not evident. Thus long double strands are not formed but short stretches of base pairing occurs, producing loops. *See* poly (AU). In all types of cells there are three kinds of RNA: (*See* figure facing.)

(*1*) *ribosomal RNA* (*rRNA*) forms about 80% of the total. It is of high mol. wt. and is metabolically stable. It is of two main types. *See* ribosomes.

(*2*) *transfer RNA* (*tRNA*) forms about 15% of the total. Mol. wt. 23,000–28,000. There are tRNA molecules specific for each amino acid and on each molecule is an ANTICODON which locates to a CODON on the mRNA and so brings the amino acids into correct sequence in the polypeptide being formed.

(*3*) *DNA-like RNA* forms about 5% of the total and has a base composition corresponding very closely to DNA. It includes messenger RNA (mRNA) of mol. wt. $0{\cdot}5$–10^6. The DNA base sequence is transcribed to the mRNA and it is used to determine the sequence of

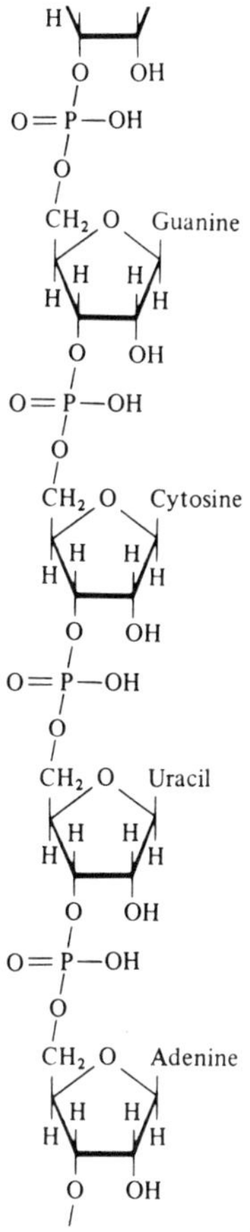

Four nucleotide units forming part of an RNA molecule.

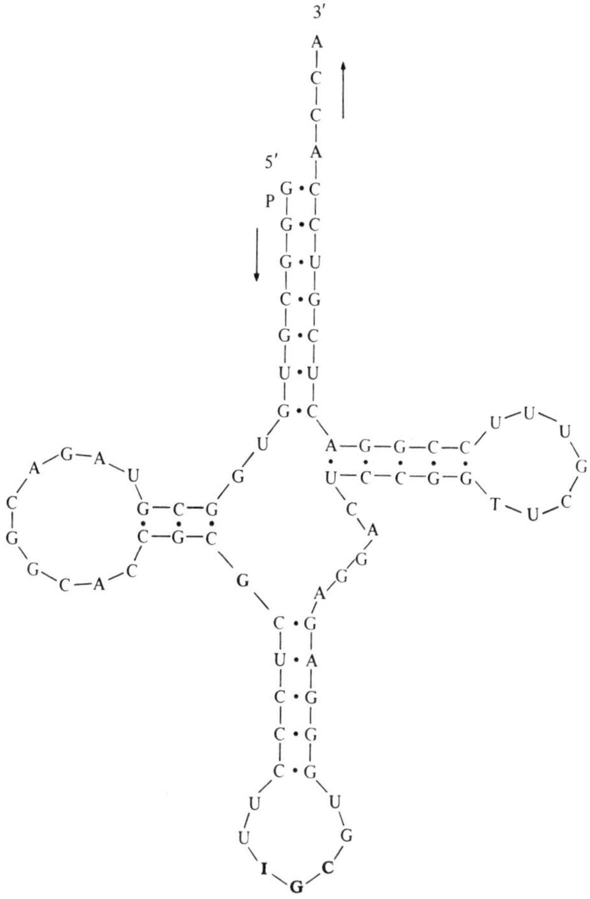

tRNA molecule showing short stretches of base pairing and the anticodon in heavy type.

amino acids in the polypeptide chain. There are other RNAs of different mol. wt. present in small amounts, often ephemeral and with no known function.

ribosomal RNA *See* ribonucleic acid *and* ribosomes.

ribosomes Small, round, electron-dense particles, 10–20 nm in diameter, found on the outer surface of the limiting membrane of the rough-surfaced endoplasmic reticulum. Also found free in the cytoplasm, sometimes in the nucleus and mitochondria, and present in all types of living cells. Name introduced in 1957 to distinguish the particulate ribosomes from membrane-associated ribosomes known as MICROSOMES, obtained on cell fractionation. They contain 40% protein and 60% RNA, and play a vital part in protein synthesis, attaching to mRNA to form POLYSOMES. Ribosomal RNA comprises almost 80% of total cellular RNA and is predominantly of high mol. wt. It has two main components: 30s and 50s. mRNA becomes associated with the 30s component and aminoacyl tRNA molecules bind to the 50s component in the order determined by the mRNA as the ribosome moves along it, the ANTI-CODONS recognising the CODONS. The amino acids carried by the tRNA are linked to the carboxyl end of the growing peptide chain under the influence of PEPTIDYL TRANSFERASE. The growing chain is linked to the ribosome by the last tRNA molecule until the next amino acid is attached. The former tRNA is then released to unite with another amino acid molecule.

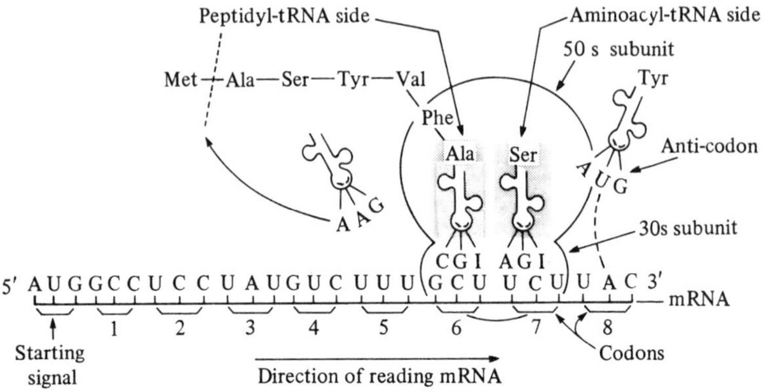

Diagram of a ribosome passing along a strand of mRNA.

Ribovirus RNA-containing viruses.

Rida virus An Icelandic form of SCRAPIE, probably imported from Scotland.

RIF Resistance-inducing factor.

rifampicin *See* rifamycin.

rifamycin An antibiotic which inhibits RNA synthesis in sensitive strains of *Esch. coli* by binding to a subunit of the bacterial RNA polymerase. Does not inhibit eukaryotic cell RNA polymerases, although 3-oxime derivatives with some inhibitory action against mammalian RNA polymerases have been described (rifamycins AF/05 and AF/013). Rifamycin also has some unexplained effects on virus-infected eukaryotic cells.

Will prevent focus formation by ROUS SARCOMA VIRUS (Vaheri A. & Hanafusa H. (1971) *Cancer Res.* **31**, 2032) and inhibits maturation of POXVIRIDAE (Pennington T.H. *et al.* (1970) *J. gen. Virol.* **9**, 225).

rifamycin-SV

Heller E. *et al.* (1969) *Nature, Lond* **222**, 273

Subak-Sharpe J.H. *et al.* (1969) *Nature, Lond.* **222**, 341

An antibiotic, and a derivative of rifamycin B, obtained from cultures of *Streptomyces*

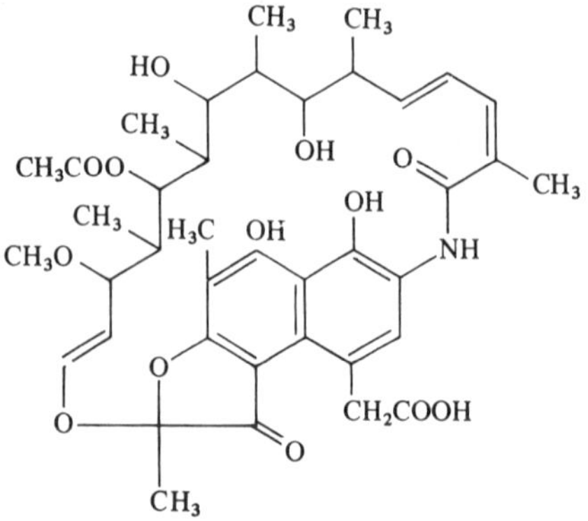

mediterranei. Inhibitory to VACCINIA VIRUS, various other poxviruses, adenovirus and trachoma agent (Chlamydia). Inactive against HERPESVIRUS and a variety of RNA viruses. Unfortunately, concentrations adequate for inhibition of 'sensitive' viruses are in the region of 75–150 μg/ml, unobtainable in human body fluids. The appearance of drug-resistant mutants of vaccinia virus suggests that the GENOME codes for a protein concerned with TRANSCRIPTION of viral DNA. Experiments *in vitro* show that transcription is inhibited before formation of the initiation complex, and that there is no effect if the drug is added after the DNA-DEPENDENT RNA POLYMERASE has started to transcribe.

Rift Valley fever virus

Imam I.Z.E. *et al.* (1979) *Bull. W.H.O.* **57**, 441

Ellis D.S. *et al.* (1979) *J. gen. Virol.* **42**, 329

Tomori O. (1979) *Res. vet. Sci.* **29**, 152, 160

An unclassified ARBOVIRUS, morphologically like BUNYAVIRUS but serologically unrelated to members of that genus. Found in central and southern Africa. Causes abortion and many deaths in pregnant and new-born sheep, goats and cattle. Lambs develop fever, vomiting, mucopurulent nasal discharge and bloody diarrhoea. Cattle are less seriously affected. Herdsmen often become infected and develop a biphasic illness which is usually mild, though retinal damage may occur. Buffalo, camels and antelopes may be naturally infected and die. Infection is mosquito-borne, but contact infection probably also occurs. Control is by protection from mosquitoes and by vaccination with mouse-adapted virus. Mice die of hepatitis when infected experimentally. Guinea pigs, ferrets and young dogs can also be infected, but birds are resistant. Virus replicates in cultures of chick, rat, mouse and human cells, and on the CAM, causing thickening. Virus diameter 90nm. Infectivity more stable than most arboviruses, but inactivated by ether. Haemagglutinates day-old chick cells at pH 6·5 and 25°.

Riley virus Synonym for lactic dehydrogenase virus.

rimantadine hydrochloride

Galegov G.A. *et al.* (1979) *Lancet* **i**, 269

α-methyl-1-adamantane-methylamine hydrochloride. A derivative of AMANTADINE HYDROCHLORIDE and an anti-viral agent. Good results have been reported from its use in the treatment of patients with INFLUENZA VIRUS A infections. Toxic effects include anxiety, nightmares and vomiting.

Rinderpest virus A species in the genus MORBILLIVIRUS. A serious natural infection of wild and domestic bovines in many parts of Asia and Africa. Ox, zebu, buffalo, yak, sheep, goats, pigs, camels, hippopotamus, warthog, giraffe and several other wild animals are naturally infected. In the acute disease there is high fever and constipation followed by diarrhoea. Inflammation and ulceration of the whole alimentary tract is the main pathological lesion, but patchy pneumonia may occur. Transmission is by direct contact and outbreaks usually start by the introduction of an infected animal. Control is by slaughter and use of vaccines. The virus is similar in structure to KATA, MEASLES and DISTEMPER VIRUS and contains cross-reacting antigens. Serum from rinderpest virus-infected cattle prevents haemagglutination by measles virus.

SYN: cattle plague virus.

Ring-necked pheasant leukosis virus

Hanafusa T. & Hanafusa H. (1973) *Virology* **51**, 247

A strain of subgroup F CHICKEN LEUKOSIS SARCOMA VIRUS. An ENDOGENOUS VIRUS present in normal ring-necked pheasant *Phasianus colchicus* cells, with genetic information to give group F host-range specificity to virus particles produced with it as HELPER VIRUS.

ring vaccination Vaccination of contacts and people who may come into contact with an infected person, so as to form a ring of non-susceptibles. A method used to control diseases such as smallpox.

Rio Bravo virus A species in the genus FLAVIVIRUS. Isolated from the salivary gland of a

bat caught in California. Similar viruses have been isolated in Texas and Mexico. No known arthropod vector and did not replicate in any of several mosquito species. In mice shows tropism for kidney, mammary and salivary gland tissue. Has caused laboratory infections associated with orchitis. No evidence that it causes disease in bats.
SYN: bat salivary virus.

Rio Grande virus
Calisher C.H. *et al.* (1977) *Am. J. trop. Med. Hyg.* **26**, 997
An unclassified ARBOVIRUS morphologically like BUNYAVIRUS but serologically unrelated to members of that genus. A member of the PHLEBOTOMUS FEVER ANTIGENIC GROUP. Isolated from pack rats *Neotoma micropus* in Texas, U.S.A. On injection into suckling mice causes death in 5–6 days. Replicates in VERO CELLS with CPE. Serological surveys suggest the pack rat is the principal natural host. Has not been isolated from haematophagous insects, so the vector is uncertain. Levels of VIRAEMIA are low in experimentally infected pack rats, so mode of transmission is uncertain. Not reported to cause disease.

RNA Ribonucleic acid.

RNA-dependent DNA polymerase An enzyme present in the VIRION of all RETROVIRIDAE. It uses RNA as a template for the formation of a DNA transcript. Like DNA polymerase, the enzyme requires a primer for DNA synthesis. The natural primer is a species of tRNA bound some 100 or so NUCLEOTIDES from the 5′ end of the GENOME RNA 35s subunit. The primer varies according to the virus species. It is $tRNA^{Trp}$ for avian sarcoma virus and probably for all avian leukosis viruses; $tRNA^{Pro}$ for MOLONEY LEUKAEMIA VIRUS, all other murine leukaemia viruses which have been examined, SIMIAN SARCOMA VIRUS, and AVIAN RETICULOENDOETHELIOSIS VIRUS; and $tRNA^{Lys3}$ for MOUSE MAMMARY TUMOUR VIRUS.

During establishment of retrovirus infection, the end product of RNA-dependent DNA polymerase activity is a linear double-stranded DNA molecule containing terminal repeats which subsequently becomes integrated into the cell genome. The enzyme has been purified free of the natural TEMPLATE and in this form is widely used for genetic manipulation and NUCLEIC ACID sequencing.

RNA-dependent RNA polymerase An enzyme unique to viruses, encoded by the viral GENOME, specific for its own viral RNA, and does not function for other viruses. It brings about TRANSCRIPTION of viral RNA to complementary RNA and this is in turn transcribed back to more viral RNA. It is not yet clear whether the enzymes involved in the transcription of VIRION RNA and of virion complementary RNA are separate gene products; most probably the two events are accomplished by the same protein which is modified during infection to accept the appropriate TEMPLATE. In viruses where the RNA is a POSITIVE STRAND and can act as mRNA, TRANSLATION commences immediately on infection and RNA-dependent RNA polymerase molecules are produced. These attach to the viral RNA and pass along from the 3′ end producing a COMPLEMENTARY STRAND which is thus synthesized from 5′ to 3′. This complex of one positive strand with about 6 or 7 complementary strands growing on it is called the replicative intermediate. The presence of positive strands and complementary strands results in the formation of some double helical strands, which are known as the 'replicative form'. This is an irrelevant end product and much of it may be formed during the process of extraction from the cells, particularly if phenol is used. In those viruses where the RNA is a NEGATIVE STRAND, the viral ribonucleoprotein has RNA-dependent RNA polymerase activity which means that mRNA can be made, as well as RNA to act as template for new virion negative strand RNA synthesis. RNA-dependent RNA polymerases which catalyse the transcription of mRNA from the virion negative strand are also termed RNA transcriptases; those which catalyse the formation of new virion RNA of whatever polarity are called RNA replicases.

RNA–DNA viruses A name sometimes used for the family RETROVIRIDAE.

RNase Ribonuclease. *See* nucleases.

RNase III

Robertson H.D. & Dunn J.J. (1975) *J. biol. Chem.* **250**, 3050

Dunn J.J. (1975) *J. biol. Chem.* **251**, 3807

An endoribonuclease from *Escherichia coli* which cleaves double-stranded RNA to single-stranded RNA of approximately 15 NUCLEOTIDES chain length. The enzyme also cleaves specific sequences in single-stranded RNA, and is responsible for processing large RNA transcripts of BACTERIOPHAGE T7 DNA into individual early mRNAs.

RNA ligase An enzyme isolated from BACTERIOPHAGE T4-infected *Esch. coli* which adds single residues (pNp) to the 3′ termini of RNA chains. Used experimentally to label RNA prior to sequencing by the gel method.

RNA polymerase An enzyme which catalyses either the formation of RNA from DNA, in which case it is DNA-DEPENDENT RNA POLYMERASE, or the formation of RNA from RNA, in which case it is RNA-DEPENDENT RNA POLYMERASE.

RNA processing *See* post-transcriptional modification.

RNA synthetase Synonym for RNA-dependent RNA polymerase.

Rocio virus

Monath T.P. *et al.* (1978) *Am. J. trop. Med. Hyg.* **27**, 1251

Lopes O.S. *et al.* (1978) *Am. J. Epidemiol.* **107**, 444; **108**, 394

A species in the genus FLAVIVIRUS, isolated from the brain of a patient with encephalitis in São Paulo, Brazil, by i/c injection into new-born mice. Caused an epidemic of encephalitis in several coastal counties of São Paulo in 1975. There were 462 cases, 61 of which were fatal. No virus was isolated from 420 sera from patients with encephalitis but 9 isolations were made from brain tissue. Isolated from 2 of 395 SENTINEL mice exposed in the epidemic area, and from a rufous collared sparrow *Zonotrichia capensis* collected in the same area. Epidemiology suggested a mosquito vector and possibly a bird natural host. Haemagglutinin present in mouse brain tissue. Serologically related to other Flavivirus but distinguishable from them. Pathogenic on injection into mice and hamsters. Replicates in VERO CELLS and BHK-21 CELLS with CPE.

Rodent paramyxoviruses

Jun M.H. *et al.* (1977) *Aust. J. exp. Biol. med. Sci.* **55**, 645

There are six species in the genus Paramyxovirus:

1 Parainfluenza virus type 1 murine
2 Pneumonia virus of mice
3 Peromyscus virus
4 Nariva virus
5 J virus
6 Mossman virus

Rodent parvoviruses Can be divided on their serological properties into four groups:

1 Latent rat virus
  H-3 virus
  X-14 virus
  L-S virus
  Haemorrhagic encephalopathy virus of rats
  Kirk virus.
2 H-1 virus
  HT virus
3 HB virus
4 Minute virus of mice.

H-1, HT and HB may be human viruses as they were apparently recovered from human tissues, but antibodies to them are rare in humans and they are pathogenic to newborn hamsters, a feature not yet observed with parvoviruses outside the rodent group.

Rodent (wild in Turkmenia) pox virus

Marennikova S.S. *et al.* (1978) *Arch. Virol.* **56**, 7

A species in the genus ORTHOPOXVIRUS, isolated in 1974 from the kidneys of a wild big gerbil, *Rhombomys opimus* caught in Turkmenia. It resembles COW POX VIRUS and CARNIVORA POX VIRUS but was markedly different from ECTROMELIA VIRUS. Apparently identical to viruses isolated from *Felidae* in Moscow Zoo. Experimental infection of the natural hosts, big gerbil, and yellow suslik, *Citellus fulvus* caused severe disease and high mortality. Transmission between cage mates occurred. Virus is present in urine for at least 3 weeks and in kidneys for at least 5 weeks.

rolling circle

Gilbert W. & Dressler D. (1968) *Cold Spring Harbor Symp. quant. Biol.* **33**, 473

A model for DNA replication which involves a circular intermediate molecule.

Ross River virus

Aaskov J.G. & Davies C.E.A. (1979) *J. immunol. Meth.* **25**, 37

A species in the genus ALPHAVIRUS. Isolated from birds and mosquitoes in Fiji, and Queensland and N. S. Wales, Australia. Causes a febrile illness and rash with arthralgia in man. The vectors are the mosquitoes *Aedes vigilax* and *Culex annulirostris*. Antibodies are present in horses, cattle, sheep, dogs, rats, bats and kangaroos in N. and E. Australia, New Guinea and northern Solomon Islands.

Rotavirus

McNulty M.S. (1978) *J. gen. Virol.* **40**, 1

Flewett T.H. & Woode G.N. (1978) *Arch. Virol.* **57**, 1

Brade L. & Schmidt W.A.K. (1979) *Med. Microbiol. Immunol.* **167**, 55

A genus of the family REOVIRIDAE. VIRION diameter 70–75 nm. The CAPSID is double-shelled with a clearly defined outer layer, appearing like the rim of a wheel, while the inner layer gives the appearance of spokes, hence the name. The outer layer is often removed spontaneously so that both double-shelled smooth and single-shelled rough virions are found in the gut contents. Virus replicates in intestinal epithelial cells. In vesicles within these cells it appears enveloped with a diameter of 87–90 nm. RNA double-stranded with 11 segments. BUOYANT DENSITY of 1·57 g/ml in $CsSO_4$. On polyacrylamide gel fractionation, 8 or possibly 9 polypeptides can be identified. There are species causing acute gastroenteritis in humans, especially infants, and in calves, mice piglets, lambs, foals, rabbits, antelope, hares, turkeys and chimpanzees. Very large numbers of particles are present in the faeces and are detected by EM. Species vary in the ease with which replication can be demonstrated in cell culture. Strains vary in the range of species which they can infect experimentally. Viruses from different animal species appear to be antigenically related by CFT, the common antigens being associated with the inner capsid. Species-specific antibodies are demonstrable by immunofluorescence or immuno-electron microscopy and the antigens appear to be in the outer capsid. Maternal antibodies probably provide some protection from overt disease and may permit SILENT INFECTIONS.

SYN: reovirus-like agent; stellavirus.

Rougeole virus Synonym for measles virus.

Rous-associated virus An avain leukaemia virus which acts as a HELPER for defective ROUS SARCOMA VIRUS, providing information for the COAT and thus controlling surface antigens and host range (*see* chicken leukosis sarcoma virus).

Rous sarcoma virus An avian sarcoma virus. A subspecies of the species CHICKEN LEUKOSIS SARCOMA VIRUS. The first virus demonstrated to cause a solid malignant tumour. There are a number of strains varying in their oncogenicity and host range. Some will produce tumours in mammals such as rats, cotton-rats, guinea pigs, mice, hamsters and monkeys. They are mostly DEFECTIVE and require a leukaemia virus to code for the viral COAT which determines host range. Transforms cells in culture which do not produce infective virus unless also infected with a leukaemia virus. Transformed cells cannot be maintained indefinitely in culture. The GENOME of the virus has a 'Src' sequence which is not present in leukaemia viruses and is responsible for cell transformation.

Rowson–Parr virus

Rowson K.E.K. & Parr I.B. (1970) *Int. J. Cancer* **5**, 96

A strain of MOUSE LEUKAEMIA VIRUS or LYMPHOID LEUKAEMIA VIRUS isolated from a FRIEND VIRUS preparation by end-point dilution. Causes a very minor degree of splenomegaly but is a potent depressor of the immune response. After a long latent period of 6 to 8 months neoplastic lymphoid cells appear in the germinal centres of the spleen and later in other lymphoid tissues.

Royal Farm virus A species in the genus FLAVIVIRUS. Isolated from a tick *Argas hermanni* in Afghanistan. Not reported to cause disease in humans.

RR 1022 cells (CCL 47) A heteroploid cell line derived from a tumour induced in inbred Amsterdam rats *Rattus norvegicus* by i/m injection of the Schmidt-Ruppin strain of ROUS SARCOMA VIRUS.

RTG-2 cells (CCL 55) A heteroploid cell line derived from pooled trypsinized male and female gonadal tissue of yearling rainbow trout *Salmo gairdneri*. The first cell line to be established from poikilothermic animals. Cells do not survive above 26°.

RT virus

Kawase S. & Kang S.K. (1976) *J. seric. Sci. Tokyo* **45**, 87

Hallauer C. *et al.* (1971) *Arch. Virol.* **35**, 80

A species in the genus PARVOVIRUS. Isolated from a line of rat fibroblasts, RT. Antigenically different from KBSH, TVX and LU III VIRUSES.

R type virus particles ('R' because of the structures radiating from the core)

Albu E. & Holmes K.V. (1973) *J. Virol.* **12**, 1164

Bergman D.G. *et al.* (1977) *J. natn. Cancer Inst.* **58**, 295

Enveloped virus particles 100 nm in diameter with a clear space between the central CORE and outer ENVELOPE. Across this space are radial threads. First described in BHK-21 CELLS, and later in calf kidney cells and hamster tumours induced by POLYOMA, SV40, ROUS SARCOMA and MOUSE SARCOMA VIRUSES. They are usually seen singly or in small groups within cell vacuoles. They have REVERSE TRANSCRIPTASE and can rescue mouse sarcoma virus from NON-PRODUCER CELLS. No known pathological role.

Rubarth's disease virus Synonym for canine adenovirus.

Rubella virus

Rawls W.E. (1974) *Prog. med. Virol.* **18**, 273

Vaccine: Banatvala J.E. (1977) *Recent Adv. clin. Viol.* **1**, 171

A species in the genus RUBIVIRUS. Causes a mild illness in man with generalized rash and enlarged lymph nodes. Usually little fever or constitutional disturbance. Incubation period 16–18 days. Meningo-encephalitis and other complications are rare but infection during the first 3–4 months of pregnancy often results in infection of the foetus and congenital abnormalities such as cataract, hearing loss, cardiac and dental malformations and microcephaly. Congenitally infected children have rubella virus antibodies but continue to excrete virus for many months. A very few cases of progressive rubella panencephalitis have occurred, commencing in the second decade of life and slowly progressive. Monkeys, rabbits, hamsters, guinea pigs, rats and mice can be infected experimentally, but show no disease except leucopenia and rash in some rhesus monkeys, and growth retardation in congenitally infected animals. Major epidemics occur every 9–10 years and 80–90% of young adults have antibodies. An active attenuated vaccine is available and should be given to all girls at the age of 12–14 years, if they were not immunized at 12–15 months of age. The virus is 50–70 nm in diameter, has a triple-layered ENVELOPE 8 nm thick surrounding an electron-lucent layer 11 nm thick and an electron-dense CORE 30 nm in diameter. Matures by budding from cytoplasmic membranes. The NUCLEIC ACID is single-stranded RNA in a single piece of mol. wt. 3×10^6. Infectivity sensitive to lipid solvents and pH 3. Day old chick erythrocytes are agglutinated at 4°. No antigenic differences have been observed between strains. Replication occurs in duck eggs and a wide variety of cell cultures, in which it may be demonstrated by INTERFERENCE with growth of another virus, by CPE or immunofluorescence. For isolation primary African Green monkey kidney cell cultures or BHK 21 CELLS are best. SYN: German measles virus.

Rubeola virus Synonym for measles virus.

Rubivirus A genus of the family TOGAVIRIDAE. Antigenically unrelated to viruses in other genera of the family. RUBELLA VIRUS is the only species in this genus.

Runde virus

Traavik T. & Brunvold, E. (1978) *Acta Path. Microbiol. Scand.* B **86**, 349

Traavik T. (1979) *Acta Path. Microbiol. Scand* B **87**, 1

A species in the genus CORONAVIRUS. An ARBOVIRUS isolated from the tick *Ixodes uriae* collected in sea bird colonies at Runde, Norway. No antigenic relationship to AVIAN INFECTIOUS BRONCHITIS VIRUS or to major arbovirus groups. Lethal to new-born mice but in two week old mice produces a persistent infection and chronic disease may result. Antibodies fail to neutralize virus infectivity completely. Replicates with CPE in BHK-21 CELLS. Haemagglutinates chicken erythrocytes. Antibodies are present in sea birds. Not reported to cause disease in humans.

Russian autumn encephalitis virus Synonym for Japanese B virus.

Russian spring–summer encephalitis virus Synonym for tick-borne encephalitis virus (eastern subtype).

Sabo virus A species in the genus BUNYAVIRUS. Belongs to the SIMBU ANTIGENIC GROUP. Isolated from cattle, goats and flies of *Culicoides* sp. in Nigeria. Not reported to cause disease in humans.

Saboya virus A species in the genus FLAVIVIRUS. Isolated from Kemp's Gerbil *Tatera kempi* in Senegal. Antibodies present in many mammals, birds and reptiles. Not reported to cause disease in humans.

Sacramento River chinook salmon disease virus

Klontz G.W. (1965) *Ann. N.Y. Acad. Sci.* **126**, 531

A species in the genus VESICULOVIRUS. Causes necrosis of haematopoietic tissues of spleen and anterior kidney in trout and salmon. Occurs as epidemic disease in fish hatcheries. The fish do not feed and often have a dark red subdermal lesion dorsally located at the back of the head. Replicates in FAT HEAD MINNOW CELLS or other fish cell lines with CPE. Closely related to INFECTIOUS HAEMATOPOIETIC NECROSIS VIRUS.
SYN: chinook salmon virus.

Sagiyama virus A species in the genus ALPHAVIRUS. Isolated from mosquitoes in Japan. On injection kills new-born mice. Not reported to cause disease in humans.

Saint-Floris virus An unclassified ARBOVIRUS. Isolated from a gerbil of *Tatera* sp. in the Central African Republic. Not reported to cause disease in humans.

Saint Louis encephalitis virus A species in the genus FLAVIVIRUS. The wild host is birds. Transmission by mosquito bites. Occurs in Canada, Western U.S.A., Central and S. America. In man most infections cause a brief febrile illness but encephalitis may occur. Sequelae are uncommon. Disease in horses not reported. Injection i/c of certain strains of mice causes encephalitis. Virus can be propagated in eggs. Causes diffuse oedematous lesions with proliferative and necrotic elements on the CAM. Replication occurs in cell cultures of chick, mouse and other species with CPE. No effective vaccine available for man.

Sakhalin group viruses Three antigenically related but unclassified viruses isolated from ixodid ticks taken from seabirds' nests.

Avalon
Clo Mor
Sakhalin

Sakhalin virus

Lvov D.K. *et al.* (1972) *Arch. ges. Virusforsch.* **38**, 133

An unclassified ARBOVIRUS. The first member of the SAKHALIN ANTIGENIC GROUP. Isolated from the tick *Ixodes putus* collected on Tyuleniy Island off the S.E. coast of Sakhalin Island where there is a colony of *Uria aalge* guillemots. Geographical distribution of the virus appears to coincide with that of *I. putus* and probably involves the Kuril, Commodore and Aleutian Islands and the N. coasts of Europe, Canada and U.S.A. It may also be associated with penguin colonies in the southern hemisphere. Virus 100–120 nm in diameter, contains RNA, inactivated by ether and sodium deoxycholate, and is pathogenic for suckling mice on i/c injection. No antigenic relationship to arboviruses of other groups. Replicates in experimentally infected *Culex modestus* mosquitoes. Antibodies are present in guillemots but not in a variety of other birds. Not reported to cause disease in humans.

Salanga virus An unclassified ARBOVIRUS. Isolated in suckling mice from the blood of a young specimen of the Kaiser's rat *Aethomys kaiseri medicatus* trapped in Salanga, Central African Republic. No haemagglutinin detected. Not reported to cause disease in humans.

Salehabad virus An unclassified ARBOVIRUS morphologically like BUNYAVIRUS but serologically unrelated to members of the genus. A member of the PHLEBOTOMUS FEVER ANTIGENIC GROUP. Isolated from female sand-flies of *Phlebotomus* sp. in Iran. Probably also present in Pakistan, as antibodies are present in humans and sheep. Not reported to cause disease in the wild.

Salisbury virus Synonym for human rhinovirus.

Salivary gland virus *See* cytomegaloviruses.

salmonid rhabdoviruses

1 Egtved virus
2 Infectious haematopoietic necrosis virus
3 Oregon sockeye disease virus
4 Sacramento River Chinook salmon disease virus

2, 3 and 4 are probably closely related. They are found in U.S.A. and Canada and cause disease in young fish. 1 is found in Europe and causes disease in young and sexually mature fish.

SAM S-adenosyl-L-methionine, an intracellular carrier and donor of activated methyl groups including those required for RNA or DNA methylation. Also required for the initial binding of class 1 RESTRICTION ENDONUCLEASES. The requirement for SAM may act as a device to prevent the enzyme cutting host cell DNA if methylation has been limited, due to methionine deprivation.

Samford virus

Doherty R.L. *et al.* (1972) *Aust. vet. J.* **48**, 81

Miura Y. *et al.* (1978) *Microbiol. Immunol.* **22**, 651

A species in the genus BUNYAVIRUS, belonging to the SIMBU ANTIGENIC GROUP. Isolated from *Culicoides brevitarsis* in S.E. Queensland, Australia. Antibodies are present in cattle and horses. Antigenically indistinguishable from AINO VIRUS, a name which has priority. Not reported to cause disease in humans.

San Angelo virus A species in the genus BUNYAVIRUS and a member of the CALIFORNIA ANTIGENIC GROUP. Isolated from mosquitoes in Texas, U.S.A. Antibodies found in raccoons and opossums. Not reported to cause disease in humans.

Sandfly fever (Naples) virus An unclassified ARBOVIRUS, morphologically like BUNYAVIRUS but serologically unrelated to members of that genus. A member of the PHLEBOTOMUS FEVER ANTIGENIC GROUP. Antigenically distinct from SANDFLY FEVER (SICILY) VIRUS.

Sandfly fever (Sicily) virus

Robeson G. *et al.* (1979) *J. Virol.* **30**, 339

An unclassified ARBOVIRUS morphologically like BUNYAVIRUS but serologically unrelated to members of that genus. A member of the PHLEBOTOMUS FEVER ANTIGENIC GROUP. Antigenically distinct from SANDFLY FEVER (NAPLES) VIRUS.

Sandfly fever viruses Synonym for phlebotomus fever viruses.

Sandjimba virus An unclassified ARBOVIRUS, belonging to the SIMBU ANTIGENIC GROUP. Isolated from a bird *Acrocephalus schoenobaenus* in the Central African Republic. Not reported to cause disease in humans.

Sand rat nuclear inclusion virus Synonym for cricetid herpesvirus 2.

Sango virus A species in the genus BUNYAVIRUS. Isolated from cattle and from flies of *Culicoides* sp. in Nigeria and Kenya. Not reported to cause disease in humans.

San Miguel sea-lion virus

Smith A.W. *et al.* (1978) *Am. J. vet. Res.* **39**, 287

Burroughs J.N. *et al.* (1978) *Intervirology* **10**, 51

A species in the family CALICIVIRIDAE. Isolated from sea-lions on San Miguel Island off the coast of California and St Paul Island, Alaska. Serological evidence suggests the virus is widely distributed in Pacific marine mammals. May be a cause of abortions in sea-lions. Causes a vesicular disease in swine, and it has been suggested that marine mammals may be a reservoir of virus for terrestrial mammals. There are five serological types. Indistinguishable from VESICULAR EXANTHEMA OF PIGS VIRUS and FELINE CALICIVIRUS in morphology and in having a single CAPSID polypeptide of mol. wt. 65×10^3, but differentiated by NEUTRALIZATION TESTS. Immunodiffusion tests indicate San Miguel sea lion virus is closely related to the pig virus, but not to the cat virus. RNA homology tests show the same association. Experimental infection of African green monkeys caused a mild febrile reaction. Antibodies have been found in laboratory workers but there is no evidence that disease is produced in man. Isolated in VERO CELLS. Causes CPE in primary porcine and human cells but not in cells of marine mammals and rodents.

Sarcoma viruses Part of the LEUKOSIS–SARCOMA VIRUS GROUP. Sarcoma viruses have been isolated from a number of species of birds and mammals but the most extensively studied are the fowl, mouse and cat viruses. They are generally DEFECTIVE and require a HELPER leukaemia virus to code for the ENVELOPE (*see* phenotypic mixing) They transform cells in culture and produce infective virus if a helper virus is present. Sarcomas are produced on injection into animals, usually after a short latent period of a few days. Some tumours show spontaneous regression. Transformed cells may have a limited life and tumour growth may require infection and TRANSFORMATION of new cells. At least a portion and possibly the entire viral GENOME shares NUCLEOTIDE sequences with cellular DNA from the host species.

sarkosyl A detergent used to break up virus particles, or infected cells.

satellite virus An absolutely DEFECTIVE VIRUS which, in nature, depends on the presence of a HELPER VIRUS to provide some factor necessary for its replication. *See* adeno-associated virus.

Sathuperi virus A species in the genus BUNYAVIRUS and a member of the SIMBU ANTIGENIC GROUP. Isolated from mosquitoes in Madras, India, and Ibadan, Nigeria. Also isolated from cattle. Not reported to cause disease in humans.

Saumarez Reef virus

St George T.D. *et al.* (1977) *Aust. J. exp. Biol. med. Sci.* **55**, 493

A species in the genus FLAVIVIRUS. Isolated from sea-bird ticks *Ornithodoros capensis* collected from the nests of sooty terns on islands off the coast of Queensland, Australia and *Ixodes eudyptidis* from dead silver gulls in northern Tasmania. Antigenically most closely related to TYULENIY VIRUS. Causes paralysis on i/c injection in new-born mice. Not known to cause disease in humans, or other animals.

SA virus

Schultz E.W. & Habel, K. (1959) *J. Immunol.* **82**, 274

A designation given to a virus isolated in hamster brain from nasal washings of a patient with a 'common cold'. A strain of PARAINFLUENZA VIRUS TYPE 5. Pathogenic for hamsters on i/c injection. Antigenically identical to SIMIAN VIRUS SV 5 and DA VIRUS.

SA virus series *See* simian viruses SA series.

Sawgrass virus

Ritter D.G. *et al.* (1978) *Canad. J. Microbiol.* **24**, 422

Unclassified ARBOVIRUS, probably a rhabdovirus. Isolated from the Eastern Dog Tick *Dermacentor variabilis* and the Rabbit Tick *Haemaphysalis leporis-palustris* in Florida. Antigenically related to NEW MINTO VIRUS. Not reported to cause disease in humans.

Scabby mouth virus Synonym for orf virus.

Scandinavian epidemic nephropathy virus

Svedmyr A. *et al.* (1979) *Lancet* **i**, 100

Synonym for, or a strain of KOREAN HAEMORRHAGIC FEVER VIRUS. In northern Scandinavia causes a disease similar to Korean haemorrhagic fever but usually less severe and without haemorrhagic features.

Sciurid herpesvirus 1

Diosi P. *et al.* (1967) *Arch. ges. Virusforsch.* **20**, 383

Diosi P. & Babusceac L. (1970) *Am. J. vet. Res.* **31**, 157

A species in the family HERPESVIRIDAE. Seventeen of 81 European ground squirrels *Citellus citellus* trapped in the Timisoara area of Rumania were found to have typical CYTOMEGALOVIRUS inclusion bodies in their salivary gland cells. These animals appeared to be in good health. Cultures of the salivary gland cells developed foci of round refractile cells after 4 days, and in 10 days these spread to involve half the culture. The virus could not be passaged in mouse, rat or human cultures.

SYN: ground squirrel cytomegalovirus.

Sciurid herpesvirus 2

Diosi P. *et al.* (1975) *Path. Microbiol.* **42**, 42

Barahona H. *et al.* (1975) *Lab. Anim. Sci.* **25**, 735

A species in the family HERPESVIRIDAE. Isolated from a spontaneously degenerating primary kidney cell culture from a N. American species of ground squirrel *Citellus* in which it is a LATENT INFECTION. Kills suckling mice on injection i/c. Produces pocks on the CAM. Replicates well in rabbit, hamster, marmoset and owl monkey cells, but poorly in dog foetal lung and VERO CELLS. Virus is readily released from cells. Neutralized by HERPESVIRUS SAGUINUS antiserum but there is no reciprocal NEUTRALIZATION. Not neutralized by antiserum to SCIURID HERPESVIRUS 1.

SYN: ground squirrel herpesvirus.

Scrapie virus

Hunter G.D. (1974) *Prog. med. Virol.* **19**, 289

Hunter G.D. & Millson G.C. (1977) *Recent Adv. clin. Virol.* **1**, 61

Causes a natural disease of sheep and goats, mainly in the northern hemisphere. Affected animals are usually about 3 years old and have intense pruritis and ataxia, which becomes severe before death. Recovery in mild cases may be explained by misdiagnosis, which, to be certain, is by histological examination of the brain. Mode of transmission is not clear, but probably often vertical. In primates causes a condition similar to Creutzfeldt–Jakob disease. Chimpanzees are not susceptible, and there is no evidence of infection in man. Goats are more uniformly susceptible to experimental disease than sheep. Injections of brain tissue extract by any route will transmit the disease, but the shortest incubation period (6–9 months) follows i/c injection. Mice can be infected, the virus replicating first in lymphoid tissue, then in the brain. Injection into mink causes a disease similar to transmissible mink encephalopathy, but the virus so passed will not reinfect mice. Different strains of virus cause slightly different signs and symptoms, but nothing is known of antigenic structure. VIRION diameter by filtration approximately 30 nm. Nature of NUCLEIC ACID uncertain, but probably single-stranded DNA of mol. wt. 60,000.

Infectivity resists heating at 80°. Exposure to ionizing radiation indicates a target size of $1{\cdot}5 \times 10^5$. Small size probably accounts for failure to visualize the virus.

scrum-pox

Shute P. *et al.* (1979) *Br. med. J.* **4**, 1629

A contagious disease of the facial skin of rugby players. Aetiology variable, but HUMAN (ALPHA) HERPESVIRUS 1 and VACCINIA VIRUS have been implicated. Almost exclusively confined to forwards. A survey of thirty rugby clubs identified 48 infected players, of whom 47 were forwards and one a scrum-half. Of the 47 forwards, 32 played in the front row, 8 in the second row and 7 in the back row of the scrum. 23 of them reported direct contact with opponents who had obvious facial lesions: 34 had similar contacts within their own teams. Some of the cases were treated with IDOXURIDINE.

SYN: herpes gladiatorum; herpes rugbeiorum; herpes venatorum; prop-pox.

Sea-lion pox virus

Wilson T.M. & Poglayen-Neuwall I. (1971) *Can. J. comp. Med.* **35**, 174

A species in the family POXVIRIDAE. Morphologically similar to ORF VIRUS. Isolated from a captive Californian sea-lion *Zalophus californianus*. Causes a severe disease in wild and captive sea-lions.

Sebokele virus An unclassified ARBOVIRUS. Isolated in suckling mice from the pooled brain, liver, spleen and heart tissue of an adult female rodent of *Hylomyscus* sp., trapped in a banana plantation at Botambi, Central African Republic. Infectivity not sensitive to chloroform. Not reported to cause disease in humans.

sedimentation coefficient

Svedberg T. & Pedersen K.O. (1940) *The Ultracentrifuge*, London: Oxford University Press.

The sedimentation rate of a protein or other macromolecule per unit of applied gravitational force is termed the sedimentation coefficient or constant, *s*, and is defined by the equation $s = \frac{1}{\omega^2 r} \times \frac{dr}{dt}$

where r = radius (the distance in cm between the particle and the centre of rotation)

ω = the angular velocity in radians per sec of the centrifuge head

$\frac{dr}{dt}$ = the rate of movement of the particle in cm per sec.

The units of *s* are reciprocal sec; for convenience, the basic unit is taken as 10^{-13} sec, and termed one Svedberg unit (S). With this unit, the sedimentation coefficients of most proteins fall between 1 and 50 S.

sedimentation rate The velocity at which a particle (assumed to be approximately a sphere) settles under a given set of conditions. It is proportional to the square of the particle diameter and to the difference between the particle density and the density of the suspending medium. It decreases as the viscosity of the suspending medium increases and increases with the gravitational force.

$$\text{Sedimentation rate} = \frac{d^2(\rho_P - \rho_L)}{18\,\mu} \times \boldsymbol{g}$$

Where: d = diameter of the particle

ρ_P = particle density

ρ_L = suspending medium density

μ = viscosity of suspending medium

$\boldsymbol{g}$ = gravitational force

It is measured in cm per sec.

Seletar virus A species in the genus ORBIVIRUS. Belongs to the KEMEROVO ANTIGENIC GROUP. Isolated from the tick *Boophilus microplus* in Singapore and peninsular Malaysia. Antibodies found in cattle, carabao and pigs. Not reported to cause disease in humans.

Sembalam virus An unclassified ARBOVIRUS. Isolated from herons in Tamil Nadu, India. Not reported to cause disease in humans.

semi-conservative replication A model for DNA replication as it occurs in nature. The double strand becomes separated and each base in the single strands becomes attached to complementary NUCLEOTIDES to form two new double strands, in which one strand of each daughter molecule will be derived from the original DNA. As the two strands are antiparallel i.e. the 3′ end of one strand is opposite the 5′ end of the other, the new strands could in theory be synthesised in opposite directions, one from its 5′ end and the other from its 3′ end. But no polymerase has been found which will work in the 3′ → 5′ direction. Synthesis probably proceeds continuously in the 5′ → 3′ direction down the left hand strand, but in the right hand strand the process is discontinuous. As the strands separate synthesis in the right hand strand starts at a point X and proceeds backwards i.e. 5′ → 3′ end. When the growing strand has filled the gap Y a DNA LIGASE unites the newly synthesized piece with the previously formed section.

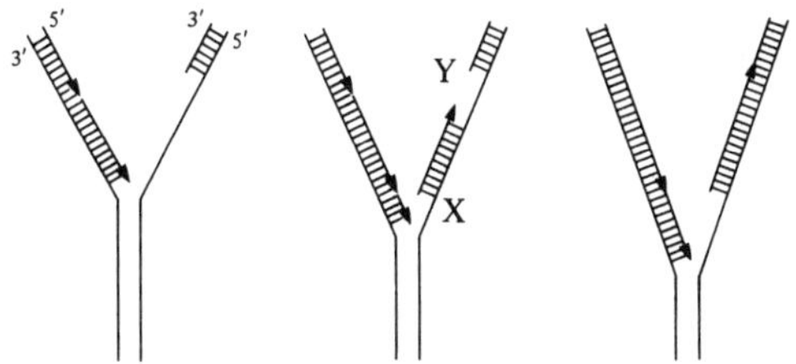

A model of DNA synthesis which occurs in the 5′ → 3′ direction in both strands.

Semliki Forest virus (*Semliki* means 'I do not know' – the reply given by natives when asked the name of the forest)

Willens W.R. *et al.* (1979) *Science* **203**, 1127

A species in the genus ALPHAVIRUS. The natural host and vector are not known but antibodies are found in man and wild primates in Uganda, Mozambique, Cameroon, Central African Republic, Kenya, Nigeria, N. Borneo and Malaya. Multiplies in the mosquito *Aedes aegypti.* Not associated with any disease, and generally considered to be non-pathogenic for man though a fatal case of encephalitis in a laboratory worker has been associated with the virus. Causes encephalitis in adult mice on experimental injection by various routes and on i/c injection in guinea pigs, rabbits and rhesus monkeys. Most inoculated animals have shown kidney damage. VIRAEMIA occurs in inoculated birds of several species and in hamsters. Virus can be propagated in eggs killing the embryo and in cell cultures of many species with CPE.

Sendai virus Synonym for parainfluenza virus type 1 murine.

sentinel animal An animal exposed captive in the wild to contract infection from the environment, usually from insects.

sentinel case An isolated case of some infectious disease or the first case in an outbreak.

Sepik virus A species in the genus FLAVIVIRUS. Isolated from mosquitoes in New Guinea. Causes a febrile illness in man.

Septicaemia anserum exudative virus Synonym for infectious myocarditis of goslings virus.

seron A name proposed for any group comprised of viruses with antigenic similarity which can be demonstrated serologically.

Serra do Navio virus A serological subtype of MELAO VIRUS. Isolated from *Aedes fulvus* mosquitoes in Amapa Territory of Brazil. Not reported to cause disease.

Serum hepatitis virus An old name for HEPATITIS B VIRUS. The name derives from the fact that the virus was often transmitted by serum in blood transfusions or in the process of giving injections, skin scarification (vaccination), ear-piercing or tattooing with inadequately sterilized instruments.

SF-4 virus *See* shipping fever virus.

Shamonda virus A species in the genus BUNYAVIRUS and a member of the SIMBU ANTIGENIC GROUP. Isolated from cattle and *Culicoides* sp. in Nigeria. Not reported to cause disease in humans.

Shark River virus A species in the genus BUNYAVIRUS and a member of the PATOIS ANTIGENIC GROUP. Isolated from mosquitoes in Florida, U.S.A., Mexico and Guatemala. Not reported to cause disease in humans.

Sheep papilloma virus

Gibbs E.P.J. *et al.* (1975) *J. comp. Path.* **85**, 327

A species in the genus PAPILLOMAVIRUS. Papillomas occur in some flocks but are not common. They may become malignant. Virus inoculated into the skin of sheep produces papillomas. Cattle and goats are resistant, but slowly-growing fibromas are produced in neonatal hamsters.

Sheep pox subgroup virus Synonym for capripoxvirus.

Sheep pox virus

Singh I.P. *et al.* (1979) *Vet. Bull. Weybridge* **49**, 145

Type species of the genus CAPRIPOXVIRUS. Causes a generalized pock disease in sheep, often with tracheitis and involvement of the lungs. Mortality 5 to 50%. Economically important. Occurs in parts of Africa, Asia, Middle East, S. Europe and Iberian peninsula. Only sheep are infected naturally. Difficult to adapt to growth in eggs. Replicates in sheep, goat and calf cell cultures with CPE. An attenuated virus vaccine is used successfully. SYN: Clavelée virus; Isiolo virus; Kedong virus; variola ovina virus.

shingles A painful local condition with rash in the region served by one nerve root. May follow exposure to HUMAN HERPESVIRUS 3 (varicella-zoster virus), but usually behaves as if it were a reactivation of a latent infection.

Shipping fever virus

Frank G.H. & Marshall R.G. (1973) *J. Am. vet. med. Ass.* **163**, 858

A bovine strain of the species PARAINFLUENZA VIRUS TYPE 3. Causes respiratory disease in cattle, especially under stress.

Shope fibroma virus Synonym for rabbit fibroma virus.

Shope papilloma virus Synonym for rabbit papilloma virus.

Show fever virus Synonym for feline panleucopenia virus.

Shuni virus A species in the genus BUNYAVIRUS and a member of the SIMBU ANTIGENIC GROUP. Isolated from man, sheep and cattle in Nigeria and S. Africa. Has been associated with disease in humans.

sialic acid Synonym for *N*-acetylneuraminic acid. *See* neuraminidase.

Sialodacryoadenitis virus

Bhatt P.N. *et al.* (1972) *J. infect. Dis.* **126**, 123

Jonas A.M. *et al.* (1969) *Arch. Path.* **88**, 613

A species in the genus CORONAVIRUS. Isolated from rats with sialodacryoadenitis. A natural infectious disease of rats, easily missed as it has a low mortality. There is fullness of the neck due to enlargement of the salivary glands. The submaxillary, salivary and Harderian glands are the glands mainly involved and there is necrosis of the ductal epithelium with acute lymphocytic infiltration and gelatinous oedema. Seromucinous glands are not affected. Red tears and staining of the fur round the eyes due to porphyrins, excreted in tears, may occur. There is repair of the tissues which is complete in two weeks. Injection i/c into new-born mice causes ataxia, paralysis and death 10 days after injection. Four week old mice are resistant. Antigenically related to RAT CORONAVIRUS and MOUSE HEPATITIS VIRUS. Does not agglutinate erythrocytes of rabbit, guinea pig or goose. Can be propagated in suckling rats and mice or adapted to replicate in primary rat kidney cell cultures with the formation of multinucleate giant cells.

sigla A contracted form of *sigilla* (Latin: *sigillum* = seal). In virology, a device formed of letters, especially initials, or other characters taken from the principal words in a compound term, e.g. PAPOVA VIRUS.

Sigmavirus

Printz P. (1973) *Adv. Virus Res.* **18**, 143

A genus in the family RHABDOVIRIDAE. The virus particles are slightly smaller than VESICULAR STOMATITIS VIRUS. The type species is drosophila virus which is congenitally transmitted in drosophila and confers carbon dioxide sensitivity.

signal peptide

Lingappa V.R. *et al.* (1979) *Nature, Lond.* **281**, 117

A short amino-acid sequence within a protein, which is recognized by cellular membranes as the signal for glycosylation of the protein. The signal peptide may be cleaved off during maturation of the protein.

signal sequence NUCLEOTIDE sequence coding for a SIGNAL PEPTIDE.

silent infection An infection with no significant signs or symptoms.

Silurid herpesvirus 1

Plumb J.A. *et al.* (1974) *J. Fish Biol.* **6**, 661

Wolf K. & Darlington R.W. (1971) *J. Virol.* **8**, 525

A species in the family HERPESVIRIDAE. Isolated from channel catfish *Ictalurus punctatus* in which it causes a severe haemorrhagic disease which may have a mortality rate in excess of 95%. The virus is only known to replicate in ictalurid cell lines. Replication takes place between 10 and 33°. Approximately half the virus remains CELL-ASSOCIATED.

SYN: CCV; channel catfish herpesvirus.

Silverwater virus An unclassified ARBOVIRUS morphologically like BUNYAVIRUS but serologically unrelated to members of the genus. A member of the KAISODI ANTIGENIC GROUP. Isolated from ticks removed from hares in Manitoulin Island and Powassan district of N. Ontario, Canada. Not reported to cause disease in humans.

Simbu antigenic group viruses Sixteen serologically related viruses in the genus BUNYAVIRUS.

Aino (C)
Akabane (C,Cu)
Buttonwillow (Cu)
Ingwavuma (C,B)
Kaikalur
Manzanilla
Mermet (B)
Nola (C)
Oropouche (C,H)
Sabo (Cu)
Samford (Cu)
Sango (C,Cu)
Sathuperi (C,Cu)
Shamonda (Cu)
Shuni (Cu,H)
Simbu (C)
Thimiri (B)

Isolated:
(C) Culicine mosquitoes
(Cu) Culicoides
(H) Humans
(B) Birds

Oropouche and Shuni viruses can also cause disease in man.

Simbu virus A species in the genus BUNYAVIRUS and member of the SIMBU ANTIGENIC GROUP. Isolated from mosquitoes in S. Africa, Central African Republic and Cameroon. Antibodies found in man but the virus is not reported to cause disease.

Simian adenovirus

Merkow L.P. & Slifkin M. (1973) *Prog. exp. Tumor Res.* **18**, 67

Kalter S.S. *et al.* (1979) Personal communication

A species in the genus MASTADENOVIRUS. Many strains were found because they produced CPE in kidney cell cultures of Asian, African and New World monkeys. Several types have been associated with respiratory and enteric disease in baboons, rhesus, *Erythrocebus* and *Cercopithecus* monkeys, but most infections are SILENT. Some strains are oncogenic in new-born hamsters. Division into groups is possible on the basis of agglutination of rat and rhesus erythrocytes. Nomenclature of strains within the species is confused.

Originally they formed part of two numbered series, SA and SV (see simian viruses). Later, an M series of simian adenoviruses was proposed, which included strains from both SA and SV, and a single isolate from a chimpanzee was designed C1. Recently, a new nomenclature has been proposed in which all simian viruses are given the virus group name followed by an 'S' number as in the table below.

Current nomenclature		Species of origin	Proposed nomenclature
Virus	Strain		Adenovirus
SV 1 (M 1)	301	*Macaca fascicularis*	S-1
SV 11 (M 5)	8045–2 WN	*M. mulatta*	S-2
SV 15 (M 4)	AP 4398	*M. mulatta*	S-3
SV 17 (M 6)	6630-IC	*M. mulatta*	S-4
SV 20 (M 7)	P 4	*M. mulatta*	S-5
SV 23 (M 2)	74932 WK	*M. mulatta*	S-6
SV 25 (M 8)	646776	*M. mulatta*	S-7
SV 30	P 5	*M. fascicularis*	S-8
SV 31	P 6	*Macaca* sp.	S-9
SV 32 (M 3)	P 7	*Macaca* sp.	S-10
SV 33 (M 10)	P 10	*M. mulatta*	S-11
SV 34	A 7644	*M. mulatta*	S-12
SV 36 (M 11)	P 9	*Macaca* sp.	S-13
SV 37	E 4382	*M. mulatta*	S-14
SV 38	702707	*M. mulatta*	S-15
SA 7	C-8	*Cercopithecus aethiops*	S-16
SA 17	B 105	*C. aethiops*	S-17
SA 18	C 626	*C. aethiops*	S-18
AA 153	AA 153	*Papio cynocephalus*	S-19
V 340	V 340	*C. aethiops*	S-20
C-1	Bertha	*Pan satyrus*	S-21
Pan 5	CV-23	*P. satyrus*	S-22
Pan 6	CV-32	*P. satyrus*	S-23
Pan 7	CV-33	*P. satyrus*	S-24

Simian agent *See* simian viruses SA series.

Simian enteroviruses

Hull R.N. (1968) *Virology Monographs*, no. 2

PICORNAVIRUSES isolated from monkey tissues or excreta in cell cultures. Often latent infections appearing in kidney cell cultures from apparently normal animals. They have been given numbers in the SA and SV series of SIMIAN VIRUSES.

SYN: ecmoviruses.

Simian foamy virus

Hooks J.J. & Gibbs C.J. (1975) *Bact. Rev.* **39**, 169

One or more species in the sub-family SPUMAVIRINAE. Nine serotypes are identified. Isolated by recognition of foamy degeneration and syncytia formation in cell cultures, from a number of different species: type 1, rhesus monkey *Macaca mulatta*; type 2, Formosan rock monkey *Macaca cyclopsis*; type 3, African green monkey *Cercopithecus aethiops*; type 4, squirrel monkey *Saimiri sciureus*; type 5, African bush baby *Galago crassicaudatus panganiensis*; types 6 and 7, chimpanzee; type 8, spider monkey *Ateles* sp. and type 9, capuchin monkeys. Cross-NEUTRALIZATION studies show only neutralization by homologous antiserum, except type 7 which is neutralized by type 2 antiserum at low dilution (1/10). Complement fixation shows some antigenic relationship between types 2 and 3 and 6 and 7. Virus has been recovered from throat washings but not from urine or faeces. Virus has also been isolated from the cervix and placenta of a pregnant rhesus monkey and from the kidney of the foetus.

Simian haemorrhagic fever virus

Madden D.L. *et al.* (1978) *Lab. Anim. Sci.* **28**, 422

Trousdale M.D. *et al.* (1975) *Proc. Soc. exp. Biol. Med.* **150**, 707

Probably a species in the genus FLAVIVIRUS, but no arthropod vector has been identified. Causes a severe disease in rhesus monkeys imported into England, U.S.A. and U.S.S.R. There is high fever, facial oedema, splenomegaly and severe haemorrhagic diathesis. Replicates in rhesus monkey cell cultures with CPE. Non-pathogenic on injection into mice. Contains single-stranded RNA and four structural proteins. Diameter 45–50 nm. Labile at pH 3 and inactivated by chloroform.

Simian papilloma virus

Lucké B. *et al.* (1950) *Fedn. Proc. Am. Socs. exp. Biol.* **9**, 336

A species in the genus PAPILLOMAVIRUS. A natural infection of *Cebus* monkeys causing papillomas. Papillomas can be transmitted experimentally to both new and old world monkeys. After injection of tissue extract, hyperaemic patches appear within 2 weeks and then the epidermis becomes thickened to form a papilloma. No evidence of invasion of normal tissue, and regression occurs in 4–6 months.

SYN: monkey papilloma virus.

Simian polyomaviruses There are two species SIMIAN VIRUS 40 and VERVET MONKEY VIRUS. The proposed classification of SIMIAN VIRUSES would designate them Polyomavirus S-1 and S-2 respectively.

Simian rotavirus

Lecatsas G. (1972) *Onderstepoort J. vet. Res.* **39**, 133

Brade L. & Schmidt W.A.K. (1979) *Med. Microbiol. Immunol.* **167**, 55

A species in the genus ROTAVIRUS. Isolated from the rectum of a healthy vervet monkey. Can be propagated in primary vervet monkey cell cultures or in a cell line from this species. Produces CPE. Morphologically similar to and antigenically related to human and bovine rotaviruses. Can be used as antigen to titrate human and bovine rotavirus antibodies.

Simian sarcoma-associated virus A species in the subgenus MAMMALIAN TYPE C ONCOVIRUS GROUP. A non-transforming virus which acts as HELPER for SIMIAN SARCOMA VIRUS. Several strains can be isolated from gibbons. Probably originated from an ENDOGENOUS C TYPE VIRUS of a S.E. Asian *Mus* sp. such as *M. caroli.*

Simian sarcoma virus A species in the subgenus, MAMMALIAN TYPE C ONCOVIRUS GROUP. Isolated from a fibrosarcoma of a woolly monkey. Causes sarcomas on injection into marmosets. It is a transforming DEFECTIVE VIRUS requiring simian SARCOMA-ASSOCIATED VIRUS as a HELPER to produce infective virus. Probably originated from an ENDOGENOUS C TYPE oncovirus of a S.E. Asian *Mus* sp. such as *M. caroli* or *M. cervicolor*.

SYN: woolly monkey sarcoma virus.

Simian vacuolating virus Synonym for simian virus 40.

Simian varicella virus Synonym for cercopithecid herpesvirus 5.

Simian virus 40 A species in the genus POLYOMAVIRUS. A natural and SILENT INFECTION of rhesus, cynomolgus, and *Cercopithecus* monkeys. Often isolated from kidney cell cultures. Replicates in a variety of cell cultures, but when first isolated was cytopathic for grivet monkey kidney cell cultures only, producing vacuolation of the cytoplasm. Does not haemagglutinate. Foci of transformed cells appear in human, bovine, porcine, hamster, rabbit and mouse cell cultures inoculated with the virus. A silent infection in man, though antibodies are formed. Produces tumours, mainly sarcomas on injection into new-born hamsters, grivets, baboons and rhesus monkeys. Was a contaminant of certain batches of poliovaccine but caused no disease. Possibly isolated from 2 patients with progressive multi-focal leukoencephalopathy.

SYN: simian vacuolating virus.

Simian viruses

Malherbe H. & Herwin R. (1963) *S. Afr. med. J.* **37**, 407
Hull R.N. (1968) *Virology Monographs*, vol. 2. Wien: Springer-Verlag.
Kalter S.S. *et al.* (1979) Personal communication.

Viruses isolated from non-human primates. Some have been isolated from excreta or diseased tissues but most have appeared as cytopathic viruses in cultures of normal tissues. The large number of monkeys used to provide cell cultures has resulted in many isolates which form a mixed group of DNA and RNA viruses. Two numbered series have been described: simian agents (SA viruses) mainly from African monkeys, and simian viruses (SV viruses) mainly from Asian monkeys. Differentiation into groups was at first made according to the type of CPE produced, but most have now been assigned to various families, and it is suggested that they should be given the name of the virus group to which they belong, followed by an 'S' number. In the list below this new nomenclature, where known, is given in brackets at the end of the entry. *See also* simian adenoviruses. Some SV and SA numbers are missing because they designated isolates which were later found not to be viruses, or to be identical with previous isolates or have been lost.

SA Series of Viruses (Simian Agents)

SA 1 Foamy virus.
SA 2 Produces CPE similar to SA 1 but there are nuclear inclusions.
SA 3 Reovirus type 1.
SA 4 Enterovirus. Isolated from the intestinal tract of *Cercopithecus aethiops*. Serologically related to SV 4 and SV 28. (Enterovirus S-16)
SA 5 Enterovirus. Isolated from the intestinal tract of *Cercopithecus aethiops*. (Enterovirus S-17)
SA 6 Cercopithecid herpesvirus 2.
SA 7 Adenovirus. (Adenovirus S-16)
SA 8 Cercopithecid herpesvirus 3.
SA 9 Isolated from the mouth of a monkey. CPE resembles that produced by a reovirus but it does not agglutinate human O erythrocytes.
SA 10 Parainfluenza virus type 3. Isolated from the mouth of a samango monkey *Cercopithecus mitis*. Agglutinates human O, guinea pig and bovine erythrocytes.
SA 11 Rotavirus.
SA 12 Vervet monkey virus.
SA 13 Is now lost. CPE resembled that of MEASLES VIRUS.
SA 14 Is now lost. Probably a virus though never proved to be so.
SA 15 Is now lost. Herpesvirus isolated from baboons *Papio ursinus*.
SA 16 Is now lost. Isolated from vervet monkeys. Produced eosinophilic cytoplasmic inclusions and was difficult to passage.
SA 17 Adenovirus. (Adenovirus S-17)
SA 18 Adenovirus (Adenovirus S-18)

SV Series of Viruses (Simian Viruses)

SV 1 Adenovirus. Type 1 of haemagglutination group 3. (Adenovirus S-1)
SV 2 Enterovirus. Isolated from intestinal tract of *Macaca mulatta*. (Enterovirus S-1)
SV 3
SV 4 Enterovirus. Serologically related to SA 4 and SV 28 viruses.
SV 5 Parainfluenza virus type 5. Antigenically identical to SA virus and DA virus.
SV 6 Enterovirus. Isolated from intestinal tract of *Macaca mulatta*. (Enterovirus S-2)
SV 7
SV 8
SV 9

SV 10
SV 11 Adenovirus. Type 2 of haemagglutination group 3. (Adenovirus S-2)
SV 12 Reovirus type 1.
SV 13 Foamy virus.
SV 14
SV 15 Adenovirus. Type 3 of haemagglutination group 2. (Adenovirus S-3)
SV 16 Enterovirus. Isolated from intestinal tract of *Macaca mulatta*. (Enterovirus S-3)
SV 17 Adenovirus. Type 4 of haemagglutination group 2. Isolated from a monkey *Erythrocebus patas*. (Adenovirus S-4)
SV 18 Enterovirus. Isolated from intestinal tract of *Macaca mulatta*. (Enterovirus S-4)
SV 19 Enterovirus. Isolated from intestinal tract of *Macaca fascicularis*. (Enterovirus S-5)
SV 20 Adenovirus. Type 5 of haemagglutination group 3. (Adenovirus S-5)
SV 21 Enterovirus. Identical to SV 4.
SV 22 Proved not to be new isolate.
SV 23 Adenovirus. Type 6 of haemagglutination group 2. (Adenovirus S-6)
SV 24 An amoeba of the genus *Acanthamoeba*.
SV 25 Adenovirus. Type 7 of haemagglutination group 3. (Adenovirus S-7)
SV 26 Enterovirus. Isolated from intestinal tract of *Macaca mulatta*. (Enterovirus S-6)
SV 27 Adenovirus. Similar or identical to SV 31.
SV 28 Enterovirus. Isolated from normal kidney cell culture of *Macaca mulatta*. Serologically related to SA 4 and SV 4 viruses. (Enterovirus S-7)
SV 29 Proved not to be a new isolate.
SV 30 Adenovirus. Type 8 of haemagglutination group 3. (Adenovirus S-8)
SV 31 Adenovirus. Type 9 of haemagglutination group 2. (Adenovirus S-9)
SV 32 Adenovirus. Type 10 of haemagglutination group 2. (Adenovirus S-10)
SV 33 Adenovirus. (Adenovirus S-11)
SV 34 Adenovirus. Type 12 of haemagglutination group 3. (Adenovirus S-12)
SV 35 Enterovirus. Isolated from intestinal tract of *Macaca mulatta*. (Enterovirus S-8)
SV 36 Adenovirus. Type 13 of haemagglutination group 1. (Adenovirus S-13)
SV 37 Adenovirus. Type 14 of haemagglutination group 2. (Adenovirus S-14)
SV 38 Adenovirus. Type 15 of haemagglutination group 3. (Adenovirus S15)
SV 39 Identical to SV 23.
SV 40 Polyomavirus species. *See main entry under* simian virus 40.
SV 41 Similar to SV 5.
SV 42 Enterovirus. Isolated from intestinal tract of *Macaca fascicularis*. (Enterovirus S-9)
SV 43 Enterovirus. Isolated from intestinal tract of *Macaca fascicularis*. (Enterovirus S-10)
SV 44 Enterovirus. Isolated from intestinal tract of *Macaca mulatta*. (Enterovirus S-11)
SV 45 Enterovirus. Isolated from intestinal tract of *Macaca fascicularis*. (Enterovirus S-12)
SV 46 Enterovirus. Isolated from intestinal tract of *Macaca* sp. (Enterovirus S-13)
SV 47 Enterovirus. Isolated from intestinal tract of *Macaca fascicularis*. (Enterovirus S-14)
SV 48 Enterovirus.
SV 49 Enterovirus. Isolated from intestinal tract of *Macaca mulatta*. (Enterovirus S-15)
SV 50–SV 58 Probably isolated by Heberling, but not included in the final SV series. (Heberling R.L. & Cheerer F.S. (1965) *Am. J. Epidemiol.* **81**, 106.)
SV 59 Reovirus type 3. Sent to Hull as agent 59 and numbered SV 59 even before SV 41 was reached.

Sindbis virus A species in the genus ALPHAVIRUS. Probably a natural infection of birds but antibodies are found in man and domestic ungulates. May be associated with fever in man. Closely related to WHATAROA VIRUS and WESTERN EQUINE ENCEPHALOMYELITIS VIRUS.

Replicates in eggs killing the embryo, and in cell cultures of chick, human and monkey tissues with CPE. Experimentally lethal for suckling mice. Causes myositis and encephalitis in infant mice. Found in Egypt, S. Africa, India, Malaya, the Philippines and Australia.

single-stranded *See* deoxyribonucleic acid.

single-stranded DNA viruses The only family is PARVOVIRIDAE, in most species + strand but in some there are + and − strands in different viral particles. On extraction the strands can form double strands.

single-stranded RNA viruses They are:

Picornaviridae, Togaviridae	Genome is + strand and acts as mRNA.
Arenaviridae	− strand, 5 segments.
Bunyaviridae	+ or − not known, 3 or 4 segments.
Coronaviridae	+ strand, unsegmented.
Orthomyxoviridae	− strand, 7 or 8 segments.
Paramyxoviridae	− strand, unsegmented.
Retroviridae	+ strand, unsegmented.
Rhabdoviridae	− strand, unsegmented.

SIRC cells (CCL 60) A heteroploid cell line derived from the cornea of a normal rabbit. Early and distinct CPE is induced in these cells by RUBELLA VIRUS, for which they are highly suitable both for propagation and for virus quantitation.

Si SV Simian sarcoma virus.

Sixgun City virus A species in the genus ORBIVIRUS, and a member of the KEMEROVO ANTIGENIC GROUP. Isolated from the tick *Argos cooleyi* in Texas and Colorado, U.S.A. Not reported to cause disease in humans.

Skin-heterogenizing virus of mice

Svet Moldavsky G.J. *et al.* (1970) *J. natn. Cancer Inst.* **45**, 475

Salaman M.H. *et al.* (1973) *Transplantation*, **16**, 583

An unclassified virus present in many mouse tumours and capable of inducing strong transplantation antigens in the skin. Some leukaemia viruses may have this property.

Slow viruses

Meulen V. ter & Hall W.W. (1978) *J. gen. Virol.* **41**, 1

A poor term for virus causing slowly progressive disease of the CNS. They are the LENTIVIRINAE but viruses of other families may perhaps cause similar disease, particularly the SPONGIFORM ENCEPHALOPATHY VIRUSES, MEASLES VIRUS, J.C. VIRUS, RUBELLA VIRUS, and MURINE POLIOENCEPHALOMYELOPATHY VIRUS.

Smallpox virus Synonym for variola virus.

SMON virus *See* subacute myelo-optico-neuropathy virus.

Snotsiekte virus Synonym for bovid herpesvirus 3.

Snowshoe hare virus

Gentsch J. & Bishop D.H.L. (1976) *J. Virol.* **20**, 351

A species in the genus BUNYAVIRUS, belonging to the CALIFORNIA ANTIGENIC GROUP. Originally isolated from the blood of an emaciated hare *Lepus americanus* caught in Bitterroot Valley, Montana, U.S.A. Isolated from lemmings, hares and mosquitoes in various parts of northern U.S.A., Canada, and Alaska. Antibodies found in man and other animals. Distinguished from other members of the group by CFT, HAI or NEUTRALIZATION TESTS. Causes subclinical infection in man.

Sockeye salmon virus Synonym for Oregon sockeye disease virus.

sodium dodecyl sulphate (SDS) A detergent used to break up virus particles, or infected cells.

Soehner–Dmochowski murine sarcoma virus

Ohtsuki Y. *et al.* (1978) *Cancer Res.* **38**, 901

A MAMMALIAN TYPE C ONCOVIRUS obtained from bone tumours induced in New Zealand black rats by injection of MOUSE SARCOMA VIRUS (Moloney strain).

Sofjin virus Prototype strain of TICK-BORNE ENCEPHALITIS VIRUS (Central European subtype).

Sokoluk virus A species in the genus FLAVIVIRUS. Isolated from bats in Kirghiz S.S.R., U.S.S.R. Not reported to cause disease in humans.

Soldado virus

Chastel C. *et al.* (1979) *Arch. Virol.* **60**, 153

An unclassified ARBOVIRUS belonging to the HUGHES ANTIGENIC GROUP. Morphologically resembles species in the genus BUNYAVIRIDAE. Isolated from a mixed pool of ticks of the *Ornithodoros* sp. infesting a common noddy *Anous stolidus* on Soldado rocks in the Caribbean Sea. Also from *O. capensis* associated with sea birds in Ethiopia, Seychelles, U.S.A. and Senegal, and from *O. maritimus* in France, Ireland and N. Wales. Kills suckling mice but not known to cause disease in man or other animals.

Sore mouth virus A poor term because it has been used as a synonym for both BLUE TONGUE VIRUS and ORF VIRUS.

Sororoca virus A species in the genus BUNYAVIRUS, belonging to the BUNYAMWERA ANTIGENIC GROUP. Isolated from mosquitoes of *Sabethini* sp. in Para, Brazil. Not reported to cause disease in humans.

Sparrow pox virus *See* avipoxvirus.

Spider monkey virus Synonym for cebid herpesvirus 3.

Sp 1 K (NBL-10) cells (CCL 78) A heteroploid cell line derived from trypsinized kidney tissue of the Atlantic spotted dolphin *Stenella plagiodon*. The line was developed to allow viral studies to be made in the cells of a marine mammal. Has a wide spectrum of susceptibility to viruses of terrestrial mammals.

Spleen focus-forming virus A strain of Friend or RAUSCHER LEUKAEMIA VIRUS which causes countable foci of tumour cells in the spleen. Used as a name for the component of FRIEND LEUKAEMIA VIRUS which is DEFECTIVE and which requires LYMPHOID LEUKAEMIA VIRUS as a HELPER.

Spleen necrosis virus A strain of AVIAN RETICULOENDOTHELIOSIS VIRUS.

splicing

Gilbert W. (1978) *Nature, Lond.* **271**, 501

Darnell J.E. (1978) *Science, N.Y.* **202**, 1257

Ligation of non-contiguous cleaved portions of an RNA molecule to produce functional mRNA. Originally discovered from work on adenovirus mRNA synthesis. Now known to be a common feature of mRNA production in eukaryotic cells; not so far discovered in bacteria. Functional mRNA in eukaryotic cells can be made up of spliced transcripts originating from widely separated regions of the DNA. The sequences of DNA, transcripts of which are present in mRNA, are termed EXONS (expressed regions); the intervening DNA sequences are termed INTRONS.

split vaccines Vaccines prepared from disrupted virus particles and purified to remove the toxic fraction of viral protein which may cause side effects. This permits the injection of a larger dose of the useful antigen.

Spondweni virus A species in the genus FLAVIVIRUS. Isolated from culicine mosquitoes in S. Africa, Nigeria, Mozambique and Cameroon. Can cause a febrile illness with hepatitis in man. Antibodies present in cattle, sheep and goats, in which it causes disease.

Spongiform encephalopathy viruses

Matthews W.B. (1977) *Recent Adv. clin. Virol.* **1**, 51

These are the SCRAPIE, KURU, TRANSMISSIBLE MINK ENCEPHALOPATHY and CREUTZFELDT-JAKOB DISEASE VIRUSES. They cause neurological disorders with a common pathological picture and progressive course to death. There is spongiform degeneration of the brain but absence of inflammatory reaction. A histologically similar change in the CNS can be produced by VISNA VIRUS and by MURINE POLIOENCEPHALOMYELOPATHY VIRUS.
SYN: subacute spongiform encephalopathy viruses.

spongoadenosine *See* adenine arabinoside.

spongothymidine (Ara T) 1-β-D-arabinofuranosylthymidine. A NUCLEOSIDE antibiotic isolated from the sponge *Cryptotethia crypta.* A selective inhibitor of HUMAN HERPESVIRUS 1 and 2.

spongouridine (Ara U) 1-β-D-arabinofuranosyluracil. A NUCLEOSIDE antibiotic isolated from the sponge *Cryptotethia crypta.*

Spring viraemia virus of carp Synonym for *Rhabdovirus carpio.*

Spumavirinae (Latin: *spuma* = foam)

Hooks J.J. & Gibbs C.J. (1975) *Bact. Rev.* **39**, 169

A subfamily of the family RETROVIRIDAE. Usually cause persistent but SILENT INFECTIONS in their natural host. Often found in primary tissue cultures, especially on prolonged passage. In cell cultures syncytium formation is induced and the cells develop a foamy appearance. The members isolated from monkeys and man are referred to as FOAMY VIRUSES: those from cattle, cats and hamsters as SYNCYTIAL VIRUSES. Nine serotypes have been isolated from monkeys of various species. Viruses of simian, bovine and feline origin do not cross-react in NEUTRALIZATION TESTS. Virus particle 100–140 nm in diameter with an electron-lucent NUCLEOID and ENVELOPE with surface projections. Maturation by budding. Inactivated by lipid solvents and pH3. Replicate slowly in a wide range of dividing cells. TRANSFORMATION or tumour production have not been observed. Genera have not yet been defined.

SP 104 virus

Quimby F.W. *et al.* (1978) *Clin. Immunol. Immunopath.* **9**, 194

A strain of mouse leukaemia virus. A B-tropic virus, weakly oncogenic but efficient at stimulating the production of anti-nuclear antibodies in mice. Isolated from an established cell line derived from a plasmacytoma in a mouse. This animal had been injected when new-born with a cell-free filtrate from the spleen of a dog with systemic lupus erythematosus. The virus shared a cross-reacting antigen with the surface of blood lymphocytes of human or canine patients with systemic lupus erythematosus. HYBRIDIZATION studies with viral NUCLEIC ACID give no evidence of viral GENOME sequences in canine or human cells from these patients.

Squirrel fibroma virus A species in the genus LEPORIPOXVIRUS, serologically related to RABBIT FIBROMA VIRUS. Causes multiple fibromas in grey squirrels *Sciurus carolinensis* in N. America. Produces fibromas in domestic rabbits but cannot be passaged in them.
SYN: fibroma virus of squirrels.

Squirrel monkey herpesvirus Synonym for cebid herpesvirus 2.

Squirrel monkey retrovirus

Colcher D. *et al.* (1977) *J. Virol.* **23**, 294

Schochetman G. *et al.* (1977) *J. Virol.* **23**, 384

A member of the subfamily ONCOVIRINAE An ENDOGENOUS xenotropic virus of squirrel monkeys *Saimiri sciureus.* Probably a D TYPE oncovirus because it is similar to MASON-PFIZER VIRUS, though VIRIONS have a central electron-dense NUCLEOID while the Mason-Pfizer virus has a bipolar tubular nucleoid. Isolated from lung cells by CO-CULTIVATION with canine cells. Infectious for cells of human, mouse, dog, chimpanzee and rhesus monkey. Buds with an intact nucleoid through the cell membrane and has a DNA polymerase with a magnesium cation preference, properties shared with the Mason-Pfizer, MOUSE MAMMARY TUMOUR and endogenous guinea pig viruses. Viral RNA hybridized with the DNA from all the squirrel monkey tissues tested, but not with DNA from other New and Old World monkeys or apes. Not immunologically related to oncoviruses of baboon, woolly monkey, rhesus monkey, cat, cattle, horses, rat, hamster or mouse.

Src gene

Halpern C.C. *et al.* (1979) *J. Virol.* **29**, 91

Brugge J.S. *et al.* (1979) *J. Virol.* **29**, 1196

One of the genes in the GENOME of the AVIAN TYPE C ONCOVIRUS. It is near the 3′ end and is presumed to code for a kinase responsible for initiation and maintenance of the transformed state. The name refers to its relation to formation of sarcoma cells. Temperature-sensitive mutants of Src have been isolated. TRANSFORMATION-defective mutants of the CHICKEN LEUKOSIS SARCOMA VIRUS lack the Src gene, but can replicate. SYN: Onc gene.

SSAV Simian sarcoma-associated virus.

SSV Simian sarcoma virus.

standard virus Term introduced by von Magnus to describe complete virus as opposed to DEFECTIVE VIRUS.

Starling pox virus *See* avipoxvirus.

statolon

Kleinschmidt W.J. *et al.* (1968) *Nature, Lond.* **220**, 167

A fermentation product of the fungus *Penicillium stoloniferum* and a potent INTERFERON inducer. This activity is due to the presence of a DOUBLE-STRANDED RNA viral GENOME. EM studies have demonstrated the presence of numerous particles of typical virus morphology, about 30 nm in diameter. They are reported to be serologically unrelated to HELENINE particles.

steady-state infection

Hotchin J. (1974) *Prog. med. Virol.* **18**, 81

Infection in a cell culture where both virus and cell multiplication proceed. Most or all of the cells are infected, virus is released continuously from the cells, but there is no CPE. The infection cannot be cured by adding anti-viral antibody to the culture medium. Superinfection with another virus is possible but there may be COMPLEMENTATION or INTERFERENCE. Examples are numerous among viruses which mature by budding: PARAMYXOVIRIDAE, RHABDOVIRIDAE, TOGAVIRIDAE and RETROVIRIDAE. *See* carrier cultures.

Stellavirus Synonym for rotavirus.

stimulon

Brailovsky C. & Chany C. (1965) *C. r. Acad. Sci. Paris.* **260**, 2634 and **261**, 4282

A factor produced in adenovirus-infected cell cultures which increases the replication of LATENT RAT VIRUS and H-1 VIRUS. Can be demonstrated in virus-free extracts of infected cells but not in extracts of uninfected cells. Stimulon is inactivated by trypsin, but not by DNase or RNase.

Stomatitis papulosa of cattle virus Synonym for bovine papular stomatitis virus, though other viruses may cause the same clinical picture.

Stomatitis/pneumo-enteritis complex virus Synonym for Kata virus.

Stoxil Trade name for IDOXURIDINE eye drops.

Stratford virus A species in the genus FLAVIVIRUS. Isolated from *Aedes vigilax* in Queensland, Australia. Not reported to cause disease in humans or other animals.

Street virus WILD STRAINS. Virulent. A term applied to RABIES VIRUS isolated from animals.

streptovitacin A A glutarimide antibiotic. A potent reversible inhibitor of protein synthesis.

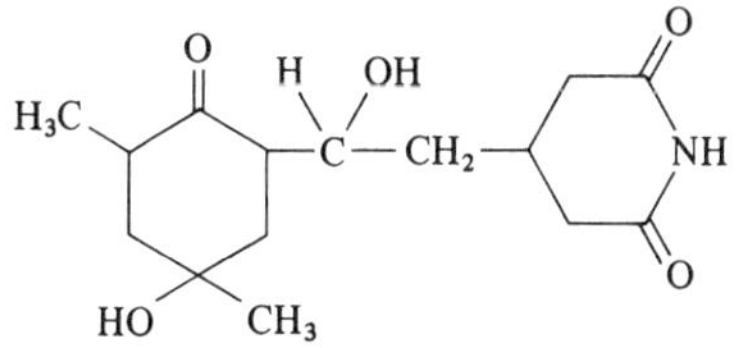

O H OH O
H_3C C — CH_2 NH
HO CH_3 O

Strigid herpesvirus 1

Burtscher H. & Sibalin M. (1975) *J. Wildl. Dis.* **11**, 164

A species in the family HERPESVIRIDAE. Isolated from owls of several species in which it

may cause paralysis. Disease can be produced experimentally in owls but not other birds. Replicates on the CAM and in the allantois.
SYN: owl herpesvirus.

Strongyloplasma hominis An old name for the molluscum body produced in epidermal cells of patients infected with MOLLUSCUM CONTAGIOSUM VIRUS. An INCLUSION BODY.

S-tropic viruses Xenotropic viruses.

Stumptailed macaque virus

Chowdhury K. *et al.* (1979) *J. gen. virol.* **45**, 223
Reissig M. *et al.* (1976) *Infect. Immun.* **14**, 225

A species in the genus POLYOMAVIRUS. Isolated from a stump-tailed macaque kidney cell culture. After a few passages the cells showed vacuolation and signs of degeneration. Infection is ubiquitous in stumptailed macaques in which it is probably congenital. Morphologically like other members of the SV_{40}-polyoma group, except that many particles had an outer ENVELOPE. DNA is 91% of the length of SV_{40} DNA. Immunologically distinct from SV_{40}, BK, POLYOMA and JC VIRUSES. The T ANTIGEN is related to that of SV_{40} and BK viruses. Probably identical to HD VIRUS.

Subacute myelo-optico-neuropathy virus

Inoue Y.K. (1975) *Prog. med. Virol.* **21**, 35
Kono R. (1975) *Lancet* **ii**, 370

A strain of GALLID HERPESVIRUS 1. Isolated from the faeces and CSF of patients with subacute myelo-optico-neuropathy. Seen mainly in Japan, the disease is characterised by sensory disturbance, especially of the lower part of the legs, abdominal symptoms, decreased muscle strength and bilateral impairment of visual acuity. There are no changes in the blood or CSF. There is degeneration of posterior and lateral tracts of the spinal cord. The virus is isolated in BAT-6 cells and causes a thinning of the cell sheet. On injection into new-born C_{57}Bl/6 mice it is reported to cause paralysis of the hind legs. It is claimed that the virus can be derived on passage of AVIAN INFECTIOUS LARYNGOTRACHEITIS VIRUS on the CAM or in new born C_{57}Bl/6 mice. It is antigenically related to this virus but is said to differ from it in being non-pathogenic for fowls, less unstable at low pH and pathogenic for C_{57}Bl/6 mice. The role of the virus in subacute myelo-optico-neuropathy has been questioned and it is suggested that the disease is due to the administration of clioquinol, an anti-diarrhoeal drug. When the use of clioquinol was stopped in Japan in September 1970, incidence of the disease fell dramatically. However, clioquinol is used outside Japan and appears to cause little disease.

Subacute sclerosing panencephalitis (SSPE) virus

Agnarsdóttir G. (1977) *Recent Adv. Clin. Virol.* **1**, 21
Thormar H. *et al.* (1978) *J. exp. Med.* **148**, 674
Hall W.W. *et al.* (1978) *Nature, Lond.* **272**, 460

MEASLES VIRUS is probably the cause of SSPE, a slow virus disease of the brain. The measles vaccine virus may possibly cause the disease but vaccinated children are less likely to develop SSPE than the unvaccinated. The disease is more common in patients who have measles before the age of two years. The majority of cases appear between the ages of 4 and 20 years. Measles virus can be isolated from the brain in cases of SSPE but only by CO-CULTIVATION of brain cells with susceptible target cells. After isolation it appears similar to other measles isolates but may have additional genetic information. Some SSPE strains of measles virus are neurovirulent in ferrets and these strains are strongly CELL-ASSOCIATED.

Subacute spongiform encephalopathy viruses Synonym for spongiform encephalopathy viruses.

subgenomic RNA

Mahy B.W.J. (1977) *Nature, Lond.* **268**, 398

A species of RNA of less than GENOME length found in RNA virus-infected cells. The genome RNA of several groups of POSITIVE-STRAND RNA viruses (TOGAVIRIDAE, RETRO-

VIRIDAE, CALICIVIRIDAE for example) contains more than one initiation site, but early in infection only the portion of the RNA coding for RNA replicating enzymes is translated. Subsequently, subgenomic RNA containing the previously masked initiation site is synthesised and can then be translated into virus COAT proteins. In togaviruses, this RNA has been termed INTERJACENT RNA. The several monocistronic species of mRNA synthesized by TRANSCRIPTION from full length genome RNA in cells infected with some NEGATIVE STRAND viruses such as PARAMYXOVIRIDAE and RHABDOVIRIDAE may also be termed subgenomic RNA.

Submaxillary virus *See* cytomegaloviruses.

Suckling mouse cataract virus

Clark H.F. (1974) *Prog. med. Virol.* **18**, 307

Bastardo J.W. *et al.* (1974) *Infect. Immun.* **9**, 444

An unusual type of mycoplasma isolated from rabbit ticks *Haemaphysalis leporis-palustris* in Georgia, U.S.A. Replicates to high titre in chick embryos. Causes cataracts in suckling mice after 20 days, sometimes with signs of neurological involvement and stunting of growth. Passes through filters of APD 220 nm but not at APD 100 nm. EM reveals mycoplasma-like bodies.

Suid (alpha) herpesvirus 1

Kaplan A.S. (1969) *Virology Monographs*, vol. 5. Wien: Springer-Verlag.

Basinger D. (1979) *Br. vet. J.* **135**, 215

A species in the family HERPESVIRIDAE. A natural infection, mainly of pigs, but cattle, sheep, dogs, cats, foxes and mink are also susceptible. In pigs the infection is usually SILENT, but in 5–10% the virus infects the tonsils from which it spreads to the CNS. There are nervous symptoms and fever but the pigs recover. In cattle, sheep and carnivores the disease is usually fatal, with intense pruritis. Horses are doubtfully susceptible. There are reports of infection in laboratory workers who developed aphthae of the mouth and local pruritis. Rabbits, guinea pigs and many other species are susceptible experimentally. Monkeys infected intranasally develop ataxia salivation and have convulsions, but there is no pruritis. Virus replicates on the CAM with plaque production and CPE in cultures of chick, rabbit, guinea pig and dog cells. All strains appear antigenically similar.

SYN: Aujesky's disease virus; infectious bulbar paralysis virus; mad itch virus; pig herpesvirus 1; pseudorabies virus.

Suid herpesvirus 1 Synonym for suid (alpha) herpesvirus 1.

Suid herpesvirus 2

Edington N. *et al.* (1976) *J. Hyg. Camb.* **77**, 283

A species in the family HERPESVIRIDAE. Causes rhinitis and destruction of the turbinates, with distortion of the snout, epistaxis and sneezing, notably in 2 week-old piglets, when death is common. Transmission is possible in piglets but not in adult pigs. Disease occurs in outbreaks and inclusions are present in the cells of many organs. Can be cultivated in primary pig cell cultures, replicating better in epithelial than in fibroblastic cells.

SYN: inclusion-body rhinitis virus of pigs; pig cytomegalovirus;

Suipoxvirus A genus in the subfamily CHORDOPOXVIRINAE containing the SWINE POX VIRUS.

Sunday Canyon virus

Yunker C.E. *et al.* (1977) *Acta Virol. Prague* **21**, 36

An unclassified ARBOVIRUS. Morphologically similar to BUNYAVIRUS but not antigenically related to members of that genus. Isolated from the tick *Argas cooleyi* collected in south-western U.S.A. in areas frequented by cliff swallows *Petrochelidon pyrrhonota*. Sensitive to ether and to low pH. Pathogenic for suckling mice. Not reported to cause disease in humans.

Svedberg units *See* sedimentation coefficient.

SV 40–PML virus

Weiner L.P. *et al.* (1972) *New Eng. J. Med.* **286**, 385

Weiner L.P. & Narayan O. (1974) *Prog. med. Virol.* **18**, 229

A species in the genus POLYOMAVIRUS. Isolated by fusion of a brain cell culture from a case of progressive multifocal leukoencephalopathy (PML) with African green monkey kidney cells and BSC-1 CELLS. Has been isolated from one further case of PML. Antigenically similar or identical to SIMIAN VIRUS 40. Antibodies are usually only found in humans in contact with monkeys, but 2–4% of humans with no monkey contacts may also have antibodies. *See* JC viruses.

SYN: PML-2 virus.

SV 40 virus Abbreviation for simian virus 40.

SV virus series *See* simian viruses SV series.

Swamp fever virus Synonym for infectious anaemia of horses virus.

Swim-bladder inflammation virus

Bachmann P.A. & Ahne W. (1974) *Arch. ges. Virusforsch.* **44**, 261

A species in the genus VESICULOVIRUS. Causes a severe and fatal disease in carp. Experimental infection of carp, *Cyprinus carpio* and *Carassius auratus* caused reduced reflex activity and in some cases loss of balance, swelling of the anus and abdomen, petechiae on the skin and muscles. Death occurs 4–8 days after signs of infection appear. Antigenically very similar to RHABDOVIRUS CARPIO. Replicates in FHM CELLS at an optimal temperature of 20°–22°.

Swine fever virus Synonym for hog cholera virus. Not to be confused with AFRICAN SWINE FEVER VIRUS.

Swine influenza virus Synonym for influenza virus A porcine.

Swine pox virus A species in the genus SUIPOXVIRUS. Cultivation in eggs not reported. Replicates with CPE in pig kidney, testis, brain and embryo lung cell cultures. Affects chiefly very young pigs causing a generalized disease. Injected i/d in rabbits causes papular lesions, but cannot be passed. Guinea pigs, suckling mice, calves, sheep and goats are insusceptible. The pig louse transmits the disease, though it may also occur in absence of lice. Pigs may also suffer from infection with VACCINIA VIRUS.

SYN: pig pox virus; variola suilla.

Swine rotavirus A species in the genus ROTAVIRUS. Causes acute enteritis with diarrhoea in young pigs. Pigs are susceptible to infection by rotaviruses of many species, but only the calf and pig rotaviruses cause disease.

Swine vesicular disease virus A species in the genus ENTEROVIRUS, antigenically related to COXSACKIE B5. Swine vesicular disease was first observed in Italy in 1966. Subsequent outbreaks occurred in Hong Kong 1971, Europe and Japan 1972–5. There are several antigenically different strains of the virus. Infectivity can be neutralized by Coxsackie B5 antiserum but the viruses can be distinguished by immuno-diffusion, NEUTRALIZATION and RNA HYBRIDIZATION. Causes a disease similar to foot and mouth disease in pigs. Fever and vesicular lesions on the feet and snout. Replicates with CPE in pig kidney cell cultures. Injected i/c in new-born mice causes paralysis and death in 5–10 days. Donkeys, cattle, rabbits, guinea pigs and chickens develop no disease on exposure to virus. Laboratory infections in man with aseptic meningitis are reported. Coxsackie B5 injected into pigs does not cause disease.

Symmetrel Trade name for AMANTADINE hydrochloride as 100 mg capsules.

Syncytial viruses

Low P.C. *et al.* (1977) *Intervirology* **8**, 204

Viruses which in cell cultures induce the formation of syncytia. There are bovine, human and feline species, similar to the FOAMY VIRUSES of simians, and hamsters. Members of the subfamily SPUMAVIRINAE. There are other viruses such as RESPIRATORY SYNCYTIAL VIRUS and MEASLES VIRUS which induce syncytia but are not included in the group. Often used as an alternative name for foamy viruses.

Syncytial virus of rabbits

Brown R.C. *et al.* (1970) *Proc. Soc. exp. Biol. Med.* **133**, 587

Probably a species in the genus REOVIRUS. Isolated from a cotton-tail rabbit and also from cell cultures of laboratory-bred rabbits. Markedly ether-sensitive.

Taarbaek disease Synonym for Bamble disease.

Tacaiuma virus An unclassified ARBOVIRUS morphologically like BUNYAVIRUS but serologically unrelated to members of the genus. Belongs to ANOPHELES A ANTIGENIC GROUP. Isolated from SENTINEL *Cebus* monkeys and mosquitoes in Para and São Paulo, Brazil. Not reported to cause disease in humans.

Tacaribe antigenic group viruses Nine morphologically identical and serologically related viruses. Members of the New World group of the genus ARENAVIRUS. Probably seldom transmitted by arthropods.

Amapari (R)	Pichinde (R,I)
Junin* (H,R)	Portillo* (H)
Latino (R)	Tacaribe (Ba)
Machupo* (H,R)	Tamiami (R)
Parana (R)	

* *Can cause disease in humans.*

Isolated from:

(I) Ixodid ticks	*(R) Rodents*
(H) Humans	*(Ba) Bats*

Tacaribe virus A species in the genus ARENAVIRUS. One of the AMERICAN HAEMORRHAGIC FEVER VIRUSES. Isolated from two species of *Artibeus* bats. Has been recovered on one occasion from mosquitoes. A SILENT INFECTION can be induced experimentally in the guinea pig. Found in Trinidad. Not reported to cause disease in humans.

Taggert virus

Doherty R.L. *et al.* (1975) *Am. J. trop. med. Hyg.* **24**, 521

An unclassified ARBOVIRUS and a member of the SAKHALIN ANTIGENIC GROUP. Isolated in suckling mice from nymphs of the tick *Ixodes uriae*, collected in tussock grass and under planks on the shore near a rookery of the royal penguin, *Eudyptes chrysolophus schlegeli* on Macquarie Island, 800 miles S.E. of Tasmania. Antibodies were found by plaque reduction test in 4 of 31 penguin sera. Not reported to cause disease in humans.

Tahyna virus

Drăgănescu N. and Gîrjabu E. (1979) *Virologie, Bucuresti* **30**, 91

Bardos V. & Danielova V. (1959) *J. Hyg. Epidemiol. Microbiol.* **3**, 264

A species in the genus BUNYAVIRUS and a member of the CALIFORNIA ANTIGENIC GROUP. Isolated in Czechoslovakia, Germany, Yugoslavia, France and Italy. Can cause a febrile illness in humans. Serologically indistinguishable from LUMBO VIRUS isolated in Mozambique.

Taka-diastase A crude preparation from the fungus *Aspergillus oryzae* which has α-amylase activity and from which several nucleases can be isolated, including RIBONUCLEASE T_1, RIBONUCLEASE T_2 and S_1 nuclease.

Talfan disease virus Synonym for porcine enterovirus. Talfan disease is a mild form of TESCHEN DISEASE, first observed in Denmark and England in 1955–57.

Tamdy virus

Lvov D.K. *et al.* (1976) *Arch. Virol.* **51**, 15

Probably a species in the genus BUNYAVIRUS. Isolated from ticks *Hyalomma a. asiaticum* and *H. plumbeum plumbeum* collected from humans working with sheep and camels in the desert regions of Turkmen S.S.R. and Uzbek S.S.R. As these ticks parasitize rodents, hedgehogs, hares and birds they may also be hosts for the virus. No antigenic relationship found to a range of viruses. Does not agglutinate goose erythrocytes. Pathogenic for suckling and three week old mice on i/c injection. Not reported to cause disease in humans.

Tamiami virus A species in the genus ARENAVIRUS. One of the AMERICAN HAEMORRHAGIC FEVER VIRUSES and a member of the TACARIBE ANTIGENIC GROUP. Isolated from cotton-rats in Florida, U.S.A. Not reported to cause disease in humans.

Tanapox virus

Downie, A.W. *et al.* (1971) *Brit. med. J.* **i**, 363

A species in the family POXVIRIDAE causing local skin lesions in children in Kenya. Appears serologically the same as a virus causing disease in captive monkeys. Antigenically related to YABA VIRUS and SWINE POX VIRUS. Does not grow in eggs but replicates in monkey kidney cell cultures. Causes single and multiple lesions in monkeys. Monkey handlers have also been infected.

SYN: benign epidermal monkey pox virus; yaba-like disease virus.

Tanga virus An unclassified ARBOVIRUS. Isolated from *Anopheles funestus* mosquitoes in Tanzania and Uganda. Not reported to cause disease in humans.

Taniguchi bodies INCLUSION BODIES found in epithelial cells of monkeys infected with JAPANESE B VIRUS.

Tanjong Rabok virus An unclassified ARBOVIRUS. Isolated from SENTINEL rhesus monkeys *Macaca nemestrina* in peninsular Malaysia. Antibodies found in wild rodents, man, birds and bats. May cause febrile illness with haemorrhagic signs in humans.

T antigen

Rigby P. (1979) *Nature, Lond.* **282**, 781

Rapp, F. & Westmoreland D. (1976) *Biochim. biophys. Acta* **458**, 167

Tumour antigen. Appears in the nucleus and in some cases also in the cytoplasm, of virus-induced tumour cells or cells transformed *in vitro* by ADENOVIRIDAE or PAPOVAVIRIDAE. Demonstrated by immunofluorescence or CF test using sera from tumour-bearing animals. T antigens are specific for the inducing virus, but not for the cell species, and are probably all coded for by the viral GENOME.

Tataguine virus An unclassified ARBOVIRUS, morphologically like BUNYAVIRUS but serologically unrelated to members of that genus. Isolated from man and mosquitoes (both *Culex* and *Anopheles* sp.) in Senegal, Cameroon, Central African Republic, Nigeria and Ethiopia. Does not appear to be a cause of significant disease in humans.

3T3 cells (CCL 92), **3T6 cells** (CCL 96)

Todaro G.T. & Green H. (1963) *J. cell Biol.* **17**, 299

Two of a number of cell lines obtained by repeated passage of random-bred Swiss mouse embryo cells. The first number indicates the passage interval, the second × 1,000 the number of cells plated per 20 cm^2. Passage at low multiplicity resulted in 3T3 cells which have not lost CONTACT INHIBITION and cease dividing at low cell density. They are therefore valuable for detecting the transforming abilities of ONCOGENIC viruses. Passage at a high cell density resulted in 3T12 cells which have lost contact inhibition and grow to a high cell density.

tegument In the HERPESVIRIDAE it is the structure located between the CAPSID and the ENVELOPE. It has been called an 'inner membrane' though it has not got the trilaminar unit structure characteristic of true membranes.

Tembe virus An unclassified ARBOVIRUS. Isolated from *Anopheles nimbus* mosquitoes in Para, Brazil. Not reported to cause disease in humans.

Tembusu virus A species in the genus FLAVIVIRUS. Isolated in Malaya, Thailand and Sarawak. Mosquito-borne. Not reported to cause disease in humans.

temperate bacteriophages Phages which can establish a LYSOGENIC relationship with the HOST CELL without killing it.

temperature-sensitive mutants Mutants the upper limit of whose temperature tolerance is lower than that of the WILD STRAIN.

template A NUCLEIC ACID or other parent molecule which determines the structure of a new molecule as it is being synthesized.

Tensaw virus A species in the genus BUNYAVIRUS, belonging to the BUNYAMWERA ANTIGENIC

GROUP. Isolated in Florida, Alabama and Georgia, U.S.A. Can cause a febrile illness with encephalitis in man. Virus has been isolated from dogs and marsh rabbits. Antibodies present in cows, chickens and humans.

terminal redundancy Presence of identical NUCLEOTIDE sequences at both ends of a GENOME NUCLEIC ACID. Occurs frequently in DNA phages which have linear chromosomes. The sequence of genes in such chromosomes may be represented as abcdef..., xyzabc.

terminal repetition Presence of a NUCLEOTIDE sequence at both ends of a GENOME NUCLEIC ACID which are either identical or may be inverted. Inverted terminal repeats occur for example in the adenovirus genome and if such a DNA molecule is denatured and reannealed, the formation of structures known as 'panhandles' may be seen in electron-micrographs of the molecules.

terminator codon *See* codon.

Teschen disease virus Synonym for PORCINE ENTEROVIRUS. Teschen is a region of Czechoslovakia where the first outbreaks of the disease were observed in 1929–30. However, the disease may already have occurred in Moravia in 1913.

Tete antigenic group viruses Four serologically related viruses in the genus BUNYAVIRUS. All isolated from birds.

Bahig
Matruh
Tete
Tsuruse

Tete virus A species in the genus BUNYAVIRUS, belonging to the TETE ANTIGENIC GROUP. Isolated from a number of species of birds in S. Africa and Nigeria. Not reported to cause disease in humans.

L-2,3,5,6-tetrahydro-6-phenylimidazo(2,1-*b*)-thiazole *See* levamisole.

Tettnang virus

Bárdoš V. *et al.* (1980) *Intervirology* **13**, 275

Thought to be an ARBOVIRUS but now identified as MOUSE HEPATITIS VIRUS probably originating from the mice used for isolation.

Theiler's virus In the 1930s Theiler isolated several viruses (GD I–VII) from the CNS of mice with spontaneous flaccid paralysis. The viruses could be passed in mice and caused necrosis of motor neurones in the chord. Mice surviving experimental infection developed demyelinating disease. The virus is now known as MOUSE ENCEPHALOMYELITIS VIRUS.

Thick leg disease virus Synonym for osteopetrosis virus.

Thimiri virus A species in the genus BUNYAVIRUS. Belongs to the SIMBU ANTIGENIC GROUP. Isolated from the pond heron or paddybird *Ardeola grayii* in Tamil Nadu, India and from the lesser white-throat *Sylvia curruca* in Egypt. Not reported to cause disease in humans.

Thogoto virus An unclassified ARBOVIRUS morphologically like BUNYAVIRUS but not related serologically to members of that genus. Isolated from man, cattle, camels and from ticks of *Boophilus* and *Rhiphicephalus* sp. in Egypt, Kenya, Nigeria and Sicily. Antibodies present in sheep, goats, cattle and camels. Causes disease in humans, sometimes severe. Optic neuritis and meningoencephalitis are reported.

Thottapalayam virus An unclassified ARBOVIRUS. Isolated from the shrew *Suncus murinus* in Vellore, N. Arcot District, Tamil Nadu, India. Not reported to cause disease in humans.

Three day stiff-sickness virus Synonym for ephemeral fever virus.

Thylaxoviridae (sacklike viruses. Greek: *thylax* = sac)

Dalton A.J. *et al.* (1966) *J. natn. Cancer Inst.* **37**, 395

A name suggested for the ONCOVIRINAE by Professor Gilbert Highet, Head of Department of Greek and Latin, Columbia University. Not adopted.

thymidine kinase An enzyme which is induced in cells infected with DNA viruses and which catalyses the phosphorylation of thymidine to thymidylic acid, in the process of DNA synthesis. In papova virus-infected cells the induced enzyme is cellular in origin, but the thymidine kinase induced by HERPESVIRUSES is specified by the virus GENOME, and differs in several properties from the cell enzyme. This is the basis for inhibition of herpesviruses by ACYCLOGUANOSINE which is phosphorylated by the virus-specified, but not the host, thymidine kinase.

Tick-borne encephalitis virus (Central European subtype) A species in the genus FLAVIVIRUS. The main vector is a tick *Ixodes ricinus* but mosquitoes and mites may be involved. The tick is probably an important reservoir of infection. Disease in man is biphasic; a febrile illness of 4–10 days is followed by meningitis or meningo-encephalitis. Mild or inapparent infections occur but in severe cases there is transient or permanent paralysis. Infection occurs in central Europe from Scandinavia to the Balkans and from Germany to western U.S.S.R. Experimentally the virus often kills mice; guinea pigs develop fever. Virus is often excreted in the milk of goats, sheep and cows and may be a source of infection for man. It is also excreted in the urine. Control is by elimination of ticks. A vaccine is avilable.

SYN: biphasic milk fever virus; biundulant meningo-encephalitis virus. Absettarov virus, Hanzalova virus, HYPR virus and Kumlinge virus are strains varying in virulence and epidemiology.

Tick-borne encephalitis virus (Eastern subtype) A species in the genus FLAVIVIRUS. The vectors are ticks *Ixodes persulcatus* and *I. ricinus*. A severe human infection causing flaccid paralysis and 30% mortality. Disease may also occur in naturally infected rodents and birds. The disease is found in eastern U.S.S.R. but a few isolations have been made in Leningrad and elsewhere in western U.S.S.R. Experimentally it causes encephalitis in mice and fever in guinea pigs. Injected i/c it causes encephalitis in rhesus monkeys, sheep, goats and some wild rodents but not in others. Control is by elimination of ticks. A vaccine is available.

SYN: far east Russian encephalitis virus; Russian spring–summer encephalitis virus.

Tilligerry virus

Gorman B.H. & Taylor J. (1978) *Aust. J. exp. Biol. med. Sci.* **56**, 369

A species in the genus ORBIVIRUS and a member of the BLUE TONGUE ANTIGENIC GROUP. RNA consists of 10 segments. Isolated from *Anopheles annulipes* caught in the Port Stephens Peninsula of N.S. Wales, Australia. Not reported to cause disease in humans.

tilorone hydrochloride

Fitzwilliam J.F. & Griffith J.F. (1976) *J. infect. Dis.* **133**, suppl. 221

2,7-Bis-[2-(diethylamino)ethoxy]-fluoren-9-one dihydrochloride. An INTERFERON inducer, active by mouth, with maximum interferon titres 24 hours after administration. Inactive in cell cultures. Protects mice against VESICULAR STOMATITIS VIRUS but not against experimental encephalitis due to HUMAN (ALPHA) HERPESVIRUS 1. Toxic for the haematopoietic and reticuloendothelial systems.

Timbo virus

Monath T.P. *et al.* (1979) *Arch. Virol.* **60**, 1

A species in the family RHABDOVIRIDAE. With CHACO VIRUS forms the Timbo antigenic group. Isolated from the lizard *Ameiva ameiva ameiva* in Para, Brazil. Not isolated from arthropods but considered to be arthropod-transmitted as it will replicate in experimentally infected mosquitoes. Will kill suckling mice but they are not as sensitive as VERO CELLS in which it replicates with CPE at 30°. Not reported to cause disease in humans.

tissue culture The growth or maintenance of living tissue in a liquid or soft gel medium *in vitro*. A large number of techniques have been described, and these can be classified under three general headings: (1) organ culture, in which the organization of the tissue is maintained, e.g. culture of kidney slices; (2) tissue culture in the strict sense of the term, in which a fragment of tissue is cultured; (3) cell culture, in which the tissue is broken down into individual cells, usually by proteolytic enzymes, before cultivation. *See* culture medium.

TK Thymidine kinase.

Tlacotalpan virus A species in the genus BUNYAVIRUS, belonging to the BUNYAMWERA ANTIGENIC GROUP. Isolated in Mexico from mosquitoes of *Anopheles* and *Aedes* sp. and *Mansonia titillans*. Not reported to cause disease in humans.

Tm Melting point: the temperature at which a transition occurs (e.g. double-stranded to single-stranded DNA) when temperature is the independent thermodynamic variable.

Togaviridae (Latin: *toga* = mantle or cloak)

Porterfield J.S. *et al.* (1978) *Intervirology* **9**, 129

A family of viruses containing single-stranded linear RNA of mol. wt. 4×10^6. VIRIONS yield infective RNA. Isometric, probably icosahedral, NUCLEOCAPSIDS surrounded by a lipoprotein ENVELOPE containing host cell lipid and virus-specified polypeptides, including one or more glycopeptides. Inactivated by lipid solvents. Multiplication occurs in the cytoplasm and the virus matures by budding. Agglutinate goose and newly-hatched chick erythrocytes. There are four genera: ALPHAVIRUS, FLAVIVIRUS, RUBIVIRUS, and PESTIVIRUS. Alphavirus and Flavivirus were formerly known as ARBOVIRUS A and B respectively.

Tollwut virus Synonym for rabies virus.

toluidine blue A photoreactive dye. *See* photodynamic inactivation.

Toure virus An unclassified ARBOVIRUS. Isolated from Kemp's gerbil *Tatera kempi* in Senegal. Not reported to cause disease in humans.

TO virus A strain of mouse encephalomyelitis virus.

transcapsidation *See* phenotypic mixing.

transcriptases Enzymes which bring about TRANSCRIPTION.

transcription The process of transferring the information encoded in the base sequence of one type of NUCLEIC ACID molecule to another. It can be either the formation of mRNA from DNA, or the production of a complementary strand from single-stranded RNA. The enzymes involved are DNA-DEPENDENT RNA POLYMERASE, RNA-DEPENDENT RNA POLYMERASE and RNA-DEPENDENT DNA POLYMERASE (reverse transcription).

transfection

Miller G. *et al.* (1979) *Proc. natn Acad. Sci. U.S.A.* **76**, 949

Transmission of genetic material (viral infectivity) by isolated NUCLEIC ACID extracted from cells or virus particles, in contrast to transmission by infective virus particles.

transferases Large class of enzymes catalyzing the transfer of groups from one molecule to another. Included are enzymes transferring one-carbon groups (e.g. transmethylases) aldehyde residues (e.g. transketolase), acyl groups (e.g. transacetylase), sugars (e.g. transglucosylase), nitrogenous groups (e.g. transaminases), phosphorus-containing groups (e.g. protein kinase) and sulphur-containing groups (e.g. CoA transferases).

transfer RNA *See* ribonucleic acid.

transformation

Macpherson I. (1970) *Adv. Cancer Res.* **13**, 169

Rapp F. & Westmorland D. (1976) *Biochim. Biophys. Acta* **458**, 167

An alteration in cell morphology and/or behaviour, involving loss of CONTACT INHIBITION and usually the acquisition of neoplastic potential. Transformation may occur spontaneously, or after exposure to certain chemical carcinogens. But it is most usually observed after infection with oncogenic viruses when it is caused by integration of the viral NUCLEIC ACID into the cell GENOME. Transformed cells can be maintained indefinitely in culture unlike non-transformed cells. *See* immortalization.

transformation assay When viruses have a sufficiently high transforming activity, it is possible to assay the frequency with which cells are transformed by observing the effect of the virus on a monolayer culture. Transformed cells grow in a manner different from that of normal cells, forming small, heaped-up colonies (plaques) of morphologically altered cells.

transition temperature Temperature at which double-stranded NUCLEIC ACID dissociates into single strands.

translation The process of making a protein chain from the information in the mRNA. The four letter language of the NUCLEIC ACID is translated into a 20 letter protein.

transmethylase Enzyme catalysing the addition of methyl groups, e.g. to RNA or DNA. Present in VIRIONS of REOVIRIDAE or RHABDOVIRIDAE and involved in formation of the 5′ cap structure on mRNA.

Transmissible enteritis of turkeys Synonym for turkey bluecomb disease virus.

Transmissible gastro-enteritis of pigs virus Synonym for porcine transmissible gastro-enteritis virus.

Transmissible mink encephalopathy virus

Burger D. & Gorham J.R. (1977) *Res. vet. Sci.* **22**, 131

The same as or a variant of SCRAPIE VIRUS. Present in mink brain tissue and infectivity will survive storage in 10% neutral formalin. On injection into mink causes progressive neurological disease after an incubation period of 6 months.

Transmissible virus-dementia virus Synonym for Creutzfeldt–Jakob disease virus.

transport medium A sterile liquid used to prevent or reduce INACTIVATION in specimens taken for virus isolation. Most transport media, of which there are many, contain a protein such as albumin, in which viruses are less readily inactivated than in solutions with low protein concentrations. They also prevent drying and change of pH.

Tree shrew herpesvirus Synonym for tupaiid herpesvirus 1.

Tree shrew retrovirus

Flügel R.M. *et al.* (1978) *Nature, Lond.* **271**, 543.

A species in the subgenus MAMMALIAN TYPE C ONCOVIRUS GROUP. An ENDOGENOUS VIRUS demonstrable in the placenta of a prosimian *Tupaia belangeri* the tree shrew at full term. Could be activated in embryo skin cultures by treatment with IDOXURIDINE.

triangulation number The number of triangles into which each face of an ICOSAHEDRON is divided when forming an ICOSADELTAHEDRON. The triangulation number $T = Pf^2$, where $P = h^2+hk+k^2$. f can be any integer, h and k are any integers with no common factor. The possible values of P are 1, 3, 7, 13, 19, 21, 31, 37....

Tribec virus A species in the genus ORBIVIRUS and member of the KEMEROVO ANTIGENIC GROUP. Isolated from the tick *Ixodes ricinus*, mice *Cleithrionomys glareolus* and *Pitymys subterraneus*, and goats in Slovakia. Antibodies are found in man, but the virus is not known to cause disease.

TRIC agent Synonym for Chlamydia.

trifluorothymidine (Trifluridine)

McNeill J.I. & Kaufman H.E. (1979) *Archs Ophthal.* **97**, 727

An anti-viral agent and an analogue of thymidine. Acts like IDOXURIDINE in inhibiting uptake of thymidine into DNA, and has a similar range of anti-viral activity though it is more potent. It is also more soluble and hence more dangerous in topical application. Will probably prove of use in the treatment of ocular herpes infection. Toxic properties require further study. Expensive to manufacture.

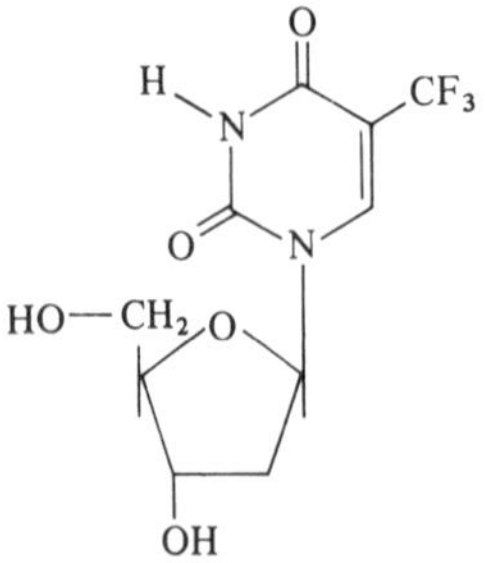

O
H N CF_3
O N
HO—CH_2 O
OH

Trinidad donkey virus A strain of Venezuelan equine encephalomyelitis virus.

Trinidad rabies A form of rabies following the bite of an infected vampire bat, most commonly *Desmodus rotundus murinus*. Clinically the infection takes the form of an acute ascending myelitis. The disease occurs in cattle in Trinidad and South America, whose blood is the normal food of the bat. Humans are attacked only if the livestock are shut away.

Triniti virus An unclassified ARBOVIRUS. Isolated from adult mosquitoes of *Trichoprosopon* sp. in Trinidad. Not reported to cause disease in humans.

trisodium phosphonoformate

Sundquist B. & Oberg B. (1979) *J. gen. virol.* **45**, 273

Helgstrand E. *et al.* (1978) *Science* **201**, 819

An anti-viral agent. Inhibits cell-free DNA POLYMERASE activity induced by HERPESVIRUSES. Therapeutically active against experimental cutaneous HUMAN HERPESVIRUS 1 infections in guinea pigs. *In vitro* inhibits human herpesvirus 1, SUID HERPESVIRUS 1 and BOVID HERPESVIRUS 1.

Trivittatus virus A species in the genus BUNYAVIRUS, belonging to the CALIFORNIA ANTIGENIC GROUP. Isolated from *Aedes trivittatus* mosquitoes in N. Dakota, Iowa, Wisconsin, Illinois, Ohio, Florida, Alabama and Minnesota, U.S.A. Probably not a significant cause of human disease.

Trubanaman virus An unclassified ARBOVIRUS, morphologically like Bunyavirus, but serologically unrelated to members of that genus. A member of the MAPUTTA ANTIGENIC GROUP. Isolated from *Anopheles annulipes* mosquitoes. Antibodies are found in humans, cattle, sheep, pigs, goats, horses, wallabies, etc. Not reported to cause disease in humans.

ts mutants Abbreviation for *T*emperature *S*ensitive Mutants.

Tsuruse virus A species in the genus BUNYAVIRUS. Isolated from a bird *Cyanopica cyaneus* in Japan. Not reported to cause disease in humans.

Tupaiid herpesvirus 1

Darai G. *et al.* (1979) *J. gen. Virol.* **43**, 541

A species in the family HERPESVIRIDAE. Originally isolated from a spontaneously degenerating lung tissue culture from an apparently normal tree shrew, *Tupaia glis*. Appears to be a common and SILENT INFECTION of tree shrews as it can often be isolated from mouth swabs and from cell cultures of various organs. Replicates in tree shrew fibroblast cell line. Another strain has been isolated from lymphosarcoma in an 8 year-old tree shrew. Probably non-pathogenic for tree shrews, but produces lymphoid granulomas in rabbit lung and spleen.

SYN: tree shrew herpesvirus.

Turbot herpesvirus Synonym for bothid herpesvirus 1.

Turkey adenovirus *See* aviadenovirus.

Turkey bluecomb disease virus

Ritchie A.E. *et al.* (1973) *Avian Dis.* **17**, 546

A species in the genus CORONAVIRUS. Causes diarrhoea in young turkeys. Replicates in embryonated turkey eggs producing damage to the lining of the embryo gut similar to that seen in poults. The term 'blue-comb' is also used to describe a similar clinical disease caused by INFECTIOUS ENTERITIS VIRUS.

SYN: transmissible enteritis of turkeys virus.

Turkey hepatitis virus A species in the genus ENTEROVIRUS. Serologically related to DUCK HEPATITIS VIRUS but infectious only for turkeys. Multiplies in fowl embryos.

Turkey herpesvirus Synonym for gallid herpesvirus 2.

Turkey meningo-encephalitis virus A species in the genus FLAVIVIRUS. Caused a progressive and fatal paralysis with enteritis of turkeys in Israel. Virus replicates in chick embryo cell cultures with CPE, and in eggs killing the embryo. Virus attentuated by egg passage can be used as a vaccine. Injected i/c in mice causes encephalitis. Chicks and other birds are resistant.

Turkey parainfluenza virus

McFerran J.B. *et al.* (1974) *Arch. ges. Virusforsch.* **46**, 281

A species in the genus PARAMYXOVIRUS. Isolated in Wisconsin, U.S.A. and in Ontario, Canada. Similar to NEWCASTLE DISEASE VIRUS but antigenically distinct from it, and from YUCAIPA VIRUS and BANGOR VIRUS.

Turkey pox virus *See* avipoxvirus.

Turkey strain T reticuloendotheliosis virus A strain of avian reticuloendotheliosis virus.

Turlock antigenic group viruses Morphologically like BUNYAVIRUS but unrelated antigenically to members of the genus.

M'Poko
Thurlock
Umbre

Turlock virus An unclassified ARBOVIRUS morphologically like BUNYAVIRUS but serologically unrelated to members of the genus. First member of the TURLOCK ANTIGENIC GROUP. Isolated from birds, rabbits, mosquitoes of *Culex tarsatis* and other *Culex* sp. in Alberta, California, Texas, New Mexico, Trinidad, and Brazil.

TVX virus

Hallauer C. *et al.* (1971) *Arch. Virol.* **35**, 80

A species in the genus PARVOVIRUS. Isolated from a line of human amnion cells originating from a Hamburg laboratory. It is the type strain of serological group 2 of the parvoviruses isolated from cell lines. Group 2 viruses are second to group 1 in frequency of isolation.

type A virus particles See A-type virus particles.

Type B oncovirus group A genus of the subfamily ONCOVIRINAE. Similar to TYPE C ONCOVIRUSES except that double-shelled A-type particles are found in the cytoplasm of infected cells; the core of these particles is located eccentrically within the VIRION. Type species MOUSE MAMMARY TUMOUR VIRUS.

type B virus particles See B-type virus particles.

Type C oncovirus group

Hung Fan (1978) *Curr. Topics Microbiol. Immunol.* **79**, 1

Levy J.A. (1978) *Curr. Topics Microbiol. Immunol.* **79**, 111

A genus of the subfamily ONCOVIRINAE. They have the morphology of C TYPE VIRUS PARTICLES. The genus embraces the leukaemia and sarcoma producing viruses and a number of related viruses which are probably non-oncogenic. Viruses spontaneously shed by infected cells are called EXOGENOUS VIRUSES but in addition there are ENDOGENOUS VIRUSES whose genetic material is intergrated into the cell GENOME and is vertically transmitted. The NUCLEIC ACID sequence of endogenous viruses hybridize with DNA from normal tissue cells. The degree of HYBRIDIZATION with different species of host can indicate the evolutionary origins of the virus. These endogenous viruses may become activated *in vivo* or *in vitro*, spontaneously or by various chemical or physical agents and produce virus particles which may be ecotropic or XENOTROPIC or AMPHOTROPIC. The role of endogenous viruses in the production of spontaneous tumours is not yet clear. The genus is divided into three subgenera containing species isolated from mammals, birds and reptiles. They are MAMMALIAN TYPE C ONCOVIRUS GROUP, AVIAN TYPE C ONCOVIRUS GROUP and REPTILIAN TYPE C ONCOVIRUS GROUP. There are type-specific or subgroup-specific glycoprotein antigens associated with the viral ENVELOPE and group-specific (gs) polypeptide antigens associated with the VIRION CORE. gs-1 antigen is shared by viruses from one species and is species-specific, but does not cross react with type B viruses. gs-3 antigen is shared by all mammalian type C oncoviruses. The avian type C oncoviruses and the B type mammalian oncoviruses do not have such interspecies gs-3 antigens.

type C virus particles *See* C-type virus particles.

Type D oncovirus group

Fine D. & Schochetman G. (1978) *Cancer Res.* **38**, 3132

A proposed genus of the subfamily ONCOVIRINAE, containing species with D type morphology, e.g. MASON–PFIZER MONKEY VIRUS, LANGUR RETROVIRUS and SQUIRREL MONKEY RETROVIRUS.

type D virus particles *See* D-type virus particles.

Tyuleniy virus

Lvov D.K. *et al.* (1971) *Am. J. trop. Med. Hyg.* **20**, 456

Clifford C.M. *et al.* (1971) *Am. J. trop. Med. Hyg.* **20**, 461

Lvov D.K. *et al.* (1972) *Arch. ges. Virusforsch.* **38**, 139

A species in the genus FLAVIVIRUS. Isolated from the tick *Ixodes putus* collected from rifts in the rocks on Tyuleniy Island, Patience Bay, SE of Sakhalin Island, in the N. of the Soviet Far East, where there is a colony of guillemots *Uria aalge*. Has also been isolated from *Ixodes uriae* collected in Three Arch Rocks Nation Wildlife Refuge, on the Oregon coast, U.S.A. and from *Ixodes putus* collected from pelagic cormorants *Phalacrocorax pelagicus* on the Commodore Islands. Pathogenic for suckling mice on i/c and i/p but kills adult mice only on i/c injection. Replicates with CPE in pig kidney cell cultures. Antibodies are found in humans, fur seals and several species of birds. The mosquito *Aedes aegypti* can be infected experimentally. Not reported to cause disease in humans.

U antigen A tumour antigen induced in cells infected with SV 40 VIRUS. It is heat-stable in contrast to the T ANTIGEN which is heat-labile

Uganda S virus A species in the genus FLAVIVIRUS. Isolated in Uganda, Nigeria and Central African Republic from mosquitoes of *Aedes* sp. and birds. Antibodies found in man and *Cercopithecus* sp. but there is no evidence that the virus causes disease.

SYN: Makonde virus.

Ulcerative dermatosis virus

Trueblood M.S. (1966) *Cornell Vet.* **56**, 521

Probably a strain of ORF VIRUS.

Ulcerative stomatitis of cattle virus Synonym for bovine papular stomatitis virus, though other viruses may cause the same clinical picture.

Umatilla virus A species in the genus ORBIVIRUS. Isolated from the sparrow *Passer domesticus*, and from mosquitoes of *Culex* sp. in Oregon, Utah, Colorado and Texas, U.S.A. Not reported to cause disease in humans.

Umbre virus An unclassified ARBOVIRUS morphologically like BUNYAVIRUS but serologically unrelated to members of that genus. Belongs to the TURLOCK ANTIGENIC GROUP. Isolated from mosquitoes and birds in Bombay State, India. Not reported to cause disease in humans.

Una virus

Cansey O.R. *et al.* (1963) *Am. J. trop. Med. Hyg.* **12**, 777

A species in the genus ALPHAVIRUS. Isolated from mosquitoes of *Psorophora*, *Aedes*, *Culex*, *Anopheles* and *Coquillettidia* sp. in Brazil, Panama, Trinidad, Colombia, French Guiana, Surinam and Argentina. Not reported to cause disease in humans.

uncoating

Lonberg-Holm K. & Philipson L. (1974) *Monographs on Virology*, vol. 9. Basel: S. Karger

The release of NUCLEIC ACID from a virus in the process of viral infection of a cell. With BACTERIOPHAGES the viral COAT remains outside the cell, and only the NUCLEIC ACID enters; thus PENETRATION and uncoating take place together. In animal cells uncoating may occur at the cell membrane or in the cytoplasm.

Upolu virus An unclassified ARBOVIRUS. Isolated from a tick *Ornithodoros capensis* on the Great Barrier Reef, Australia. Antibodies in cattle and kangaroo. Not reported to cause disease in humans.

Urucuri virus An unclassified ARBOVIRUS morphologically like BUNYAVIRUS but not serologically related to members of that genus. A member of the PHLEBOTOMUS FEVER ANTIGENIC GROUP. Isolated in suckling mice from the blood of an apparently normal male rodent *Proechimys guyannensis* found in Utinga forest, Brazil. Antibodies were found in the sera of members of this species in Para and Amapa, Brazil. Not reported to cause disease in humans.

Uruma virus A species in the genus ALPHAVIRUS. Caused an outbreak of fever and headache in Bolivia. Probably a strain of MAYARO VIRUS.

Usutu virus A species in the genus FLAVIVIRUS. Isolated from mosquitoes of *Culex*, *Mansonia* and *Aedes* sp., also birds, in S. Africa, Uganda, Cameroon, Congo, Central African Republic and Nigeria. Not reported to cause disease in humans.

Uukuniemi antigenic group viruses Five tick-borne species, serologically related and probably forming a genus in the family BUNYAVIRIDAE. Morphologically similar to the Bunyaviruses but not serologically related to members of that genus. Type species UUKUNIEMI VIRUS strain 523.

Grand Arbaud (Ar)
Manawa (Ix, Ar)
Ponteves (Ar)
Uukuniemi (Ix)
Zaliv-Terpeniya (Ix)

Isolated from:
(Ar) Argasid ticks
(Ix) Ixodid ticks

Uukuniemi virus An unclassified ARBOVIRUS, morphologically like BUNYAVIRUS but serologically unrelated to members of the genus. First member of the UUKUNIEMI ANTIGENIC GROUP. Isolated from a rodent *Apodemus flavicollis*, passerine birds, a thrush *Turdus merula*, and *Ixodes* sp. in Finland, Czechoslovakia, Poland, Hungary, U.S.S.R., Lithuania and Oregon, U.S.A. Antibodies are found in man but there is no evidence that the virus causes disease.

U virus Synonym for ECHOVIRUS 11. Found in children with respiratory illness. May cause rashes and 'colds' or gastrointestinal disturbances.

vaccine virus markers

Kantoch M. (1978) *Adv. Virus. Res.* **22**, 259

Nakano J.H. (1978) *Prog. med. Virol.* **24**, 178

Characters which can be used to distinguish vaccine strains of a virus from WILD STRAINS of the same virus. Growth characters, virulence, antigenic and biochemical markers can be used, but in some cases differentation may be difficult or impossible.

Vaccinia subgroup viruses Synonym for orthopoxvirus.

Vaccinia variolae Synonym for vaccinia virus.

Vaccinia virus Type species of the genus ORTHOPOXVIRUS. Used as an active vaccine for protection against smallpox. May have been derived from VARIOLA or COW POX VIRUS, or perhaps as a hybrid between them. Several antigens are demonstrable by precipitation, and neutralizing antibodies can be used to differentiate vaccinia from other members of the group. A heat-resistant lipoprotein haemagglutinin, separable from the virus particle, agglutinates turkey erythrocytes and those of some fowls. Virus suspensions are inactivated in 10 min at 60° but dried virus withstands 100° in the same time. Also inactivated by potassium permanganate, ethylene oxide and chloroform, but resistant to ether. The first virus to be grown in cell culture. Replicates in many cell types, including chick embryo, rabbit kidney, bovine and human cells. Pocks are produced on the CAM

up to 40·5°, are large and white, and have a slight tendency to become haemorrhagic. Scarification of the virus into the skin produces a local lesion and immunity, but can cause spreading and generalized infection in patients with skin disease or impaired immune responsiveness. Similar local lesions are caused in calf, sheep and rabbit skin, and these tissues, as well as cell cultures, can be used to produce vaccine.
SYN: vaccinia variolae.

vacuolating viruses Species of the genus POLYOMAVIRUS. *See under* simian and rabbit vacuolating viruses.

Vand endogenous type C virus
Callahan, R. *et al.* (1979) *J. Virol.* **30**, 124
A species in the subgenus MAMMALIAN TYPE C ONCOVIRUS GROUP. Released spontaneously by a kidney cell culture from the long-tailed tree mouse *Vandeleuria oleracea* after 24 weeks in culture and 12 passages. The virus-associated REVERSE TRANSCRIPTASE and major internal protein p30 are immunologically related to the analogous proteins of the SIMIAN SARCOMA VIRUS complex. The viral GENOME is present in *V. oleracea* cellular DNA, in multiple copies.

Varicella–zoster virus Synonym for human herpesvirus 3.

Variola major virus *See* variola virus.

Variola minor virus *See* variola virus.

Variola ovina Synonym for sheep pox virus.

Variola suilla Synonym for swine pox virus.

Variola virus
Baxby D. (1975) *Prog. med. Virol.* **19**, 215
A species in the genus ORTHOPOXVIRUS. Causes smallpox in man. A severe and frequently fatal disease with often confluent rash, fever and prostration. Eliminated from the world population in 1977. This was possible because SILENT human carriage of the virus does not occur and there is no natural animal reservoir. (However, *see* white pox viruses.) There were two types of smallpox. One, occurring in Asia and the middle and far East, had a high mortality and was due to variola major virus. The other, occurring in S. America and W. Africa, had a low mortality and was due to variola minor virus. Both viruses produce small white-domed pocks on the CAM after 72 hours. Variola major produces pocks at 38·5° whereas variola minor does not above 38°. Variola major is more lethal for chick embryos than variola minor. Replication is demonstrated with ease only in suckling mice. African strains may be difficult to differentiate. Control is by immunization with vaccinia virus and isolation of cases and contacts. Chemotherapy with METHISAZONE may be useful.
SYN: smallpox virus.

VEE virus Abbreviation for *V*enezuelan *E*quine *E*ncephalomyelitis Virus.

Vellore virus A species in the genus ORBIVIRUS. A member of the PALYAM ANTIGENIC GROUP. Isolated from *Culex pseudovishnui* and other species in Vellore, north Arcot District, Tamil Nadu, India. Not reported to cause disease in humans.

Vellore virus-like particles An unclassified FAECAL VIRUS type IV. No proven association with human gastroenteritis. Described from India. Morphologically enveloped particles similar to INFLUENZA VIRUS.

velogenic strains A term used to describe virulent virus strains, particularly used in relation to NEWCASTLE DISEASE VIRUS.

Venezuelan equine encephalomyelitis virus
Trent D.W. *et al.* (1979) *J. gen. Virol.* **43**, 365
Johnson K.M. & Martin D.H. (1974) *Adv. Virus Res.* **19**, 76
A species in the genus ALPHAVIRUS. Found in Venezuela, Brazil, Colombia, Ecuador, Panama, Trinidad, and in recent years also in Mexico, Texas and Florida. Antigenically very closely related to MUCAMBO and PIXUNA VIRUSES found in the Amazon area. A number

of antigenic subtypes can be differentiated. Causes disease in horses, donkeys and man. Is more viscerotropic than neurotropic. There is damage to blood vessels, and lesions are produced in many organs. In horses and donkeys there is fever, loss of condition, diarrhoea, and in some cases signs of CNS involvement and often death. In man the incubation period is 2–5 days. There is fever, severe headache, tremors, diplopia, and a death rate of up to 1%. Laboratory infections occur readily, probably by inhalation. Horses, dogs, cats, sheep and goats, but not cattle, are readily infected experimentally and develop disease. Natural reservoir probably mammalian, and mosquitoes *Aedes taeniorhynchus* and *A. scapularis* the main vectors. Replicates with CPE in a wide range of primary cell cultures and continuous cell lines of mammalian origin, and in embryonated eggs killing the embryo in less than 48 hours. A formalised vaccine has been used.

Venkatapuram virus An unclassified ARBOVIRUS. Isolated from *Culex vishnui* mosquitoes in N. Arcot district, India. Not reported to cause disease in humans.

Vero cells (CCL 81) A heteroploid cell line derived from the kidney of a normal African green monkey *Cercopithecus aethiops*. Used widely in virus replication studies and plaque assays. Useful for assay of SIMIAN VIRUS 40, PARAINFLUENZA VIRUS TYPE 5, MEASLES, ARBOVIRUSES, REOVIRUSES, SIMIAN ADENOVIRUS and HUMAN POLIOVIRUS. Susceptible to GERMISTON, GETAH, GUAROA, KOKOBERA, MODOC, MURUTUCU, NDUMU, PARAMARIBO, PIXUNA, PONGOLA, ROSS RIVER, SEMLIKI FOREST and TACARIBE arboviruses, but not to APEU, CARAPARU, MADRID, NEPUYO, OSSA or STRATFORD.

vertical transmission Spread of infection parent to the young via the egg, sperm or *in utero*. Transmission via the maternal milk is sometimes included.

Vervet monkey disease virus Synonym for Marburg fever virus.

Vervet monkey herpesvirus

Clarkson M.J. *et al.* (1967) *Arch. ges. Virusforsch.* **22**, 219

Synonym for cercopithecid herpesvirus 5.

Vervet monkey virus

Valis J.D. *et al.* (1977) *Infect. Immun.* **18**, 247

A species in the genus POLYOMAVIRUS. Isolated from a S. African vervet monkey kidney cell culture. Has been adapted to growth in primary rhesus monkey kidney cell cultures. VIRION diameter 44–45 nm. The superhelical circular double-stranded DNA has a mean length 101% of the length of SV 40 DNA and mol. wt. $3{\cdot}3 \times 10^6$. Has the internal CAPSID antigen common to all PAPOVAVIRUSES of the SV 40 polyoma group. Unrelated to other papovaviruses by NEUTRALIZATION TESTS. T antigen is indistinguishable from the T antigen of SV 40. Transforms hamster kidney cells. Natural host probably the chacma baboon *Papio ursinus*.

SYN: SA 12 virus.

Vesicular exanthema of pigs virus

Bankowski R.A. (1965) *Adv. vet. Sci.* **10**, 23

Burroughs J.N. *et al.* (1978) *J. gen. Virol.* **40**, 161

A species in the family CALICIVIRIDAE. There are at least 13 serological types identified by letters A, B, C etc. First recognized in California in 1932; spread in 1952 to most of the U.S.A. Controlled by quarantine, slaughter and cooking of pig food. Spreads by contact, but less readily than APHTHO VIRUS. Replicates in cell cultures of swine, horse, dog and cat with CPE. Only infects pigs, similar to foot and mouth disease, but milder. Vesicles appear on the snout, tongue, feet and teats. Some strains injected into the tongues of horses and dogs cause local lesions. *See* San Miguel sea lion virus.

Vesicular stomatitis virus

Cartwright B. & Brown F. (1972) *J. gen. Virol.* **16**, 391

Type species of the genus VESICULOVIRUS. Natural hosts horses, cattle, sheep and pigs, in which a disease resembling a mild form of foot and mouth disease is produced. There are small papules or vesicles in the mouth and excess salivation. Lesions last only a few days. Lesions on feet are uncommon except in pigs. Teat lesions may occur in cattle. Racoons and deer may constitute a reservoir of infection. Antibodies have been found in the turtle *Trionyx spinifer* and the snake *Natrix erythrogaster*. Laboratory workers and cattle handlers may be infected and have an influenza-like disease. Almost all animals, including birds, can be infected experimentally. Disease occurs sporadically but only between June and October. Virus has been recovered from arthropods but their role as vectors is doubtful. Virus replicates on the CAM and in the allantoic cavity. Also in chick embryo cell cultures and primary cultures of bovine, pig and monkey cells. There are a number of antigenically different strains. New Jersey and Indiana share a common CORE protein antigen. An ENVELOPE antigen allows differentiation between Indiana strains and CHANDIPURA, ISFAHAN and PIRY viruses. PSEUDOTYPE VIRUS particles are formed when a cell is infected with both V.S.V. and an enveloped virus such as PICHINDE VIRUS.

Vesiculovirus

Brown F. *et al.* (1979) *Intervirology* **12**, 1

A genus of the family RHABDOVIRIDAE. Type species VESICULAR STOMATITIS VIRUS.

vidarabine *See* adenine arabinoside.

Vilyuisk encephalitis virus

Casals J. (1963) *Nature, Lond.* **200**, 339

Encephalitis occurs in N. Siberia and following it one third of patients develop chronic progressive disease similar to amyotrophic lateral sclerosis. Virus isolated from CSF, blood and brain resembles ENCEPHALOMYOCARDITIS VIRUS. Relation to disease not established.

vinblastine An alkaloid derived from the periwinkle plant *Vinca rosea*. Inhibits synthesis of cellular RNA and protein. Mitosis is arrested in metaphase and there is ATTACHMENT and UNCOATING of infecting viruses but no viral macromolecules are made.

Viper type C oncovirus

Lunger P.D. & Clark H.F. (1977) *J. natn. Cancer Inst.* **58**, 809

Lunger P.D. & Clark H.F. (1978) *Adv. Virus Res.* **23**, 159

Andersen P.R. *et al.* (1979) *Science, N.Y.* **204**, 318

The type species of the subgenus REPTILIAN TYPE C ONCOVIRUS GROUP. However, it may have D TYPE VIRUS PARTICLES and though the viral NUCLEIC ACID has no homology with that of MASON–PFIZER VIRUS, the major structural proteins of these viruses are antigenically related. The virus was first observed in the cells of a cell line VSW, established from the spleen of a Russell's viper *Vipera russelli*. Two further strains have been obtained from two different viper heart cell lines, neither of which were producing virus particles at first but spontaneously commenced to do so. These strains have been designated VV-VH-2 and VV-VH-3 to distinguish them from the original strain VV-VSW. There appears to be no nucleic acid homology or antigenic relationship with the avian or MAMMALIAN TYPE C ONCOVIRUSES and it may well be that the virus belongs with the Mason–Pfizer virus and is an ENDOGENOUS TYPE D ONCOVIRUS.

viraemia The presence of virus particles in the blood. Occurs transiently in many infections but virus is rarely isolated, probably because the viraemia occurs very early in the infection. Chronic viraemia occurs in a few infections; for example in aleutian disease of mink, hepatitis in man and LACTIC DEHYDROGENASE VIRUS infection in mice. Infective virus may circulate as virus-antibody complexes and immune complex disease may occur.

Viral haemorrhagic fever viruses of man

Shelokov A. (1970) *J. infect. Dis.* **122**, 560

Simpson D.I.H. (1978) *Bull. W.H.O.* **56**, 819

A term with no very precise meaning applied to a group of viruses which cause diseases characterized by fever and haemorrhagic phenomena resulting from capillary damage. They have natural animal hosts, are arthropod-borne and man becomes infected through venturing into the ecological domain of the virus and its natural host. The term began to appear in the literature in the early 1950s in discussions of Korean haemorrhagic fever virus.

Virus	*Means of transmission*
Variola virus	Man to man
Chikungunya virus Dengue virus Rift Valley fever virus Yellow fever virus	Mosquito-borne
Crimean/Congo fever viruses Kyasanur Forest disease virus Omsk haemorrhagic fever virus	Tick-borne
Junin virus Machupo virus Lassa virus Korean haemorrhagic fever virus	Zoonotic
Marburg virus Ebola virus	Unknown

Viral haemorrhagic septicaemia of trout virus Synonym for Egtved virus.

viral hepatitis Most commonly caused by hepatitis virus A, B, or C but other viruses can cause hepatitis: YELLOW FEVER VIRUS, HUMAN (ALPHA) HERPESVIRUS 1 OR 2, HUMAN HERPESVIRUS 3, HUMAN (GAMMA) HERPESVIRUS 4, COXSACKIE VIRUS, RUBELLA VIRUS, MEASLES VIRUS after certain immunization procedures, and EBOLA VIRUS.

Virazole Trade name for RIBAVIRIN.

virion Synonym for virus particle.

virogenes Cell DNA sequences carrying information for production of virus particles. *See* endogenous virus.

virogenic cells Cells carrying a latent viral GENOME and not producing infective virus, but able to do so on being grafted into an animal of a suitable species, or on CO-CULTIVATION or fusion with a cell of a different species.

viroid

Diener T.O. (1979) *Science, N.Y.* **205**, 859

A term introduced by E. Altenburg (*Am. Nat.* **80** (1946), 559) to designate hypothetical symbionts, akin to viruses, supposed to occur universally within the cells of animals and to give rise by mutation to viruses. Experimental verification of this theory has not materialized. T.O. Diener (*Virology* **45** (1971), 411) has proposed that the term be redefined and used as a name for agents such as potato spindle tuber 'virus', a small infective NUCLEIC ACID with no CAPSID protein and too little nucleic acid to code for its own replication. No HELPER VIRUS has been demonstrated. The RNA is not translated and is replicated by pre-existing host enzymes. They have as yet only been found in plants where they induce important diseases such as 'hop stunt'.

virolysis

Radwan A.I. *et al.* (1973) *Virology* **83**, 372.

Irreversible structural damage which may go as far as complete disintegration of virus particles. When certain enveloped viruses are exposed to specific antiserum in the presence of complement at +2° there is NEUTRALIZATION of infectivity but no gross structural damage. However at 37° there is virolysis, presumably mediated by late acting components of complement.

viropexis The engulfment of virus particles by cells. A form of pinocytosis. An active process by the cell and perhaps an important method of virus PENETRATION.

virosomes

Almeida J.D. *et al.* (1975) *Lancet* **ii**, 899

Liposomes with viral proteins on their surfaces. The haemagglutinin and NEURAMINIDASE surface units of INFLUENZA VIRUS A can be removed from the virus and relocated on the surface of liposomes. Such virosomes can be used as antigens. Liposomes are particles consisting of aqueous dispersions of phospholipid in the form of either multi- or uni-lamellar lipid bilayers. They are formed when a dried film of a phospholipid such as lecithin is shaken with buffer and then sonicated.

virostatic Able to prevent viral replication.

virucidal Causing INACTIVATION of a virus.

viruria Presence of infectious virus in the urine (CMV).

Virus de rue renforcé A term applied to certain strains of STREET VIRUS of unusual virulence.

virus Infectious units consisting of either RNA or DNA enclosed in a protective coat. They contain no functional RIBOSOMES or other cellular organelles and no energy-producing enzyme systems. They cannot grow in size but their NUCLEIC ACID contains the necessary information for their replication in a susceptible HOST CELL. This cell provides some of the enzymes necessary for viral replication but its main function is to provide the energy-producing systems. The host cell may or may not be destroyed in the process of viral replication and release.

virus induction Activation of a PROVIRUS to replicate complete virus. May occur spontaneously or be promoted by various factors such as exposure to IDOXURIDINE.

Virus N *See* influenza virus A avian.

Virus III of rabbits Synonym for leporid herpesvirus 1.

virus rescue *See* reactivation.

Virus X of bovine serum

Verwoerd D.W. (1970) *Prog. med. Virol.* **12**, 192

A species in the genus ORBIVIRUS. Found in a culture of BHK-21 hamster cells and thought to have been derived from the bovine serum in the medium.

Visceral disease virus Synonym for human (beta) herpesvirus 5.

visceral lymphomatosis of fowls An old term for the leukoses involving the viscera: Marek's disease and the leukosis–sarcoma group of diseases.

Visna virus (Icelandic: *visna* = shrinking or wasting)

Agnarsdottir G. (1974) *Prog. med. Virol.* **18**, 336

Vigne R. *et al.* (1978) *J. Virol.* **28**, 543

Meulen V. ter & Hall W.W. (1978) *J. gen. Virol.* **41**, 1

A species of the subfamily LENTIVIRINAE. Causes a slowly progressive demyelinating disease of the CNS in sheep. Early signs are lip tremor and abnormal carriage of the head. Later there is progressive paralysis and death. Sporadic cases were first reported between 1935 and 1951 in Iceland, when an extensive slaughter policy was started to eliminate pulmonary adenomatosis and maedi as well as visna. Localised outbreaks of maedi occurred again between 1958 and 1965 but there was no recurrence of the other two diseases. VIRION 85 nm in diameter with a dense CORE. NUCLEIC ACID indistinguishable from that of MAEDI VIRUS, and shares sequences with that of PROGRESSIVE PNEUMONIA VIRUS. In Iceland, the three diseases appear to have been imported with sheep from Germany in 1933. Transmission requires close contact and seldom occurs between sheep out of doors. Antibodies are formed but virus is not eliminated from the animal. The virus undergoes antigenic change and antibodies are formed to the new antigenic type. This can occur several times. These changes appear to be limited and are probably not due to mutations so much as selection of strains expressing various alternative antigens. Replicates in cultures of sheep and human cells. Giant cells and CPE occur in 2–3 weeks.

Transforms mouse cells *in vitro*. On injection into mice these cells will form sarcomas from which the virus can be rescued.

Vomiting and wasting disease of pigs virus Synonym for porcine haemagglutinating encephalitis virus.

Von Magnus phenomenon

von Magnus P. (1954) *Adv. Virus Res.* **2**, 59

Repeated passage of INFLUENZA VIRUS A at high multiplicity results in a progressive increase in the proportion of DEFECTIVE VIRUS particles produced. The defective particles are lacking in the largest class of RNA.

Wad Medani virus A species in the genus ORBIVIRUS. Isolated from various ticks: *Rhipicephalus sanguineus*, *Hyalomma* sp. *Amblyomma* sp. and *Boophilus* sp. in Sudan, India, Jamaica and Pakistan. Not reported to cause disease in humans.

Wallal virus

Doherty R.L. *et al.* (1978) *Aust. J. biol. Sci.* **31**, 97

An unclassified ARBOVIRUS. Isolated from *Culicoides* sp. flies in Queensland, Australia. Antibodies found in wallabies, kangaroos and other vertebrates. Not reported to cause disease in humans.

Wanowrie virus

Khorshed M. *et al.* (1976) *Indian J. Med. Res.* **64**, 557

An unclassified ARBOVIRUS. Isolated from the tick *Hyalomma marginatum isaaci* and the mosquito *Culex fatigans* in India, Ceylon and Egypt. Has been isolated from the brain of a patient with hepatitis and haemorrhagic disease of the gut. Pathogenic for new-born but not for adult mice. Replicates with CPE in BHK-21 CELLS.

Warrego virus A species in the genus ORBIVIRUS. With MITCHELL RIVER VIRUS forms the Warrego antigenic group. Isolated from flies of *Culicoides* sp. in Queensland, Australia. Antibodies found in wallabies, kangaroos and cattle. Not reported to cause disease in humans.

Warthin–Finkeldey cells Syncytial lymphoid cells found in MEASLES VIRUS infection in the human tonsil, Peyer's patches, lymphoid tissue of the appendix, lymph nodes and spleen.

Wart-hog disease virus Synonym for African swine fever virus.

wart viruses Species of the genus PAPILLOMAVIRUS. For individual viruses *see under* name of host.

Wavre virus

Huygelen C. & Peetermans J. (1968) *Arch. ges. Virusforsch.* **20**, 260

Cartwright S.F. *et al.* (1969) *J. comp. Path.* **78**, 371

Described originally as a picornavirus which agglutinated erythrocytes of several species including monkeys, guinea pig, swine and chicken. However it is probably a strain of PORCINE PARVOVIRUS. Replicates with CPE in pig kidney cell cultures and was originally isolated from a pig kidney cell monolayer from an apparently normal pig. Resistant to ether and IDOXURIDINE. A pig injected i/m did not develop disease but produced antibodies.

WB virus

Liebhaber H. *et al.* 1965) *J. exp. Med.* **122**, 1135 and 1151

A strain of PARAINFLUENZA VIRUS TYPE 5. Isolated in WI-38 CELLS from two patients with infectious hepatitis.

WEE virus Abbreviation for *W*estern *E*quine *E*ncephalomyelitis virus.

Wellcome 248U *See* acycloguanosine.

Wesselsbron disease virus A species in the genus FLAVIVIRUS. EPIZOOTIC in sheep causing abortion and death of lambs and pregnant ewes. Haemorrhages and jaundice occur in the ewes and meningo-encephalitis in the foetuses. May cause abortion in cattle. Infects man causing fever and muscular pains. Transmission is by mosquito bites. Found in S. Africa, Namibia, Zimbabwe, Mozambique, Cameroon, Nigeria, Uganda, Madagascar, Botswana, and Thailand. Injection of suckling mice i/c causes encephalitis. In rabbits and guinea pigs it causes abortions. Replicates in lamb kidney cell cultures and in eggs.

Western equine encephalomyelitis virus A species in the genus ALPHAVIRUS. Maintained in the wild as a harmless infection of birds, small rodents and reptiles. Man and horses are infected by mosquito bites. Disease produced is similar to that caused by EASTERN EQUINE ENCEPHALOMYELITIS VIRUS but milder. Mortality in horses 20–30% and in man 10%. Sequelae are uncommon. Virus found in most of U.S.A. (except the eastern seaboard), southern Canada and S. America as far as Argentina. Injection i/c causes meningo-encephalomyelits in a range of rodents, monkeys, rabbits, pigs and birds. Hamsters, mice and guinea pigs can be infected by i/p and i/m injection. Virus can be propagated in eggs and cell cultures of many types in which it causes a CPE. An active virus vaccine has been used.

West Nile virus A species in the genus FLAVIVIRUS. A SILENT or short febrile infection in humans especially children. Occurs in Egypt, Uganda, S. Africa, Israel, India and south of France. Causes encephalitis on i/c injection into rodents, chicks and rhesus monkeys. Virus is propagated in eggs causing plaques on the CAM and in cell culture of chicks and many mammals as well as mosquitoes. Birds are probably the natural host, the virus being spread by mosquitoes.

wet-tail of hamsters *See* hamster enteritis.

Whataroa virus

Miles J.A.R. *et al.* (1971) *Aust. J. exp. Biol. med. Sci.* **49**, 365

A species in the genus ALPHAVIRUS. Isolated from mosquitoes and birds in New Zealand. No known association with disease. Closely related to SINDBIS VIRUS.

White pox virus

Marennikova E.M. & Shelukhina, E.M. (1978) *Nature, Lond.* **276**, 291

Svetlana S. *et al.* (1979) *Intervirology* **11**, 333

A species in the genus ORTHOPOXVIRUS. Isolated from healthy cynomolgus monkeys in Holland, a chimpanzee shot in W. Africa, a sun squirrel, and a multimammate mouse *Mastomys natalensis.* None of these animals showed signs of disease. Similar to MONKEY POX VIRUS, but produces CPE in cell cultures and white pocks on the CAM like VARIOLA VIRUS. Distinction from variola virus is almost impossible. May be a white mutant of monkey pox virus.

whooping cough viruses Though there is no doubt that *Bordetella pertussis* is the major cause of whooping cough, viruses may sometimes cause the syndrome. Virus-associated cases are most common in England in the winter and the viruses incriminated most often are adenovirus, RESPIRATORY SYNCYTIAL VIRUS, PARAINFLUENZA and INFLUENZA VIRUS types A and B.

WI-38 cells (CCL 75) A diploid cell line derived from normal female embryonic lung tissue. Has one of the broadest spectra for human viruses of any cell line tested, and is particularly useful in the isolation of RHINOVIRUSES. Has been used for the preparation of a number of human virus vaccines.

SYN: Wistar Institute 38 Cells.

Wildebeest herpesvirus Synonym for bovid herpesvirus 3.

wild strains Isolations made from naturally infected hosts. Such strains may be different from LABORATORY STRAINS. *See* vaccine virus markers.

wild type The reference or original genotype, used for comparison with strains which have arisen from it.

Windpocken Synonym for chickenpox. *See* human herpesvirus 3.

Winter vomiting disease virus A better name is ACUTE EPIDEMIC GASTROENTERITIS VIRUS as diarrhoea may be as important a symptom as vomiting which may be absent, and the winter season is not a well-documented feature.

wish cells (CCL 25) A heteroploid human amnion cell line derived from colonies of 'altered' cells which appeared after the primary cell culture had been passaged 35 times. Has been used to differentiate virulent from avirulent strains of MEASLES VIRUS.

Wistar Institute 38 cells *See* WI-38 cells.

Witwatersrand virus An unclassified ARBOVIRUS, morphologically like BUNYAVIRUS but serologically unrelated to members of that genus. Isolated from a mosquito *Culex rubirotus* and rodents in Uganda, Mozambique and S. Africa. Kills mice on injection. Probably non-pathogenic for man.

WM 1504 E virus

Oldstone M.B.A. *et al.* (1977) *Am. J. Path.* **88**, 193

A species of the subgenus MAMMALIAN TYPE C ONCOVIRUS GROUP. A non-transforming mouse virus. Wild mice trapped in Los Angeles County, U.S.A. were found to have progressive lower motor neurone paralysis of the hind legs. They also showed a high incidence of lymphomas. A C TYPE VIRUS was present and the condition could be passed by inoculation of new-born wild or laboratory mice with extracts of tissue containing the virus. The neurological disease and the lymphoma appeared to be caused by the same virus.

wobble hypothesis *See* anti-codon.

Wollan virus

Clarke S.K.R. *et al.* (1972) *Brit. med. J.* **3**, 86

An unclassified FAECAL VIRUS type 1 associated with acute epidemic gastroenteritis in man. Passed in volunteers given faecal extracts collected from boarding school outbreak in U.K. Similar to NORWALK VIRUS but serologically distinct.

Wongal virus A species in the genus BUNYAVIRUS. With KOONGOL VIRUS forms the Koongol antigenic group. Isolated from *Culex annulirostris* and *Coquillettidia crassipes* in Queensland, Australia. Not reported to cause disease in humans.

Wongorr virus An unclassified ARBOVIRUS. Isolated from *Aedes lineatopennis* mosquitoes in Queensland, Australia. Antibodies found in humans, wallabies and cattle. Not reported to cause disease in humans.

Woolly monkey sarcoma virus Synonym for simian sarcoma virus.

Woolly monkey type C oncovirus A species in the subgenus MAMMALIAN TYPE C ONCOVIRUS GROUP. A strain of simian sarcoma virus. Seen by EM in a spontaneous fibrosarcoma of a woolly monkey of *Lagothrix* sp. *See also* simian sarcoma virus.

Wut virus Synonym for rabies virus.

W virus Abbreviation for WOLLAN VIRUS. Also used in 1932 by Gay & Holden (*Proc. Soc. exp. Biol. Med.* **30**, 1051) to designate a virus which in all probability was identical with B virus (CERCOPITHECID HERPESVIRUS 1).

Wyeomyia virus A species in the genus BUNYAVIRUS and a member of the BUNYAMWERA ANTIGENIC GROUP. Isolated from birds and mosquitoes in Colombia, Panama, Brazil, Trinidad and French Guiana. Causes a febrile illness in humans.

Xenotropic murine type C viruses

Levy J.A. (1978) *Curr. Topics Microbiol. Immunol.* **79**, 111

A subspecies of the MURINE TYPE C ONCOVIRUS, which infects and replicates efficiently only in cells from a species other than the mouse. The first to be identified was that from NZB mice but they may be present in all mouse strains. They vary in host range and this may be used to classify them into groups. All show similar INTERFERENCE tests, p30 and REVERSE TRANSCRIPTASE. They differ however, in p12, gp 70 and NUCLEIC ACID sequences. α or class II viruses are inducible by IDOXURIDINE. Present in many mouse strains including some which also have an ectropic virus. β or class III viruses are not inducible and are produced spontaneously, but only by a few mouse strains and these strains do not produce ecotropic viruses.

xenotropic virus An ENDOGENOUS VIRUS which will not replicate complete virus particles in cells of the species in which it occurs naturally. Sometimes called X tropic or S tropic viruses.

XJ-cl 3 strain of Junin virus An avirulent strain non-pathogenic for guinea pigs.

X-tropic virus Xenotropic viruses.

X 14 virus

Payne F.E. *et al.* (1964) *Virology* **23**, 109

A species in the genus PARVOVIRUS. A RODENT PARVOVIRUS of group 1. Isolated from mammary tissue of a Sprague-Dawley rat treated with X rays and methylcholanthrene. Resembles LATENT RAT VIRUS in biological properties.

Yaba-like disease virus Synonym for tanapox virus.

Yaba virus

Schmidt L.H. (1970) In *Infections and Immunosuppression in Subhuman Primates*, 87, Ed. Balner H. and Beveridge W.I.B. Munksgaard.

A species in the family POXVIRIDAE causing benign fibrous tumours of the head and limbs of rhesus and cynomolgus monkeys, which may ulcerate before regressing. Natural host probably an African primate. Workers in contact with infected animals often become infected and have local disease, with fever in some cases. Experimental infection in man causes a small nodule which regresses. Virus G+C CONTENT 32·5, density of DNA 1·69 in CsCl. Inactivated after 1 hour at 56° or by pH 3 at room temperature. Replicates on the CAM and in primary human kidney, *Cercopithecus* kidney and MK2 cells.

Yaba 1 virus

Málkova D. (1972) *Acta Virol. Prague* **16**, 264

Marhoul Z. *et al.* (1976) *Acta Virol. Prague* **20**, 499

An unclassified ARBOVIRUS. First isolated in 1962 in Nigeria. A very similar or identical virus, Lednice 110 has been isolated near the small town of Lednice in S. Moravia from the tick *Culex modestus*. Inactivated by sodium desoxycholate, ether and low pH. Resistant to high pH. Replicates in goose and duck embryo cell cultures without CPE. Pathogenic for new-born mice. Not reported to cause disease in humans.

Yaquina Head virus A species in the genus ORBIVIRUS, and a member of the KEMEROVO ANTIGENIC GROUP. Isolated from *Ixodes uriae* in Oregon, U.S.A. The same or a closely related virus has been isolated in Alaska. Not reported to cause disease in humans.

Yata virus An unclassified ARBOVIRUS. Isolated from the mosquito *Mansonia uniformis* in the Central African Republic. Not reported to cause disease in humans.

Yellow fever virus A species in the genus FLAVIVIRUS. Jungle yellow fever is an infection of wild primates in forests of Africa and S. America. Yellow fever is endemic in Africa, south of the Sahara and as far south as northern Zimbabwe. Epidemics have occurred in Sudan and Ethiopia. Spreads occasionally from southern to central America and Trinidad. In the African tree tops the virus is spread by the mosquito *Aedes africanus* and *A. simpsoni*, carrying infection from the monkeys to man in the villages. In S. America *Haemagogus* sp. are the main vectors in the sylvan cycle. In the urban area *Aedes aegypti* is the vector carrying the human disease. Incubation period is 3–6 days. Infection in man may be inapparent (in natives) or a fulminating, often fatal infection, with high fever, albuminuria, jaundice, black vomit and other haemorrhages. In children it may be difficult to diagnose. Macaca monkeys, marmosets and howler monkeys may die after experimental inoculation. In most African primates there is only VIRAEMIA. The virus is fatal to hedgehogs. Replicates in cultures of chick and mouse embryo cells and after adaptation will infect eggs. The attenuated 17D strain was obtained by passage in chick embryo cells and gives few reactions when used as a vaccine. It gives protection for several years. Urban

yellow fever can be controlled by elimination of *Aedes aegypti*. The endemic prevalence of dengue and other related viruses may prevent spread to Asia.
SYN: fiebre amarilla virus.

YLD Yaba-like disease.

Yogue virus An unclassified ARBOVIRUS. Isolated from a *Rousettus aegyptiacus* bat in Senegal. Not reported to cause disease in humans.

Yucaipa virus
Dinter Z. *et al.* (1964) *Virology* **22**, 297
A species in the genus PARAMYXOVIRUS. Isolated in southern California from tracheal exudate of chickens with severe laryngotracheitis in which the main cause of disease was INFECTIOUS LARYNGOTRACHEITIS VIRUS. Yucaipa virus causes only mild disease. Similar to NEWCASTLE DISEASE VIRUS but antigenically distinct.

Zaliv Terpeniya virus
Lvov, D.K. *et al.* (1973) *Arch. ges. Virusforsch.* **41**, 165
An unclassified ARBOVIRUS morphologically like BUNYAVIRUS but serologically unrelated to members of that genus. A member of the UUKUNIEMI ANTIGENIC GROUP. Isolated from ticks *Ixodes putus* collected on Tyuleniy island in Patience Bay (Zaliv Terpeniya), Sakhalin region, and Commodore island, Kamchatka region in the U.S.S.R. where there are sea bird colonies. Pathogenic for suckling mice. Not reported to cause disease in humans.

Zaysan virus
Slavik I. *et al.* (1976) *Acta Virol. Prague* **20**, 177
A species in the genus ALPHAVIRUS, related to SEMLIKI FOREST VIRUS. Isolated from mosquitoes in the far east of the U.S.S.R.

Zegla virus A species in the genus BUNYAVIRUS and a member of the PATOIS ANTIGENIC GROUP. Isolated from the cotton-rat *Sigmodon hispidus* in Almirante, Panama, also in Honduras, Guatemala and Mexico. Not reported to cause disease in humans.

Zika virus
Fagbami A.H. (1979) *J. Hyg. Camb.* **83**, 213
A species in the genus FLAVIVIRUS. Isolated from humans, wild monkeys and *Aedes africanus* mosquitoes in Uganda, Nigeria, Central African Republic, Senegal and Malaya. Experimental infection of rhesus monkeys causes a fever. In humans there is a febrile illness with rash.

Zinga virus An unclassified ARBOVIRUS. Isolated from *Mansonia africana* and *Aedes* sp. mosquitoes, and also from humans. Antibodies found in birds, rodents, elephants, hogs, buffalo and hartebeest. Causes a febrile illness in humans.

Zingilamo virus An unclassified ARBOVIRUS. Together with BOTEKE VIRUS forms the Boteke antigenic group. Isolated from a bird *Bycanistes sharpei* in the Central African Republic. Not reported to cause disease in humans.

Zirqa virus An unclassified ARBOVIRUS, belonging to the HUGHES ANTIGENIC GROUP. Isolated from *Ornithodoros muesebacki* ticks collected on Zirqa Island, Persian Gulf. Not reported to cause disease in humans.

zona Synonym for shingles.

zoonosis
World Health Organisation/FAO Expert Committee on Zoonoses (1959) *Tech. Rept. Series no. 169*
A disease or an infection naturally transmitted between vertebrate animals and man. However, the term has been frequently misunderstood. *See* Fiennes R., *Zoonoses of Primates* (London: Weidenfeld and Nicolson, 1967, pp. 2–6) for a discussion of the etymology of this term and the various interpretations which have been placed upon it.

Zovirax Trade name for acycloguanosine.

Zwoegerziekte virus Synonym for Maedi virus in the Netherlands.

Taxonomy of vertebrate viruses

DNA VIRUSES

Family	*Subfamily*	*Genus*	*Type species*
Adenoviridae		Mastadenovirus	adenovirus type 2
		Aviadenovirus	chicken embryo lethal orphan virus
Herpesviridae	Alphaherpesvirinae	Not named	human (alpha) herpesvirus 1
	Betaherpesvirinae	Not named	human (beta) herpesvirus 5
	Gammaherpesvirinae	Not named	human (gamma) herpes-virus 4
Poxviridae	Chordopoxvirinae	Orthopoxvirus	vaccinia virus
		Avipoxvirus	fowl pox virus
		Capripoxvirus	sheep pox virus
		Leporipoxvirus	myxoma virus
		Parapoxvirus	orf virus
		Suipoxvirus	swine pox virus
	Entomopoxvirinae	Entomopoxvirus	three subgenera A, B and C
Papovaviridae		Papillomavirus	rabbit papilloma virus
		Polyomavirus	polyoma virus
Parvoviridae		Parvovirus	latent rat virus
		Adeno-associated virus	adeno-associated virus type 1
		Densovirus	densovirus of *Galleria mellonella**
Iridoviridae		Iridovirus	tipula iridescent virus type 1*
		Not named	African swine fever virus

* *Insect viruses, not defined in the text.*

RNA VIRUSES (part two: Retroviridae)

Family	*Subfamily*	*Genus*	*Subgenus*
Retroviridae	Oncovirinae	Type C oncovirus group	Mammalian type C oncoviru
			Avian type C oncovirus grou
			Reptilian type C oncovirus g
		Type B oncovirus group	
		Type D oncovirus group	
	Spumavirinae	Not named	
	Lentivirinae	Not named	

RNA VIRUSES (part one)

Family	*Genus*	*Type species*
Reoviridae	Reovirus	reovirus type 1
	Orbivirus	blue-tongue virus
	Rotavirus	human rotavirus
	Phytoreovirus	
	Fujivirus	
Togaviridae	Alphavirus	Sindbis virus
	Flavivirus	yellow fever virus
	Rubivirus	rubella virus
	Pestivirus	pestivirus diarrhoea virus
Coronaviridae	Coronavirus	Avian infectious bronchitis virus
Picornaviridae	Enterovirus	human poliovirus type 1
	Cardiovirus	encephalomyocarditis virus
	Rhinovirus	human rhinovirus 1A
	Aphthovirus	aphtho virus
Caliciviridae		vesicular exanthema of pigs virus
Rhabdoviridae	Vesiculovirus	vesicular stomatitis virus
	Lyssavirus	rabies virus
	Sigmavirus	drosophila virus*
Paramyxoviridae	Paramyxovirus	Newcastle disease virus
	Morbillivirus	measles virus
	Pneumovirus	human respiratory syncytial virus
Orthomyxoviridae	Influenzavirus	influenza virus A
	Influenzavirus C	influenza virus C
Arenaviridae	Arenavirus	lymphocytic choriomeningitis virus
Bunyaviridae	Bunyavirus	Bunyamwera virus

’s	*Subspecies*
: type C oncovirus	ecotropic murine type C virus
	xenotropic murine type C virus
	amphotropic murine type C virus
rcoma and leukaemia viruses	feline leukaemia virus A, B and C
e type C oncovirus	
n type C oncovirus	
en leukosis and sarcoma viruses	subgroup A–G
reticuloendotheliosis virus	
type C oncovirus	
e mammary tumour virus	
n–Pfizer monkey virus	
n foamy virus	
i/Visna virus